SNORRI STURLUSON

HEIMSKRINGLA

VOLUME III

The printing of this book is made possible by a gift to the University of Cambridge in memory of Dorothea Coke, Skjæret, 1951

SNORRI STURLUSON
HEIMSKRINGLA

VOLUME III
MAGNÚS ÓLÁFSSON TO MAGNÚS ERLINGSSON

TRANSLATED BY

ALISON FINLAY

AND

ANTHONY FAULKES

VIKING SOCIETY FOR NORTHERN RESEARCH
UNIVERSITY COLLEGE LONDON
2015

ISBN: 978-0-903521-93-2

The cover illustration is of a scene from the Battle of Stamford Bridge in the Life of St Edward the Confessor in Cambridge University Library MS Ee.3.59 fol. 32v. Haraldr Sigurðarson is the central figure in a red tunic wielding a large battle-axe.

Printed by Short Run Press Limited, Exeter

CONTENTS

Introduction

King Óláfr inn helgi (the Saint) casts a long shadow over the third and last part of *Heimskringla*. It has been pointed out that in writing the *Óláfs saga helga* that is the centrepiece of *Heimskringla* Snorri was amplifying the version of the same narrative he had written earlier in the *Separate Saga of St Óláfr*, whereas the process of constructing the sagas of subsequent kings involved cutting down the earlier texts he was using as sources. Thus, 'if Snorri was indeed the author of the whole of *Heimskringla*, it . . . seems likely that it was a matter of importance for him that *Óláfs saga helga* should be large enough to dominate the other parts of his narrative' (Ármann Jakobsson 2005, 397). It is in keeping with the planned dominance of the saga of St Óláfr that reference to the saint should continue throughout the sagas of his successors that cover the historical period from Óláfr's death in 1030 up to 1177. The groundwork was already laid by the inclusion in the *Separate Saga* of stories of miracles attributed to the saint in the years after his death; these are repeated in their chronological contexts in the sagas of his son Magnús (*Magnúss saga ins góða* ch. 27) and half-brother Haraldr (*Haralds saga Sigurðarsonar* chs 14, 55–57), and in the joint reign of the sons of Haraldr gilli (*Haraldssona saga* chs 24–25). Alongside conventional hagiographical accounts of miraculous cures, the saint's interventions repeatedly testify to his benevolent protection of his son: he appears to Magnús in a dream before his significant battle against the Wends at Hlýrskógsheiðr—in which Magnús carries his father's axe, named Hel—and is explicitly said to have ensured his victory. In a second dream Óláfr appears to Magnús to presage his death (ch. 28), a scene clearly recalled by the saint's later appearance to Haraldr harðráði before his fall at Stamford Bridge in 1066 (*Haralds saga Sigurðarsonar* ch. 82), where Haraldr's predicted death in battle, not caused by God, is set against his brother's 'holy fall' (stanza 152). One effect of these interventions is that Haraldr's character and reign are directly contrasted, not only with those of his predecessor (and, for a short time, joint ruler) Magnús, but also with those of his sainted half-brother.

On a secular level, Haraldr is compared more positively with Óláfr in the testimonial of Halldórr Brynjólfsson, who knew them both, and declares that 'I never came across two men more alike in character'. His assessment, occupying its own chapter near the end of *Haralds saga Sigurðarsonar*, can be seen as a specimen of the traditional *mannjafnaðr* 'comparison of men', another example of which occurs in a later saga in the exchange between the jointly ruling brothers Sigurðr Jórsalafari and Eysteinn (*Magnússona saga* ch. 20). It has been noted that *Heimskringla* (following its main source, *Morkinskinna*; see below) bases its account of Norwegian history on 'two contrastive sets of kings . . . the "foreign adventurer" type [Haraldr harðráði, Magnús berfœttr, Sigurðr Jórsalafari] and the "builder and lawmaker" type [Magnús góði, Óláfr kyrri, Eysteinn Magnússon]' (Andersson 2012, 120; see also Andersson 1993, 16–19; Bagge 1991, 139, 156; Lönnroth 1978, 53–80).

It is notable in this context that St Óláfr, in the stanza in which he predicts his half-brother's death in defeat, aligns himself with the stay-at-homes: 'I had, since at home I lingered, I a holy fall to earth'.[1]

As has been pointed out with reference to *Morkinskinna*, the literary technique of comparison of kings was encouraged by the prevalence of joint kingship in this period of Norwegian history: 'A good deal of [the] narrative deals with periods when there are two kings in Norway at the same time, thus providing an opportunity for comparison' (Ármann Jakobsson 2005, 396). This phenomenon resulted from the conditions under which a claim to kingship could be made (Bagge 2010, 40–41):

> In the case of Norway, the rules of succession—or perhaps the lack of such rules—have often been regarded as a serious problem. All male descendants of a king, at least the agnatic descendants, whether they were born in wedlock or not, had an equal right to claim the throne and could in principle be recognised by any local assembly . . . If two or more kings were recognised at the same time, they had to make an arrangement between them or fight over the throne.
>
> If a peaceful arrangement was made, as happened several times in the period 1045–1157, no territorial division took place. The king had no fixed residence in this period, but travelled around the country, largely receiving his incomes in the form of *veizla*, i.e. provisions for himself and his men in the local region. When there were several kings, they usually travelled in different parts of the country, probably according to some pre-arranged pattern, occasionally meeting for eating, drinking, and discussion. It is clear that this arrangement implied great risks for conflict. No rule forced the pretenders to agree to divide the throne between them; a stronger candidate, or a candidate believing himself to be the stronger, might easily try to fight his rival. Once an agreement was made, plenty of situations might lead to conflicts between the co-rulers, such as the sharing of common incomes, who was to preside over the common meetings, and quarrels between their adherents. The sagas give many examples of such conflicts. Division between the kings meant a division of wealth and power but not necessarily of ambition.

Bagge's remarks are made in the context of the so-called 'civil wars', the term conventionally designating the turbulent period from the death of Sigurðr Jórsalafari in 1130, to 1240. But even the 'period of peace' of the preceding century begins with the uneasy collaboration of the young king

---

[1] This contrastive theme is found only in the *Heimskringla* (and *Fagrskinna*) text of the stanza, since *Morkinskinna* has a different version of these lines: 'If you stayed at home you would have had a holy fall to earth'.

Magnús inn góði with his half-uncle Haraldr, clearly forced on Magnús by the greater age, wealth and charisma of the returned adventurer from Byzantium, and includes the shared rule of Haraldr Sigurðarson's two sons and, in turn, of the three sons of Magnús berfœttr, Sigurðr, Eysteinn and Óláfr. The prevalence of rival claimants was exacerbated by the appearance of pretenders, self-declared sons of Magnús berfœttr: first Haraldr gilli who successfully legitimises his claim to royal descent by undergoing the ordeal of walking over hot iron bars (*Magnússona saga* ch. 26), then the less successful Sigurðr slembidjákn (*Magnús saga blinda ok Haralds gilla* ch. 13). This chaos of competing claims reaches its nadir in *Haraldssona saga*, where factions fighting in the names of the sons of Haraldr gilli, aged respectively five and three, defeat Sigurðr slembidjákn, who has bolstered his own claim by an alliance, voluntary or not, with the blind and mutilated Magnús inn blindi, whom he has taken out of the monastery in which he had taken refuge after his own reign was ended by enemies who brutally mutilated him 'in such a way that he could not call himself a king from then on'. Throughout these struggles the puppet child-kings are used as figureheads for the warring factions and carried in person into battle, which leads in the case of the one-year-old Ingi to permanent physical deformity: 'It is said that Þjóstólfr Álason had King Ingi in his lap while the battle was raging . . . people say that it was then that Ingi caught the sickness that he suffered from all the rest of his life, and his back became crooked and one leg was shorter than the other, and he was so lacking in strength that he had difficulty in walking as long as he lived' (*Haraldssona saga* ch. 2).

To some extent the evolution of the monarchy throughout the period narrated in *Heimskringla* III reveals the increasing influence of Christianity and the church on the ideology of kingship and government. It begins with the divine authority conferred (retrospectively) on St Óláfr by virtue of his martyrdom, continues with the establishment of the new see of Niðaróss in 1152/53 (*Magnúss saga Erlingssonar* ch. 16) and culminates in the involvement of Archbishop Eysteinn in the institution of the ceremony of coronation, beginning with that of the seven-year-old Magnús Erlingsson in 1163/64 (*Magnúss saga Erlingssonar* ch. 21). Haki Antonsson traces the continuing importance of martyrdom in the ideology of kingship in this period and points out the mutual support existing between monarchy and church: 'the fledgling Scandinavian Church was not averse to bestowing sanctity on royal or princely figures. After all it was only with the support of the secular authority that the Church was able to establish itself within a deeply traditional society' (Haki Antonsson 2004, 75).

Against this background, the striking figure of Haraldr Sigurðarson stands out as the contrastive embodiment of secular values. His nickname *harðráði*—which does not appear in the Old Norse texts until it is added in chapter headings in thirteenth-century and later manuscripts of historical works—has been rendered variously as 'tyrant' or 'hard-ruler', 'ruthless', 'savage in counsel, tough, tyrannical', 'severe', but is perhaps best translated as 'resolute' (Finlay 2015, 99–100). While *Óláfs saga helga* dominates *Heimskringla* as a whole, *Haralds saga Sigurðarsonar* achieves this status over the sagas of its final third, by virtue both of its length and of the compelling character of Haraldr himself. It falls into three parts, Haraldr's early adventures as a mercenary in Byzantium, an amalgam of historical kernel and legendary enhancement; his rule in Norway, first jointly with his nephew Magnús and then as sole king, and his dealings particularly with King Sveinn Úlfsson of Denmark (a further opportunity for comparison of kings); and finally his doomed expedition—condemned outright by both Snorri and his poetic sources as imprudent—to extend his rule to England, and his death at Stamford Bridge in 1066.[2] This final exploit has been seen by later historians as the end of an era, and Haraldr labelled 'the last of the formidable Viking kings of Scandinavia' (Magnusson and Pálsson 1966, 9).

While Haraldr is not presented by Snorri explicitly in these terms, he does emerge as a fascinatingly mixed character; 'a chameleon king' to Theodore Andersson (2006, 93); described by Ármann Jakobsson as 'a rogue king' (2005, 396). The comparison of him with St Óláfr at the end of his saga emphasises his ambition: 'But Haraldr fought for fame and power and forced all the people to submit to him, as far as he could'. The episode in Byzantium harnesses legendary stories to attribute to him cunning, resourcefulness, a capacity for leadership and equally, for treachery; once Haraldr is established in authority in Norway these attributes are revealed in a more realistic mode, for instance in his treatment of Kálfr Árnason, former enemy of his brother Óláfr, with whom he arranges an ostensible truce, but then engineers his fall in a fight against the Danes (*Haralds saga Sigurðarsonar* chs 51–53).[3]

Despite the evidence of thoughtful planning in its construction, *Heimskringla* ends seemingly abruptly some years before the death of the last king named in it, Magnús Erlingsson; the last recorded event is the Battle

---

[2] Haraldr's service as a mercenary with the Varangian Guard is attested in Greek sources, principally the *Consilia et Narrationes* of Kekaumenos, a composite text, from the mid- to late 1070s. For the Greek text and English translation by Charlotte Roueché see http://www.ancientwisdoms.ac.uk/library/kekaumenos-consilia-et-narrationes/. Three versions of *The Anglo-Saxon Chronicle*, A, C and E, include contemporary accounts of the Norwegian invasion. That of the C version is the fullest (*Anglo-Saxon Chronicle*, I 194–98). See Finlay 2015.

[3] For a more detailed account of the construction of Haraldr's reign in *Heimskringla* and earlier sources, see Finlay 2015.

of Ré in 1177, in which Magnús and his father defeated the Birkibeinar, the rebel band that were promoting the claim of yet another pretender to royal power. The ending of *Heimskringla* here is in line with earlier texts, *Ágrip* and *Fagrskinna*, that cover the same time span, and was probably dictated by the pre-existence of *Sverris saga*, believed to have been written before 1210. Sverrir, brought up in the Faroes, arrives in Norway in 1177 claiming to be the son of King Sigurðr Haraldsson; his saga, the first part of which is said in the saga's Prologue to have been written by the Icelandic abbot Karl Jónsson under the instruction of Sverrir himself, tells of his ultimately successful campaign to establish himself as king by defeating Magnús and his father Erlingr, and then his defence of the kingdom against new contenders for the throne, until his death in 1202 (*Sverris saga* 2007). Snorri's choosing to end his work with the events of 1177 suggests that he saw *Heimskringla* not as a text to be read in isolation, but as part of the continuing documentation of the history of his time.

Sources

A general account of the sources of *Heimskringla* has been given in the Introduction to Volume I. This is supplemented here with some further consideration of the specific sources of the sagas in the final part of the work. As is the case throughout *Heimskringla* the primary source must be considered the skaldic stanzas incorporated in the text, though these tail off towards the end of the work; only five stanzas are cited in the whole of the last two sagas, *Hákonar saga herðibreiðs* and *Magnúss saga Erlingssonar*. On the other hand, as events progress towards Snorri's own time, reference is made more frequently to named individuals as oral informants. This is already evident in the account of Haraldr Sigurðarson's exploits in Byzantium, where it is made clear repeatedly that Haraldr himself and his followers were the sources for the narrative; singled out in particular is the Icelander Halldórr Snorrason ('he brought this story back to this country [i.e. Iceland]', ch. 9). Though Haraldr's feats are celebrated after the fact by his poets, it is made clear that they derived their material from the king's own account: 'So says the poet Stúfr, who had heard the king himself tell about these events' (ch. 12); 'it was Haraldr himself that transmitted this story, together with the other men who were there with him' (ch. 14).

The primary written source for the third part of *Heimskringla* is *Morkinskinna*, a history covering most of the same chronological ground, written probably about 1220, and marking 'a key moment in the genre's development ... *Morkinskinna* is the first extant work in Old Norse in which a saga dealing with many kings is narrated in such detail; it may even be the case that it is the first kings' saga in Old Norse concerned with the lives of more than a single king' (Ármann Jakobsson 2014, 11). It shares with *Heimskringla* the technique of citing skaldic stanzas (frequently the same ones, though the wording sometimes differs) as authorities, and is emphatic in presenting an Icelandic perspective, showing a particular interest in the relations of Icelanders with kings.

The one surviving manuscript (from about 1275) is damaged and probably about a third of the original work is missing; it probably extended, like *Heimskringla* and other texts, to cover events up to 1177, but the existing narrative breaks off in 1157. Material missing from the earlier part of the text can be supplied from the part of *Flateyjarbók* written in the fifteenth century, which has a version of *Morkinskinna*'s account of Magnús inn góði and Haraldr Sigurðarson.

Because the original version does not survive, scholars have differed as to how closely *Morkinskinna* is represented by the surviving text, and in particular whether the many *þættir*—short semi-independent narratives, including many anecdotes of encounters between Icelanders, most of them poets, and Norwegian kings—are part of the original text or later interpolations. The latter view undoubtedly owes much to the fact that *Heimskringla*, while following its source closely on the whole, does not include these interludes. *Morkinskinna* has generally been compared to *Heimskringla*, to its detriment, but has recently been rehabilitated by studies such as that of Ármann Jakobsson (2014), who argues that the *þættir*, which he considers original, are among the features of *Morkinskinna* that give it a distinctive focus, not just on the character and role of kings as individuals, but on the dealings between kings and retainers, with a particular interest in Icelandic retainers. Theodore Andersson has recently contrasted the differing, but commonly Icelandic, viewpoints of *Morkinskinna* and *Heimskringla* in the light of political relations between Iceland and Norway, speculating that the Icelandic suspicion and distrust of Norwegian kings in *Morkinskinna* reflects strained relations, amounting to a trade war, between the two countries in the period 1215–20, and that Snorri, writing a few years later, made 'adjustments' which 'may reflect a desire to remove the signs of Icelandic distrust in order to promote better relations with the mother country' (Andersson 2012, 134). While this argument is based on suppositions about the dates of composition of both texts that cannot be verified, it gives a useful account of how *Heimskringla* differs from its source, at least in its coverage of the period 1030–1130.

The narrative in chapters 39–72 of *Haralds saga Sigurðarsonar* in *Heimskringla* differs substantially from that of the corresponding sequence in *Morkinskinna*, which suggests that Snorri based it on another text, *Hákonar saga Ívarssonar*. This tells of the Norwegian chieftain Hákon Ívarsson, great-grandson of Jarl Hákon inn ríki of Hlaðir, and the growing friction between him and King Haraldr. This sequence contributes strongly to the negative aspects of the overall portrait of Haraldr, involving not only his mounting envy of the popular and successful Hákon, but also his enmity with other magnates, Einarr þambarskelfir and the brothers Kálfr and Finnr Árnason.

A fragmentary text of the saga survives in a fifteenth-century manuscript, supplemented by a Latin digest of the whole saga, and its version corresponds closely to that of *Heimskringla*, including the eight stanzas (and two half-stanzas) preserved in the fragments. It has generally been considered that *Hákonar saga* was written early, but not early enough to have been a source for *Morkinskinna*, which gives a different account of the period in question; Andersson speculates that they may have been written at the same time but without reference to each other, in a response to Sverre Bagge's recent claim that *Hákonar saga* is a late text based on *Heimskringla* (Andersson 2015, Bagge 2014). Andersson further suggests a relationship of some kind between *Hákonar saga* and a supposed **Hlaðarjarla saga*, a history of the jarls of Hlaðir that he argues may have ended with the death of Einarr þambarskelfir (Andersson 1998), but this takes us into the realm of speculation as this text does not survive.

For his account of the death of the pretender Sigurðr slembidjákn (or slembir) in 1139 Snorri refers us to a named source, a book (*Morkinskinna* calls it a saga) called *Hryggjarstykki* by one Eiríkr Oddsson (*Haraldssona saga* ch. 11). Unfortunately nothing more is known about either the author or the mysterious title. Eiríkr must be Icelandic, as implied by the statement that he 'was at this time for a long period in Norway'. The name *Hryggjarstykki* has been translated as 'Backbone-Piece', which could suggest that it gives just a summary of events; other suggestions have been that *stykki* 'piece' may be a technical term for a piece of parchment, implying that the work was short enough to be confined to a single sheet, or that *hryggr* 'backbone' could refer metaphorically to a powerful man, alluding to the ownership of the book. But all interpretations are speculative. Snorri's own account of the contents of the work is ambiguous: 'In that book it tells about Haraldr gilli and his two sons [*Morkinskinna* specifies Sigurðr and Ingi] and about Magnús blindi and about Sigurðr slembir, right up until their deaths'. This could refer just to the deaths of Magnús and Sigurðr in 1139, or to the deaths of the sons of Haraldr as well, which would take the narrative up to the death of Ingi in 1161. Bjarni Guðnason (1978) argues that the work was a hagiographical treatment of the life, and especially the martyrdom, of Sigurðr slembidjákn. *Hryggjarstykki* has been referred to as the first 'contemporary saga', since Eiríkr is said to have drawn on his own experience and that of contemporary witnesses:[4]

---

[4] There are two further references to Eiríkr and his named informants, in chs 7 and 10.

He wrote some of his account according to what Haraldr's sons' landed man Hákon magi dictated. Hákon and his sons were in all these conflicts and strategies. Eiríkr further mentions others that told him about these events, intelligent and reliable people, and were nearby, so that they heard or saw what happened, and some things he wrote according to what he himself had heard or seen.

Other sources that may have existed in written form, or may perhaps have circulated as more or less fixed oral legends, lend some passages in the later sagas of *Heimskringla* a distinctly hagiographical tone and style, quite different from those of Snorri himself and of literary sources such as *Morkinskinna*, and are evidently derived almost verbatim from near-contemporary accounts. One of the most striking of these is the account in *Magnúss saga blinda ok Haralds gilla* (chs 9–11) of the sack of the town of Konungahella by a heathen Wendish force, events not recorded in any other source. The clerical rhetoric of the narrative is especially noticeable in the miraculous elements of its account of the preservation of the Holy Cross relic from the heathen onslaught. It may be no accident that the prominent Icelander Jón Loptsson, later Snorri Sturluson's foster-father at Oddi, was present in Konungahella as a child, fostered by the priest Andreas Brúnsson who plays a leading part in the rescue of the Cross relic preserved in his church: 'At the time there was with him being fostered and brought up Jóan Loptsson and he was eleven winters old' (ch. 9). If such narratives existed in written form, quite probably at Oddi, Snorri may have instructed an amanuensis to copy them without making any stylistic changes.

This Translation

This volume completes the three-volume translation of *Heimskringla* published by the Viking Society. Volume I appeared in 2011, Volume II in 2014. The translation is based on the *Íslenzk fornrit* edition of *Heimskringla* by Bjarni Aðalbjarnarson (*Íslenzk fornrit* XXVI–XXVIII, *Hkr* I–III). Volume III of the edition and of this translation includes the sagas of Norwegian kings in the period 1030–1177. Page numbers of the edition appear here in square brackets, and internal page references as well as those in the index and introduction are to this edition. The prose has been translated by Anthony Faulkes and the verse by Alison Finlay, who also wrote this Introduction. Both have contributed footnotes, but as in previous volumes, many of these are closely based on those of Bjarni Aðalbjarnarson.

To the right of each stanza is noted the name of the poem (if any) and the stanza number. As in Volume II, this information is based on the attributions in the recent edition of the skaldic corpus, of which the relevant volumes are *Skaldic Poetry of the Scandinavian Middle Ages* I. *Poetry from the Kings' Sagas* 1: *From Mythical Times to c. 1035* (*Skald* I) and *Skaldic Poetry of the*

Scandinavian Middle Ages. II. *Poetry from the Kings' Sagas* 2. *From c. 1035 to c. 1300 (Skald* II). These attributions sometimes differ from those in the older edition of Finnur Jónsson (FJ), which was used in *Heimskringla* I. The page number on which the stanza appears in *Skald* I or II is also noted here, so that this edition can be referred to for full information on the meaning and manuscript status of each stanza. This edition has proved invaluable for the interpretation of the stanzas in this translation, and in specific instances the editors of particular poems have been acknowledged in the footnotes. The interpretations sometimes differ, however, since our translation has followed manuscripts of *Heimskringla* that are not always the ones chosen as primary manuscripts by the editors of the skaldic edition.

The stanzas sometimes preserve archaic spellings of names, appropriate to the presumed date of composition of the stanza, thus 'Ǫleifr' for 'Óláfr' and 'Hǫkon' for 'Hákon'. Although these are more often the reconstructions of editors than spellings found in surviving manuscripts, they are retained here in accordance with the conventions used in the *Íslenzk fornrit* edition. Similarly, when names appear in alternative forms in the text (such as Fiðr/ Finnr), the identity of the characters is made clear in the Index of names.

In the translation of directions, 'north' generally describes any journey, wherever from, that ended up in Þrándheimr (Þrœndalǫg) or further north. 'East' describes any journey that ended up in the Vík or by Göta Elv. The directions do not actually refer at all closely to the direction(s) travelled from starting point to destination (See Jackson 1998–2001).

We are most grateful to Carl Phelpstead, who has read and commented on a draft of this volume.

Bibliographical References

This bibliography incorporates those published in Volumes I–II, with the addition of references made in this volume.

1GT = The First Grammatical Treatise 1972. Ed. Hreinn Benediktsson. Reykjavík.

3GT = The Third Grammatical Treatise. In *Den Tredje og Fjærde Grammatiske Afhandling i Snorres Edda*. 1884. Ed. Björn Magnússon Ólsen. København, 1–119.

Adam of Bremen 1959. *History of the Archbishops of Hamburg-Bremen*. Trans. Francis J. Tschan. New York.

Ágrip. In *Ágrip af Nóregskonunga sǫgum*. *Fagrskinna—Nóregs konunga tal* 1984. Ed. Bjarni Einarsson. Reykjavík, 1–54. *ÍF* XXIX.

Ágrip 2008 = *Ágrip af Nóregskonunga sǫgum*. 2008. Ed. M. J. Driscoll. London.

A History of Norway and The Passion and Miracles of the Blessed Óláfr 2001. Trans. Devra Kunin. Ed. with introduction and notes by Carl Phelpstead. London.

Andersson, Theodore M. 1993. 'Snorri Sturluson and the Saga School at Munkaþverá'. In *Snorri Sturluson. Kolloquium anläßlich der 750. Wiederkehr seines Todesdages*. Ed. Alois Wolf. Tübingen, 9–25. ScriptOralia 51.

Andersson, Theodore M. 1998. The Continuation of **Hlaðajarla saga*'. *Journal of English and Germanic Philology* 97: 2, 155–67.

Andersson, Theodore M. 2006. *The Growth of the Medieval Icelandic Sagas (1180–1280)*. Ithaca, NY, and London.

Andersson, Theodore M. 2008. 'The Oral Sources for *Óláfs saga helga* in *Heims-kringla*'. *Saga-Book* XXXII 5–38.

Andersson, Theodore M. 2012. *The Partisan Muse in the Early Icelandic Sagas (1200–1250)*. Ithaca, NY. Islandica 55.

Andersson, Theodore M. 2015. 'Hákonar saga Ívarssonar Once Again'. *Maal og minne*, 1: 61–77.

Andersson, Theodore M. and K. E. Gade (trans.) 2000. *Morkinskinna: The Earliest Icelandic Chronicle of the Norwegian Kings (1030–1157)*. Ithaca and London. Islandica LI.

Anglo-Saxon Chronicle = Two of the Saxon Chronicles Parallel 1892–99. Ed. John Earle and Charles Plummer. Oxford.

Ármann Jakobsson 2005. 'Royal Biography'. In *Companion to Old Norse-Icelandic Literature*. Ed. Rory McTurk. Oxford, 388–402.

Ármann Jakobsson 2014. *A Sense of Belonging. Morkinskinna and Icelandic Identity, c. 1220*. Trans. Fredrik Heinemann. Odense.

Ásgeir Blöndal Magnússon 1989. *Íslensk orðsifjabók*. Reykjavík.

Bagge, Sverre 1991. *Society and Politics in Snorri Sturluson's Heimskringla*. Berkeley.

Bagge, Sverre 2010. *From Viking Stronghold to Christian Kingdom. State Formation in Norway, c. 900–1350*. Copenhagen.

Bagge, Sverre 2014. 'Hákonar saga Ívarssonar—en kompilasjon fra senmiddelalderen'. *Maal og minne*, 2: 1–17.

Bjarni Guðnason 1978. *Fyrsta sagan*. Reykjavik. Studia Islandica 37.

Boulhosa, Patricia Pires 2005. *Icelanders and the Kings of Norway. Mediaeval Sagas and Legal Texts*. Leiden and Boston. The Northern World 17.

Clunies Ross, Margaret 1999. 'From Iceland to Norway. Essential Rites of Passage for an Early Icelandic Skald'. *Alvíssmál* 9, 55–72.

Dillmann, François-Xavier 2000. 'Pour l'étude des traditions relatives à l'enterrement du roi Halfdan le Noir'. In *International Scandinavian and Medieval Studies in Memory of Gerd Wolfgang Weber*. Ed. Michael Dallapiazza et al.Trieste, 147–56.

Edda Magnúsar Ólafssonar 1979. Ed. Anthony Faulkes. Reykjavík.

Egils saga Skalla-Grímssonar 1933. Ed. Sigurður Nordal. Reykjavík. *ÍF* II.

Ellis Davidson, Hilda 1943. *The Road to Hel. A Study of the Conception of the Dead in Old Norse Literature*. Cambridge.

Fagrskinna. In *Ágrip af Nóregskonunga sǫgum. Fagrskinna—Nóregs konunga tal* 1984. Ed. Bjarni Einarsson. Reykjavík, 55–364. *ÍF* XXIX.

Falk, Hjalmar 1912.'Altnordisches Seewesen'. *Wörter und Sachen* 4, 1–122.

Falk, Hjalmar 1914. *Altnordische Waffenkunde*. Kristiania.

Farrell, R. T. 1972. *Beowulf, Swedes and Geats*. London.

Faulkes, Anthony 1966. *Rauðúlfs þáttr. A Study*. Reykjavík. Studia Islandica 25.

Faulkes, Anthony (ed.) 2011. *Two Icelandic Stories*. London. Viking Society Text Series IV.

Fell, Christine 1981. '*Víkingarvísur*'. In *Speculum norroenum. Norse Studies in Memory of Gabriel Turville-Petre*. Ed. U. Dronke et al. Odense, 106–22.

Fidjestøl, B. 1982. *Det norrøne fyrstediktet*. Øvre Ervik. Universitet i Bergen Nordisk institutts skriftserie 11.

Finlay, Alison 2011. 'Risking one's Head. *Vafþrúðnismál* and the Mythic Power of Poetry'. In *Myths, Legends, and Heroes. Essays on Old Norse and Old English Literature*. Ed. Daniel Anlezark. Toronto, 91–108.

Finlay, Alison 2015. 'History and Fiction in the Kings' Sagas: The Case of Haraldr harðráði'. *Saga-Book* XXXIX, 77–102.

FJ = Finnur Jónsson (ed.) 1912–15. *Den norsk-islandske skjaldedigtning* A I–II, B I–II. København.

Flb = Flateyjarbók I–IV 1944–45. Ed. Sigurður Nordal. Reykjavík.

Foote, Peter 1978. 'Wrecks and Rhymes'. In *The Vikings*. Ed. T. Andersson and K. I. Sandred. Uppsala, 57–66. Reprinted in Peter Foote 1984. *Aurvandilstá. Norse Studies*. Ed. M. Barnes, H. Bekker-Nielsen and G. W. Weber. Odense, 222–35. The Viking Collection 2.

Foote, Peter and David Wilson 1970. *The Viking Achievement*. London.

Fóstbrœðra saga. In *Vestfirðinga sǫgur* 1943. Ed. Björn K. Þórólfsson and Guðni Jónsson. Reykjavík, 119–276. *ÍF* VI.

Frank, Roberta 1984. 'Viking Atrocity and Skaldic Verse: The Rite of the Blood-Eagle'. *English Historical Review* 99, 332–43.

Fritzner, Johan 1886–96. *Ordbog over det gamle norske Sprog* I–III. Kristiania.

Fsk = Fagrskinna.

Grettis saga Ásmundarsonar 1936. Ed. Guðni Jónsson. Reykjavík. *ÍF* VII.

Grønlie, Siân (trans.) 2006. *Íslendingabók, Kristni saga. The Book of the Icelanders, The Story of the Conversion*. London. Viking Society Text Series XVIII.

Gylf = Gylfaginning. In Snorri Sturluson 2005. *Edda. Prologue and Gylfaginning*. Ed. Anthony Faulkes. London.

Haki Antonsson 2004. 'Some Observations on Martyrdom in Post-Conversion Scandinavia'. *Saga-Book* XXVIII, 70–94.

Hákonar saga Ívarssonar 1952. Ed. Jón Helgason and Jakob Benediktsson. Copenhagen. Samfund til udgivelse af gammel nordisk litteratur 62.
Hálfs saga ok Hálfsrekka 1981. Ed. Hubert Seelow. Reykjavík.
Halldór Halldórsson 1954. *Íslenzk orðtök*. Reykjavík.
Hallfreðar saga. In *Vatnsdœla saga*. *Hallfreðar saga*. *Kormáks saga* 1939. Ed. Einar Ól. Sveinsson. Reykjavík, 133–200. *ÍF* VIII.
Háttatal = Snorri Sturluson 2007. *Edda*. *Háttatal*. Ed. Anthony Faulkes. London. [Referred to by stanza and, where appropriate, line no.]
Heimskringla 1893–1901 = Snorri Sturluson. *Heimskringla* I–IV. Ed. Finnur Jónsson. Copenhagen.
Heinrichs, Anne 1993. 'Óláfs saga helga'. In *Medieval Scandinavia. An Encyclopedia*. Ed. Phillip Pulsiano et al. New York and London, 447–48.
Hemings þáttr Áslákssonar 1962. Ed. Gillian Fellows Jensen. Copenhagen. Editiones Arnamagnæanæ B 3.
Historia Norwegie 2003. Ed. Inger Ekrem and Lars Boje Mortensen. Trans. Peter Fisher. Copenhagen.
Hkr = Snorri Sturluson 1941–51. *Heimskringla* I–III. Ed. Bjarni Aðalbjarnarson. Reykjavík. *ÍF* XXVI–XXVIII.
Hkr 1991 = Snorri Sturluson. *Heimskringla*. Ed. Bergljót Kristjánsdóttir et al. Reykjavík.
ÍF = *Íslenzk fornrit* I ff. 1933– . Reykjavík.
Íslendinga saga. In *Sturlunga saga* I.
Íslendingabók = Ari Þorgilsson 1968. *Íslendingabók*. In *Íslendingabók. Landnámabók*. Ed. Jakob Benediktsson. Reykjavík, 1–28. *ÍF* I.
J = Jöfraskinna (See Vol. 1, p. xiii).
Jackson, Tatiana 1998–2001. 'On the Old Norse System of Spatial Orientation'. *Saga-Book* XXV, 72–82.
Jesch, Judith 2001. *Ships and Men in the Late Viking Age. The Vocabulary of Runic Inscriptions and Skaldic Verse*. Woodbridge.
Jiroušková, Lenka 2010. 'Textual Evidence for the Transmission of the Passio Olavi Prior to 1200 and its Later Literary Transformations'. In *Saints and their Lives on the Periphery: Veneration of Saints in Scandinavia and Eastern Europe (c. 1000–1200)*. Ed. Haki Antonsson and Ildar H. Garipzanov. Turnhout, 219–39.
Johnsen, A. O. and Jón Helgason (eds) 1941. *Den store saga om Olav den hellige*. Oslo.
Jóms (291) = *Jómsvíkinga saga* 1969. Ed. Ólafur Halldórsson. Reykjavík [ÁM 291 4to].
Jóms (510) = *Jómsvíkinga saga (efter cod. AM 510, 4to) samt Jómsvíkinga drápa* 1879. Ed. Carl af Petersens. Lund.
Jón Hnefill Aðalsteinsson 1997. *Blót í norrænum sið. Rýnt í forn trúarbrögð með þjóðfræðilegri aðferð*. Reykjavík.
Jónas Kristjánsson 1977. 'Egils saga og konungasögur'. In *Sjötíu ritgerðir helgaðar Jakobi Benediktssyni, 20 júlí 1977*. Ed. Einar G. Pétursson and Jónas Kristjánsson. Reykjavík, 449–72.
Jónas Kristjánsson 1990. 'Var Snorri Sturluson upphafsmaður íslendingasagna?' *Andvari* 115, 85–105.
Jørgensen, Jon Gunnar 1995. ' "Snorre Sturlesøns Fortale paa sin Chrønicke". Om kildene til opplysningen om *Heimskringlas* forfatter'. *Gripla* 9, 45–62.
Jørgensen, Jon Gunnar 2007. *The Lost Vellum Kringla*. Trans. Siân Grønlie. Copenhagen. Bibliotheca Arnamagnæana 45.

K = Kringla (see Vol. II, Introduction p. xi).

Keraliunas, Simas 1994. 'The Information on the Aistians in Olafs saga Tryggvasonar and its Importance for the History of the East Baltic Region'. In *Samtíðar sögur*. Preprints of the ninth International Saga Conference II, 450–54. Akureyri.

Knýt = Knýtlinga saga. In *Danakonunga sǫgur* 1982. Ed. Bjarni Guðnason. Reykjavík, 91–321. *ÍF* XXXV.

Krag, Claus 1989. 'Norge sem odel i Harald hårfagres ætt'. [Norwegian] *Historisk tidsskrift* 68, 288–302.

Krag, Claus 2002. 'Myten om Hårfagreættens odel—et svar til Knut Dørum'. [Norwegian] *Historisk tidsskrift* 81, 381–94.

Landn = Landnámabók. In *Íslendingabók. Landnámabók* 1968. Ed. Jakob Benediktsson. Reykjavík, 29–397. *ÍF* I.

Laws of Early Iceland I 1980. Trans. Andrew Dennis, Peter Foote and Richard Perkins. Winnipeg.

Legendary saga = Olafs saga hins helga. *Die 'Legendarische saga' über Olaf den Heiligen (Hs. Delagard. saml. nr. 8¹¹)* 1982. Ed. Anne Heinrichs, Doris Janshen, Elke Radicke and Hartmut Röhn. Heidelberg.

Leland, Charles Godfrey 1892. *Etruscan Roman Remains in Popular Tradition*. New York and London.

Lind, E. H. 1920–21. *Norsk-isländska personbinamn från medeltiden*. Uppsala.

Lindow, John 2007. 'St Olaf and the Skalds'. In *Sanctity in the North: Saints, Lives, and Cults in Medieval Scandinavia*. Ed. T. A. DuBois. Toronto, 103–27.

Lindquist, I. 1929. *Norröna Lovkväden från 800- och 900-Talen*. Lund.

LP = Sveinbjörn Egilsson 1931. *Lexicon Poeticum Antiquæ Linguæ Septentrionalis*. Rev. Finnur Jónsson. Copenhagen.

Lönnroth, Lars 1978. *Den dubbla scenen. Muntlig diktning från Eddan till Abba*. Stockholm.

Magnusson, Magnus and Hermann Pálsson, trans, 1966. *King Harald's Saga*. Harmondsworth.

Maríu saga 1871. Ed. C. R. Unger. Christiania.

Mork = Morkinskinna 2011. Ed. Ármann Jakobsson and Þórður Ingi Guðjónsson. *ÍF* XXIII–XXIV.

Mork (Flb) = Passages in *Flb* taken to be derived from the original *Morkinskinna*, printed in *Mork* (and other editions of *Morkinskinna*).

NGL = Norges gamle love indtil 1387 1846–95. Ed. R. Keyser et al. Christiania.

NN = E. A. Kock 1923–44. *Notationes Norrœnæ* I–XXVIII. Lund. [References are to section numbers]

Oddr = Oddr munkr Snorrason 2006. *Óláfs saga Tryggvasonar*. In *Færeyinga saga. Óláfs saga Tryggvasonar eptir Odd munk Snorrason*. Ed. Ólafur Halldórsson. Reykjavík, 123–380. *ÍF* XXV.

O'Donoghue, Heather 2005. *Skaldic Verse and the Poetics of Saga Narrative*. Oxford.

ÓH = Den store saga om Olav den hellige 1941. Ed. O. A. Johnsen and Jón Helgason. Oslo.

Ólafur Halldórsson 1965. 'Flutningur handrita milli Íslands og Noregs fyrr á öldum'. *Tíminn*, 17th June. Reprinted in *Grettisfærsla. Safn ritgerða eftir Ólaf Halldórsson gefið út á sjötugsafmæli hans 18. apríl 1990*. 1990. Reykjavík, 339–47.

Ólafur Halldórsson 1979. 'Sagnaritun Snorra Sturlusonar'. In *Snorri: átta alda minning*. Reykjavík, 113–38. Reprinted in *Grettisfærsla. Safn ritgerða eftir Ólaf Halldórsson gefið út á sjötugsafmæli hans 18. apríl 1990*. 1990. Reykjavík, 376–95.

Oldest saga of St Óláfr = Anhang. In *Olafs saga hins helga. En kort saga om kong Olaf den hellige fra anden halvdeel af det tolfte aarhundrede* 1849. Ed. R. Keyser and C. R. Unger. Christiania, 90–95.

Olrik, Axel 1909. 'At sidde paa Hoj'. *Danske Studier*, 1–10.

ONP = Ordbog over det norrøne prosasprog at http://onp.ku.dk

Orkn = Orkneyinga saga 1965. Ed. Finnbogi Guðmundsson. Reykjavík. *ÍF* XXXIV.

ÓTM = Óláfs saga Tryggvasonar en mesta I–III 1958–2000. Ed. Ólafur Halldórsson. Copenhagen. Editiones Arnamagnæanæ A 1–3.

Phelpstead, Carl 2000. 'In Honour of St Óláfr. The Miracle Stories in Snorri Sturluson's *Óláfs saga helga*'. *Saga-Book* XXV, 292–306.

Phelpstead, Carl 2001. 'Introduction'. In *A History of Norway*.

Phelpstead, Carl 2007. *Holy Vikings. Saints' Lives in the Old Icelandic Kings' Sagas*. Tempe.

Poetic Edda = *Edda. Die Lieder des Codex Regius* I 1962. Ed. Hans Kuhn. Heidelberg.

Rauðúlfs þáttr: in *ÓH* 655–82; normalised text with notes and translation at www. vsnrweb-publications.org.uk/Raudulfs%20thattr.%20text.pdf

Rowe, Elizabeth Ashman 2005. *The Development of Flateyjarbók. Iceland and the Norwegian Dynastic Crisis of 1389*. Odense. The Viking Collection 15.

Roueché, Charlotte (ed. and trans.). Kekaumenos, *Consilia et Narrationes*. http:// www.ancientwisdoms.ac.uk/library/kekaumenos-consilia-et-narrationes/

Separate Saga of St Óláfr = ÓH.

Skald I = Diana Whaley (ed.) *Skaldic Poetry of the Scandinavian Middle Ages* I. *Poetry from the Kings' Sagas* 1: *From Mythical Times to c. 1035* 2012. Turnhout.

Skald II = Kari Ellen Gade (ed.). *Skaldic Poetry of the Scandinavian Middle Ages*. II. *Poetry from the Kings' Sagas* 2: *From c. 1035 to c. 1300* 2009. Turnhout.

Skáldsk = Snorri Sturluson 1998. *Edda. Skáldskaparmál*. Ed. Anthony Faulkes. London.

Skjǫldunga saga: in *Danakonunga sǫgur* 1982. Ed. Bjarni Guðnason. Reykjavík, 3–90. *ÍF* XXXV.

SnE II = *Edda Snorra Sturlusonar* II 1852. Ed. Jón Sigurðsson et al. Hafniæ.

Snorri Sturluson 1987. *Edda*. Trans. Anthony Faulkes. London.

Stefán Karlsson 1976. 'Kringum Kringlu'. *Landsbókasafn Íslands: Árbók*, 5–25. Reprinted in *Stafkrókar. Ritgerðir eftir Stefán Karlsson gefnar út í tilefni af sjötugsafmæli hans* 2000. Reykjavík, 253–73.

Stefán Karlsson 1979. 'Islandsk bogeksport til Norge i middelalderen'. *Maal og minne*, 1–17. Reprinted in *Stafkrókar. Ritgerðir eftir Stefán Karlsson gefnar út í tilefni af sjötugsafmæli hans* 2000. Reykjavík, 188–205.

Straubhaar, Sandra Ballif 2002. 'Ambiguously Gendered. The Skalds Jórunn, Auðr and Steinunn'. In *Cold Counsel. Women in Old Norse Literature and Mythology*. Ed. Sarah M. Anderson and Karen Swenson. New York and London, 261–72.

Sturlunga saga I–II 1946. Ed. Jón Jóhannesson et al. Reykjavík.

Sverrir Tómasson 1994. 'The Hagiography of Snorri Sturluson, especially in the Great Saga of St Olaf'. In *Saints and Sagas: A Symposium*. Ed. Hans Bekker-Nielsen and Birte Carlé. Odense, 49–71.

Sverrir Tómasson 1998. *Formálar íslenskra sagnaritara á miðöldum. Rannsókn bókmenntahefðar.* Reykjavík.

Sverris saga 2007. Ed. Þorleifur Hauksson. Íslenzk fornrit XXX.

Theodoricus monachus 1998. *An Account of the Ancient History of the Norwegian Kings.* Trans. David and Ian McDougall. London.

Turville-Petre, E. O. G. 1953. *Origins of Icelandic Literature.* Oxford.

Turville-Petre, E. O. G. 1976. *Scaldic Poetry.* Oxford.

Turville-Petre, Joan 1988. 'A tree dream in Old Icelandic'. *Scripta Islandica* 39, 12–20.

de Vries, J. 1977. *Altnordisches etymologisches Wörterbuch.* 2nd revised edition. Leiden.

Wanner, Kevin J. 2008. *Snorri Sturluson and the Edda. The Conversion of Cultural Capital in Medieval Scandinavia.* Toronto.

Whaley, Diana 1991. *Heimskringla. An Introduction.* London.

Whaley, Diana (ed.) 1998. *The Poetry of Arnórr jarlaskáld.* London.

Widding, Ole, Hans Bekker-Nielsen and L. K. Shook 1963. 'The Lives of the Saints in Old Norse Prose. A Handlist'. *Mediaeval Studies* 25, 294–337.

Örvar-Odds saga. In *Fornaldarsögur norðurlanda* 1950. Ed. Guðni Jónsson. Reykjavík, II 199–363.

SNORRI STURLUSON

HEIMSKRINGLA
III

[3] Magnúss saga ins góða

CHAPTER ONE

After Yule Magnús Óláfsson got ready to set out from the east in Hólmgarðr down to Aldeigjuborg. They begin to prepare their ships when the ice broke up in the spring. Arnórr jarlaskáld (Jarls' Poet) speaks of this in *Magnússdrápa*:[1]

1. Now I mean, for well I know them,   *Magnússdrápa* 1
    to name to men the exploits   *Fsk* 208–09
    of the strife-quick sword's-edge   *ÓH* 614
    stainer[2]—let gold-breakers[3] listen!   *Skald* II 207–08
    The serpent's home's hater[4]
    had not reached eleven winters
    fully when the bold friend of Hǫrðar[5]
    fitted warships to leave Garðar.

[4] King Magnús laid his course in the spring from the east to Svíþjóð. So says Arnórr:

2. The young edge-reddener[6] called men   *Magnússdrápa* 2
    out to an assembly;   *Fsk* 208–09
    the trim troop of the eagle-feeder[7]   *ÓH* 614
    took up, war-clad, rowing stations.   *Skald* II 209
    The great king with hull rime-crusted   *Skáldsk* 94
    clove, bold, the salt westwards;
    keen gales carried the surf-fire's
    quencher[8] to Sigtúnir.

---

[1] Arnórr jarlaskáld Þórðarson was the son of another court poet, Þórðr Kolbeinsson (see Vol. I, note 473), from Hítarnes in western Iceland. His nickname refers to his service of the Orkney jarls Rǫgnvaldr and Þorfinnr, for whom he composed the memorial poems *Rǫgnvaldsdrápa* and (some twenty years later) *Þorfinnsdrápa*. He is said to have composed for the kings Magnús and Haraldr during their joint rule, and memorial poems for them both, which survive in only fragmentary form. His poem *Hrynhenda*, for Magnús, is the first known praise poem to use the expanded *hrynhent* metre, which has eight rather than six metrical positions in each line (see stanzas 7, 8, 36, 39, 40 and 74 below).

[2] *hneitis eggja rjóðandi*: 'reddener of the sword's edges', warrior.

[3] *seimbroti*: 'breaker, distributor of gold', generous man.

[4] *ormsetrs hati*: 'hater of the dragon's home (treasure, on which a dragon lies)', generous man, who gives away treasure.

[5] *Hǫrða vinr*: 'friend of people of Hǫrðaland', king of Norway (Magnús).

[6] *eggrjóðandi*: 'blade-reddener', warrior.

[7] *ara brœðir*: 'feeder of the eagle', warrior.

[8] *brimlogs rýrir*: 'destroyer of surf-fire (gold)', generous man.

Here it says that King Magnús, when he travelled from the east in Garðaríki, he first of all sailed to Svíþjóð and up to Sigtúnir. At this time the king in Svíþjóð was Emundr Óláfsson.[9] Also there then was Queen Ástríðr, who had been married to the blessed King Óláfr. She welcomed her stepson[10] Magnús extremely warmly, and immediately had a large assembly summoned in the place that is known as at Hangrar. And at this assembly Ástríðr spoke, saying as follows:

'There is now come here with us the son of the blessed King Óláfr, who is called Magnús, now planning [5] his expedition to Norway to claim his patrimony. I have a great obligation to support him on this journey, since he is my stepson, as is known to everyone, both Svíar and Norwegians. I shall in this spare nothing that is within my power by which his support may be as great as can be, both in regard to the numbers of men that I have at my disposal, and also the wealth. Moreover all those that commit themselves to this expedition with him will have access to my complete friendship. I also wish to announce that I shall undertake this expedition with him. It will then be plain to all that I shall not spare anything else for his support that I am able to grant him.'

After this she spoke long and eloquently. But when she stopped, then many replied, saying that the Svíar had gained little glory from their travels to Norway when they had followed his father King Óláfr.

'And there is now little better prospect with this king,' they say. 'People are therefore not keen on this expedition.'

Ástríðr replies: 'All those that would like to be men of valour at all will not be fearful about that. But if people have lost their relatives with the blessed King Óláfr, or have themselves been wounded, then it is now a manly thing to go to Norway now and take vengeance for it.'

Ástríðr managed her words and support so that a great number of troops came forward to go with him to Norway with Ástríðr. The poet Sigvatr mentions this:

3.   With my praise I'll reward for   Poem about Queen Ástríðr 1
    a wealth of treasures, grandly,   *Skald* I 646
    Qleifr's daughter,[11] spouse of
    the stout prince, most victorious.
[6]   A host met at Hangrar,
    huge, from the land of Svíar,
    in the east, as Ástríðr
    Qleifr's son supported.

[9] It must actually have been Qnundr (Jákob) Óláfsson at this date. Emundr Óláfsson did not succeed until 1050.

[10] Not strictly speaking stepson. Ástríðr was St Óláfr's first wife, Magnús's mother was St Óláfr's second wife.

[11] Daughter of King Óláfr of the Svíar.

4. Wise in counsel, she could not   Poem about Queen Ástríðr 2
   the keen Svíar have handled   Skald I 648
   better had brisk Magnús
   been her own offspring.
   She most, with Christ the mighty,
   made sure that King Magnús
   happily could inherit
   Haraldr's[12] whole legacy.

5. He owes Ástríðr a debt for   Poem about Queen Ástríðr 3
   her action, and we are glad of it;   Skald I 649
   it made generous Magnús,
   men's friend,[13] wide-landed.
   She has aided, as will few
   others, her step-son, deeply
   wise woman; I honour
   with words of truth that lady.

[7] So says the poet Þjóðólfr in *Magnússflokkr*:[14]

6. You launched, all-ruler, a warship—   *Magnússflokkr* 2
   the yard shivered, driven—   Skald II 65
   sent then over sea the thirty-
   seater at full stretch, gliding.
   The wild storm did not spare the
   swayed mast above you, lord;
   fine retainers took down the masthead-
   tapestry[15] at Sigtúnir.

CHAPTER TWO

Magnús Óláfsson began his expedition from Sigtúnir, now taking a large troop that the Svíar had provided him with. They travelled on foot across Svíþjóð and so to Helsingjaland. So says Arnórr jarlaskáld:

[12] Haraldr hárfagri, founder of the dynasty, or Magnús's grandfather, Haraldr grenski.

[13] *virða vinr*: 'friend of men', king.

[14] The Icelandic poet Þjóðólfr Arnórsson is said in *Skáldatal* to have composed for Magnús inn góði and for Haraldr harðráði, and many of his surviving verses are assigned to a named poem in honour of each of these kings: the *Magnússflokkr* named here, and the *Sexstefja* for Haraldr, named in Snorri's *Separate Saga of St Óláfr* (see Vol. II, note 455). In addition there are fragments of a *runhent* (rhyming) poem in honour of Haraldr, and verses that may have belonged to further poems about these kings. *Sneglu-Halla þáttr* refers to Þjóðólfr as Haraldr's *hǫfuðskáld* 'chief poet' and locates his origin in Svarfaðardalr, Iceland.

[15] *húnskript*: 'pictured cloth of the mast-head', decorated sail.

[8]   7.   Afterwards crimson shields you carried,   *Hrynhenda* 5
            combat-Yggr,[16] through Swedish settlements,   *ÓH* 615
            no poor pick of troops you garnered,   *Skald* II 189
            people of the land sought your faction.
            From east you came, tongue-colourer
            of the company of wolves,[17] known to people,
            to proud meetings, picked warriors
            with pale shields and inlaid javelins.

After that Magnús Óláfsson travelled from the east across Jamtaland and over Kjǫlr and down into Þrándheimr, and immediately all the people of these places welcomed him. But King Sveinn's people, as soon as they learned that King Óláfr's son Magnús was come into their country, then they all scattered in flight to safety. No resistance was offered to Magnús there. King Sveinn was in the south of the country. So says Arnórr jarlaskáld:

      8.   You held west with the highest   *Hrynhenda* 6
            of helms of terror into Þrœndish homes;   *ÓH* 615
            they say your foemen faltered,   *Skald* II 190–91
            feather-reddener of Yggr's seagull.[18]
[9]   Your enemies, sater of the swarthy
            surf-of-wounds vulture,[19] felt their misery—
            they said your foemen were, fearful,
            forced to save their lives—increasing.

CHAPTER THREE

Magnús Óláfsson travelled with his troops out to Kaupangr. He was welcomed there. After that he had Eyraþing summoned. And when the farming community got to the assembly, then at it Magnús was accepted as king over the whole country as widely as his father King Óláfr had ruled. After that King Magnús took on a following for himself and set up landed men.[20] In every area he appointed men to stewardships and to prefectures. In the autumn King Magnús immediately called out a levy from the whole of Þrándheimr, getting plenty of troops, afterwards taking his army south along the coast.

[16] *rimmu Yggr*: 'Óðinn of battle', warrior.

[17] *ulfa ferðar tungu rjóðr*: 'tongue-reddener of the pack of wolves', warrior.

[18] *Yggjar mós fiðrirjóðr*: 'reddener of the feathers of the seagull (raven) of Óðinn', warrior.

[19] *benja kolgu blágams fœðir*: feeder of the dark vulture (raven) of the wave of wounds (blood)', warrior.

[20] A *lendr maðr* 'landed man' was one who held land in fief from the king. He was next in rank to a jarl in Norway.

[10] CHAPTER FOUR

Sveinn Álfífuson was staying in Sunn-Hǫrðaland at the time he heard about the news of this martial activity. He immediately had a war arrow issued and sent out in all directions from where he was, summoning the farming people to come to him and adding that the whole population was to come out with troops and ships and defend the country with him. All the troops from that area that were nearest to the king went to see him. The king then held an assembly and discussion with the farmers and announced his intention, saying this, that he plans to go against King Óláfr's son King Magnús and fight a battle with him if the farmers were willing to go with him. The king spoke for rather a short time. The farmers gave little applause to his speech. Then the leading Danes that were with the king made long and eloquent speeches, but the farmers replied, opposing them. Many said that they were willing to go with King Sveinn and fight by his side, but some refused. Some were entirely silent, some said this, that they would make their way to King Magnús as soon as they could. Then King Sveinn replies:

'It seems to me that few of the farming people that we had sent word to are come here. But these farmers that are here say to our face that they want to side with King Magnús, so it seems to me that they will all be the same support to us as those that say they want to stay put, and also those that say nothing about it. But as for those others that say that they will go with us, it will be every other one or more of them that will be no use to us to turn to if we engage in battle with King Magnús. It is my opinion that we should place no trust in these farmers, rather let us go there where the people are all reliable and faithful to us. We have there sufficient support to subject this country to ourself.'

And as soon as the king had delivered this opinion, then [11] all his men followed this advice. They then turned the prows of their ships around and hoisted their sails. King Sveinn then sailed east along the coast and did not stop until he got to Denmark. He was welcomed there. And when he met his brother Hǫrða-Knútr, then he invited King Sveinn to hold power with him there in Denmark, and Sveinn agreed to this.

CHAPTER FIVE

In the autumn King Magnús travelled east right to the border, and he was accepted as king over the whole country, and all the people of the country were glad that Magnús had become king. That same autumn Knútr inn ríki (the Great) died in England on the Ides of November.[21] He was buried in Winchester. He had by then been king over Denmark for seven and twenty

---

[21] 13th November 1035.

winters, and over both there and over England for four and twenty winters, and over Norway as well for seven winters.[22] Then Knútr's son Haraldr was accepted as king in England. That same winter Sveinn Álfífuson died in Denmark. Þjóðólfr said this of King Magnús:

9. Eagle's sole-reddener, you stepped on   *Magnússflokkr* 3
    soil on your way from Svíþjóð;   *Skald* II 67
    a brave force followed you
    from the east, lord, to Norway.
    Sveinn fled; sometime later,
    surely let down, from the country
[12]   I heard that off abroad
    Álfífa's son went rushing.

Bjarni Gullbrárskáld (Gullbrá's Poet) composed about Kálfr Árnason:

10. You helped young princes have the   *Kálfsflokkr* 6
    inheritance due to them;   *Fsk* 208 (1–4 after 5–8)
    it's true that Sveinn could be sovereign   *ÓH* 619
    solely over Denmark.   *Skald* I 886
    Kálfr, to the country
    keen Magnús you conducted
    from Garðar; 'twas you gave the ruler
    governance of the kingdom.

King Magnús was that winter ruling over Norway, and Hǫrða-Knútr over Denmark.

CHAPTER SIX

The following spring both the kings called out levies, and the word got around that they would be engaging in battle by the Elfr. But as the two armies advanced on each other until they were close to meeting, then landed men from each host sent intelligence to their relatives and friends, and with the messages from both sides they included the request that people were to make peace between the kings. And because the kings were both like children and young, at that time the government of the land was in the hands of powerful men on their behalf that had been appointed for this in each country. So it came about that a peace conference was arranged

[22] This is rather inaccurate. After Sveinn Forkbeard's death in 1014 (1008 according to Snorri) his son Haraldr was sole king over Denmark, and Knútr did not become king there until 1019, on Haraldr's death (1018 according to Snorri), three years after the Anglo-Saxons had submitted to Knútr. Knútr was thus king of Denmark for 16 years and king of England for 19 years.

between the kings. After that they met in person and a settlement was discussed, [13] and the terms of it were that the kings were to swear oaths of brotherhood and establish peace between them for as long as both their lives lasted, but if one of them died without leaving a son, then the one that survived was to inherit from him territories and subjects. Twelve men, those who were of highest rank from each kingdom, swore to this along with the kings that this agreement should be kept as long as any of them lived. Then the kings parted, and each went back to his kingdom, and this agreement was kept as long as they lived.

CHAPTER SEVEN

Queen Ástríðr, who had been married to King Óláfr the Saint, came to Norway with her stepson King Magnús, and stayed with him in high honour, as [14] was fitting. Then there also came to the court King Magnús's mother Álfhildr. The king immediately welcomed her with the greatest affection and settled her down honourably. But it was with Álfhildr as can happen with many that receive power, that her ambition grew in proportion, so that she did not like it that Queen Ástríðr was rather more highly honoured than she in precedence with seating and other treatment. Álfhildr wanted to sit closer to the king, but Ástríðr called her her servant woman, which was what she had been before, when Ástríðr was queen over Norway, while King Óláfr was ruling the land. Ástríðr wanted by no means to share a seat with Álfhildr. They could not bear to be in the same room.

The poet Sigvatr had been travelling to Rome when the battle at Stiklarstaðir took place. And while he was on his way back from the south, he learned of King Óláfr's fall. This was a very great sorrow to him. Then he said:

> 11. I stood on Mont,[23] remembered, *ÓH* 617
>   one morning, near castles,[24] *Skald* I 722
>   where many broad shields and masking[25]
>   mailcoats flew asunder.
>   I recalled the king who in his
>   country in early bud-time[26]
>   once was happy; my father
>   was there that time: Þórrøðr.

---

[23] *mont*: presumably the Italian *monte*, referring to either the Alps or the Appenines.

[24] Each of the phrases *borgum nær* 'near castles, cities' and *of morgin* 'in the morning' could alternatively refer to the remembered battle rather than to the poet's current situation.

[25] *síðar*: literally 'long, hanging'.

[26] *ǫndverðan brum*: the beginning of bud-time, spring; i.e. in his youth.

[15] One day Sigvatr was walking through a certain village and heard that some husband was lamenting bitterly that he had lost his wife, beating his breast and tearing his clothes off, weeping a lot, saying he would willingly die. Sigvatr said:

> 12. A man claims, if he misses   *ÓH* 442
>   a maid's embrace, he's ready   *Skald* I 725
>   to die; love's bought dear if even
>   the dignified must weep for her.
>   But fierce tears[27] the fearless,
>   flight-shy man sheds, bereft of
>   his lord; worse looks our grievous
>   loss to the king's servants.

CHAPTER EIGHT

Sigvatr got back to Norway. He had an estate and children in Þrándheimr. He travelled from the south along the coast on a trading ship. And when they were lying in Hillarsund, then they saw where many eagles were flying. Sigvatr spoke:

> 13. I see ravens to the harbour   *Skald* I 726
>   hurry, recalling carrion,
> [16] where rode once a ship under
>   the worthy son of Northmen.[28]
>   Greedy eagles yell shrilly
>   each day between Hillar—
>   those that Óleifr often
>   once fed—and the mainland.

And when Sigvatr got north to Kaupangr, King Sveinn was then there, and invited Sigvatr to go and be with him, for he had previously been with King Sveinn's father Knútr inn ríki. Sigvatr says that he wants to go back to his estate.

It happened one day when Sigvatr was walking out on the street, he saw where the king's men were entertaining themselves. Sigvatr spoke:

> 14. I turn aside from the sport of   *Skald* I 727
>   soldiers of the king's retinue;
>   am pale as bast,[29] burdened
>   my breast is with feeling.

[27] *vígtǫr*: 'battle-tears', i.e. 'tears of rage shed by a warrior in a murderous mood'.
[28] Óláfr Haraldsson.
[29] bast, the pale inner bark of the birch or lime tree, used for making rope.

I recall where once my
widely-praised lord and I often
played on his people's ancestral
properties formerly.

After that he went home. He heard many men [17] criticising him and saying
that he had deserted King Óláfr. Sigvatr spoke:

15. May White-Christ punish me   *ÓH* 618
     if I meant to depart from   *Skald* I 728
     Óleifr—I'm innocent
     of that—with hot fire.
     Such witness, plentiful as water—
     I went to Rome in peril—
     of others I have; from people
     I shall never hide it.

Sigvatr was discontented at home. He went out during the day and spoke:

16. The high leaning cliffs looked to me   *Skald* I 729
     laughing, over all Norway—
     once I was known on the vessels—
     while Óleifr was living.
     Now the slopes seem to me—
     such is my sorrow;
     I lost all the king's favour—
     unhappier since then.

At the beginning of winter Sigvatr travelled east across Kjǫlr to Jamtaland
and on to Helsingjaland, coming out in Svíþjóð and going straight to Queen
Ástríðr, and stayed with her in high [18] honour for a long time. And he also
stayed with her brother King Ǫnundr, and received from him ten marks of
pure silver. So it says in *Knútsdrápa*. Sigvatr would often ask, when he met
merchants who travelled to Hólmgarðr, what they could tell him of Magnús
Óláfsson. He spoke:

17. From the east I am still eager   *Skald* I 730
     to ask, from Garðar, about
     the young prince; the praises
     often brought are not sparing.
     I ask about little, though the littlest
     of love-birds, between us creeping,
     fly; I am cheated of the coming
     of the king's heir hither.

CHAPTER NINE

So when Magnús Óláfsson got to Svíþjóð from Garðaríki, Sigvatr was then there with Queen Ástríðr, and they were all very pleased. Then Sigvatr spoke:

18.   You rebounded home boldly,   *Skald* I 734
    but well may rejoice in
    lands and men, King Magnús;
    your might I endorse.
[19]   I would have gone to Garðar
    given my closeness to you;
    my godson got a writing,
    great king, from your stepmother.[30]

After that Sigvatr joined Queen Ástríðr on her journey accompanying Magnús to Norway. Sigvatr spoke:

19.   I speak my mind, Magnús,   *Skald* I 736
    to men, that I rejoice in
    your life, attending assemblies;
    it is God's endowment.
    The lord of men would leave an
    illustrious son, if he turned out
    like his father; few peoples
    could foster such a ruler.

[20] And when Magnús had become king in Norway, then Sigvatr followed him and was very dear to the king. He then spoke this, when Queen Ástríðr and the king's mother Álfhildr had been having some words together:

20.   Let Ástríðr be higher,   *Skald* I 736
    Álfhildr, than yourself,
    though your status greatly—
    God willed it—is improving.

CHAPTER TEN

King Magnús had a shrine made and ornamented with gold and silver and set with precious stones. And this shrine was both in size and its shape made in other respects like a coffin, except that there were legs underneath and on

[30] Literally, 'a document of the sister, kinswoman was written to [my] godson'. Sigvatr was Magnús's godfather; hence their closeness, mentioned in the previous line. It has been suggested that this refers to a document written by Magnús's stepmother, Ástríðr; either a letter to him (*Hkr* III 19) or a statement of his eligibility to reign as king of Norway (*Hkr* 1991 567).

top the lid was shaped like a roof and up above it figureheads and a ridge. On the lid there are hinges at the back and hasps in front, and these are locked with a key. After that King Magnús had the holy relics of King Óláfr laid in this shrine. There were many miracles performed there at the holy relics of King Óláfr. The poet Sigvatr mentions this:

21. For him whose heart was noble   *Erfidrápa Óláfs helga* 24
     has a gold shrine been made, for my   *ÓH* 616
     lord; the leader's sanctity   *Skald* I 693
     I laud; to God he journeyed.
[21] Soon many a sword-tree[31] goes from
     the unsullied king's glorious
     tomb, with his sight healed,
     who had come blind thither.

Then the celebration of the holy feast of King Óláfr was made law all over Norway. That day[32] was then straight away celebrated there as one of the highest feasts. The poet Sigvatr mentions this:

22. It befits us the feast of Óleifr,   *Erfidrápa Óláfs helga* 25
     father of Magnús, in my dwelling   *ÓH* 617
     to celebrate—God strengthens   *Skald* I 695
     the sovereign—sincerely.
     I must uphold honestly
     the holy death-day, lamented,
     of the king who fitted
     the forks of my arm[33] with red gold.

[22] CHAPTER ELEVEN

Þórir hundr (Dog) left the country soon after King Óláfr's fall. Þórir travelled out to Jórsalir, and there are many that say that he has never come back. Þórir hundr's son was called Sigurðr, father of Rannveig who was married to Árni Árnason's son Jóan. Their children were Víðkunnr in Bjarkey and Sigurðr hundr (Dog), Erlingr and Jarðþrúðr.

CHAPTER TWELVE

Hárekr from Þjótta stayed at home on his estates right on until Magnús Óláfsson got to the country and he was king. Then Hárekr travelled south to Þrándheimr to see King Magnús. At this time there was there with King

---

[31] *hrings meiðr*: 'sword's tree', warrior, man.
[32] 29th July.
[33] *handar tjǫlgur*: 'branches of the hand, arm', arms or fingers.

Magnús Ásmundr Grankelsson. And when Hárekr went ashore from his ship on his arrival at Niðaróss, and Ásmundr was standing on a balcony by the king, they saw Hárekr and recognised him. Ásmundr said to the king: 'Now I am going to pay back Hárekr for the killing of my father.' He had in his hand a small and thinly forged broad-bladed axe. The king looked at him and said: 'Use my axe instead.' This one was wedge-shaped and thick. The king spoke again: 'You must expect, Ásmundr, that the bones in that fellow will be hard.' Ásmundr took the axe and went down from the building, and when he got down onto the cross-street, then Hárekr and his men were coming up towards him. Ásmundr struck at Hárekr's head so that the axe immediately stuck down in his brain. This caused Hárekr's death. So Ásmundr went back up into the building to the king, and the edge had all broken off the axe. Then said the king: 'What use would the thin axe have been then? It looks to me as though this one is no good now.'

After this King Magnús gave Ásmundr revenues and [23] stewardship in Hálogaland, and there are many long stories about the dealings between Ásmundr and Hárekr's sons there.

CHAPTER THIRTEEN

Kálfr Árnason was largely in charge of the government together with King Magnús for a time to start with. But then people began to remind the king about Kálfr's whereabouts at Stiklarstaðir. Then Kálfr began to find it more difficult to cope with the king's moods. It came about on one occasion when there was a lot of people round the king and people were pleading their cases, then there came before him with his own urgent business a man who has been mentioned before, Þorgeirr of Súla from Veradalr. The king paid no heed to what he was saying and was listening to those that were nearer to him. Then Þorgeirr spoke to the king in a loud voice so that everyone could hear that was nearby:

23.   Speak to me,   *ÓH* 621
       Magnús king!   *Skald* II 9
       In your father's
       following I was.
       From there I carried
       my cloven skull,
       when they stepped over
       the stricken king.

You give love to
the loathsome crowd
of lord-betrayers
who delighted the devil.'

[24] Then people made an uproar about it, and some of them told Þorgeirr to leave. The king called him over to himself and afterwards settled his business in such a way that Þorgeirr was well pleased, and he promised him his friendship.

CHAPTER FOURTEEN

It was somewhat later, when King Magnús was at a banquet at Haugr in Veradalr. And while the king was sitting at table, then Kálfr Árnason was sitting on one side of him and on the other side Einarr þambarskelfir (Bowstring-shaker). It had reached the point where the king was beginning to treat Kálfr rather coldly, and was now honouring Einarr most highly. The king spoke to Einarr:

'Today we shall ride to Stiklarstaðir. I want to see the traces of what took place there.'

Einarr replied: 'I cannot tell you about that. Let your foster-father Kálfr go. He will be able to to tell you about what happened there.'

So when the tables had been taken away, then the king got ready to go. He said to Kálfr:

'You must go with me to Stiklarstaðir.'

Kálfr says that this was not necessary. Then the king stood up and spoke rather angrily:

'You shall go, Kálfr!'

Then the king went out. Kálfr got his clothes on quickly and said to his servant:

'You must ride in to Egg and tell my men to have all the luggage on board ship before sunset.'

The king rode to Stiklarstaðir and Kálfr with him. They dismounted from their horses and went to where the battle had been. Then said the king to Kálfr:

'Where is the place that the king fell?'

Kálfr replies, stretching out his spear-shaft: 'Here he lay when he had fallen,' he says.

The king said: 'Where were you then, Kálfr?'

He replies: 'Here where I am standing now.'

The king spoke, and was now red as blood: 'He was within range of your axe, then.'

Kálfr replies: 'My axe did not reach him.'

He then went off to his horse, leapt on its back and rode on his way and [25] all his men, but the king rode back to Haugr. In the evening Kálfr got in to Egg. His ship was ready by the shore and all his movable property on board and it was manned with his men. They immediately made their way during the night out along the fiord. After that Kálfr travelled day and night as fast as the wind would take him. He then sailed to the west across the sea and stayed there a long time, raiding round Scotland and round Ireland and the Suðreyjar. Bjarni Gullbrárskáld mentions this in *Kálfsflokkr*:

24. I've heard that Haraldr's nephew   *Kálfsflokkr* 7
     held you dear, Þorbergr's brother;   *ÓH* 624
     you earned that; it lasted   *Skald* I 887
     until men[34] destroyed it.
     Between you envious men
     kindled constant strife.
     I think Ǫleifr's heir
     was harmed by this affair.

CHAPTER FIFTEEN

King Magnús took possession of Vigg, which had been owned by Hrútr, and Kviststaðir, which had been owned by Þorgeirr, also of Egg, and all the property that Kálfr had left behind, and many other great possessions that had been owned by those on the farmers' side that had fallen at Stiklarstaðir he arranged to be appropriated by the royal treasury. He also inflicted heavy punishments on many of the men that had opposed [26] King Óláfr in that battle. Some of them he drove out of the country, and from some he exacted very heavy payments, for some he had their livestock destroyed. Then the landowners began to grumble and said among themselves:

'What can this king mean by acting towards us contrary to the laws that King Hákon inn góði (the Good) established? Does he not remember that we have never put up with loss of our rights? He will go the same way as his father or some of the other rulers that we have deprived of life when we got tired of their tyranny and lawlessness.'

This grumbling was widespread in the country. The people of Sogn had mustered troops, with the public announcement that they would engage in battle with King Magnús if he came there. King Magnús was at the time in Hǫrðaland and had been staying there a very long time and had a large troop and acted as though he would now be going north to Sogn. The king's friends

---

[34] *herr*: 'men'. This is the reading of the main *Hkr* manuscript; others have *hann* 'he' (see *Skald* I 887).

became aware of this, and twelve men held a conference and it was agreed between them to choose by lot one person to tell the king of this grumbling. And it was settled that the poet Sigvatr was chosen.

CHAPTER SIXTEEN

Sigvatr composed a *flokkr*[35] that is known as *Bersǫglisvísur* ('Plain-speaking verses'), and it opens to begin with about how they felt the king was hesitating too much about putting a stop to the landowners that were threatening to start hostilities against him. He spoke:

25. I've heard that south among Sygnir   *Bersǫglisvísur* 1
Sigvatr has dissuaded   *ÓH* 625
the king from waging warfare.   *Skald* II 12
I will go, if we yet must battle.
[27]   Let us arm, and with no
argument, defend, eager,
the lord and his lands with ring-swords;
how long till this encounter?

In the same poem there are these verses:

26. He who fell at Fitjar   *Bersǫglisvísur* 5
foremost[36] was called, and punished   *Mork* I (*Flb*) 33–34
hostile looting, Hǫkon,   *ÓH* 625
he was loved by people.   *Skald* II 16
Men held fast to the most friendly
foster-son of Aðalsteinn's
laws later; still farmers are slow
to relinquish what they remember.

27. I think they made just choices,   *Bersǫglisvísur* 6
farmers and jarls also,   *Mork* I (*Flb*) 34
for people's property was given   *ÓH* 625
peace by the two Óleifrs.   *Skald* II 17
[28]   Haraldr's heir, ever trusty,
and Tryggvi's son, supported
leek-straight[37] laws that the namesakes
laid down for the people.

---

[35] A series of stanzas without a refrain; a less formal style of poetry than a *drápa*.
[36] *fjǫlgegn*: 'effective in many ways'; perhaps a periphrasis for Hákon's nickname *inn góði* 'the Good'.
[37] *laukjǫfn*: 'straight as a leek', i.e. just.

28. King, at your counsellors you must not
become angry for plain speaking;
this command of our lord will
make clear, prince, the way for glory.
Other laws, unless the landsmen
lie, the farmers say they have,
worse than those you in Ulfasund
once promised to people.

Bersǫglisvísur 9
Mork (Flb) 36
ÓH 626
Skald II 20
Fsk 213

29. Who counsels you to cancel,
king intent on hatred—
often you assay slender
swords—your promises?
[29] A prosperous king of people
his pledges must honour.
To break your bond never,
battle-enlarger,[38] befits you.

Bersǫglisvísur 1
Mork I *(Flb)* 38–39
ÓH 626
Skald II 24

30. Who incites you to slay your
subjects' cattle, war-leader[39]?
It is arrogance for a ruler
in his realm to act so.
None had earlier offered
a young king such counsel;
your troops, I think, tire of plunder;
people, prince, are angry.

Bersǫglisvísur 11
Mork I *(Flb)* 37–38
Fsk 213–14
ÓH 626
Skald II 22

31. Take notice, thief-toppler,
of talk of men now going
about here; the hand must be
held back by moderation.
[30] It is a friend who offers—
you must heed, gladdener
of the tear-hawk of warm wounds,[40]
what the farmers want—a warning.

Bersǫglisvísur 10
Mork I *(Flb)* 37
Fsk 213 (ll.1–4)
ÓH 626
Skald II 21

32. The threat is grave that greybeards
against the king, as I hear it,
mean to rise; measures
must for that be taken.

Bersǫglisvísur 12
Mork I *(Flb)* 38
Fsk 214–15
Ágrip 2008, 46–48

---

[38] *hjaldrmǫgnuðr*: 'battle-increaser', warrior.

[39] *hjaldrgegnir*: 'advancer of battle', warrior.

[40] *varmra benja tármútaris teitir*: 'gladdener of the hawk (raven) of the tears of
warm wounds (blood)', warrior.

It's harsh when thing-men hang their	*3GT* 30, 114 (ll. 1–4)
heads, and under mantles—	*ÓH* 626
your servants are stricken	*Skald* II 23
with silence—stick their noses.	

33. All say the same: 'Of his   *Bersǫglisvísur* 14
subjects' ancestral properties   *Mork* I (*Flb*) 38
my lord claims ownership.'   *ÓH* 627
Honourable farmers turn against him.   *Skald* II 25
He who his inheritance
hands out to king's barons
according to rushed rulings
will reckon that robbery.

[31] After this warning the king changed for the better. Many people also used the same arguments with the king. So it came about that the king held discussions with the wisest people, and they then agreed on their laws. After this King Magnús had the law code written down that still applies in Þrándheimr and is known as Grágás. King Magnús became popular and beloved of all the people in the country. He was for this reason known as Magnús inn góði (the Good).

CHAPTER SEVENTEEN

King Haraldr of the English died four winters after the death of his father Knútr inn ríki.[41] He was buried beside his father in Winchester. After his death Haraldr's brother Hǫrða-Knútr, old Knútr's second son, took the kingdom in England. He was now king of both England and the realm of the Danes. He ruled this realm for two winters. He died of sickness in England and is buried in Winchester beside his father.[42] After his death [32] Eatvarðr inn góði (the Good), son of King Aðalráðr of the English and Jarl Ríkarðr of Rúða's daughter Queen Emma, was taken as king in England. King Eaðvarðr was half-brother[43] to Haraldr and Hǫrða-Knútr. Old Knútr and Emma's daughter was called Gunnhildr. She was married to Emperor Heinrekr in Saxland. He was known as Heinrekr mildi (the Gracious). Gunnhildr was three winters in Saxland before she got ill. She died two winters after the death of her father King Knútr.[44]

---

[41] 17th March 1040.

[42] 8th June 1042.

[43] *bróðir sammœðri* 'son of the same mother'. This is not correct. Haraldr was not son of Knútr's second wife Emma (who had previously been married to Æþelræd II), but of his first wife Ælfgifu (Álfífa).

[44] Gunnhildr was married to Henry 29th June 1036, and died 18th July (?) 1038. Henry became Emperor in 1046. In 1036 he was only king of Germany. Knútr died in 1035.

CHAPTER EIGHTEEN

King Magnús Óláfsson heard of the death of Hǫrða-Knútr. Then he immediately sent his men south to Denmark carrying messages to the men who had sworn oaths to him when their settlement and special agreements had been made between Magnús and Hǫrða-Knútr, and reminded them of their promises, adding also that he would immediately in the summer be coming to Denmark in person with his troops, and adding finally that he was going to take possession of the whole realm of the Danes as the special agreements and oaths had stated, or else himself fall in battle with his army. So says Arnórr jarlaskáld:

34. Extreme was the eloquence   *Magnússdrápa* 5
    the jarls' lord was endowed with.   *Mork* I (*Flb*) 48
    Fulfilment followed the words of   *Fsk* 216
    the fooler of she-wolf's sorrow,[45] *Skald* II 213
[33] when the prince said, in the cruel clash
    of carved shield,[46] under the raven's
    claw, he'd fall on his face, happy,
    fated, or else have Denmark.

CHAPTER NINETEEN

Then King Magnús mustered troops, summoning to come to him landed men and powerful landowners, providing himself with longships. And when these forces assembled then they were very splendid and very well fitted out. He had seventy ships when he sailed from Norway. So says Þjóðólfr:

35. Boldly you made use of, battle-   *Magnússflokkr* 4
    brave lord, long vessels,   *Skald* II 68
    in that men steered seventy
    sailing ships eastward.
    South sang linked boards; high-hoisted
    sails whispered with forestay.
    The creek was cut by an oak[47] high-masted;
    its curved rim Visundr lowered.

[34] Here it mentions that King Magnús now had the great Visundr (Bison) that the blessed King Óláfr had had built. It numbered more than thirty rowing benches. There was a bison-head on the prow and a fishtail aft. The

---

[45] *ylgjar angrtælir*: 'beguiler of the grief of the she-wolf', warrior who gladdens wolves by feeding them carrion, here Magnús.
[46] *grafnings gný*: 'clash of the graven shield', battle.
[47] *eiki*: a ship made of oak.

figurehead and the tail and both necks were all covered in gold. This is mentioned by Arnorr jarlaskáld:

36. Foam drove in on the afterdeck,   *Hrynhenda* 10
ugly; the red gold shivered   *Mork* I (*Flb*) 45
on the ship's helm; the fir-tree's hardy   *Skald* II 195
hound[48] set the rushing fir-ship plunging.
Strong prows from the north around Stafangr
you steered. The sea shook before you.
Blizzard-horse's[49] mastheads shone like
fire, up into the realm of Danes.

King Magnús sailed out from Agðir and across to Jótland. So says Arnórr:

37. I shall relate how, listing,   *Magnússdrápa* 6
the lee-side bison,[50] rime-swollen,   *Mork* I (*Flb*) 49
carried the king of the Sygnir,[51]   *Skald* II 215
courageous, southwards.
[35]   The caller of the mailcoat-meeting,[52]
the monarch, steered—gladly
people greeted the gods of
girdle-pins[53]—for broad Jótland.

CHAPTER TWENTY

And when King Magnus got to Denmark, then he was warmly welcomed there. He soon held assemblies and meetings with the people of the country and asked to be accepted in accordance with the special agreements. And since the national leaders that were most distinguished in Denmark were bound by oaths to King Magnús and wanted to keep their words and oaths, then they spoke much in favour of this before the people. There was another reason too, that Knútr inn ríki was now dead and all his progeny; and the third thing was that now the sainthood of King Óláfr was universally acknowledged throughout all countries, and his performance of miracles.

CHAPTER TWENTY-ONE

After this King Magnús had Vébjargaþing summoned. That is where the Danes have chosen themselves kings in both ancient and modern times.

---

[48] *fýris garmr*: 'hound of the fir-tree', stormy wind.

[49] *élmarr*: 'storm-horse', ship.

[50] *hléborðs visundr*: 'bison of the lee-side', ship. *Visundr*, in other verses the name of Magnús's ship, here has a dual function as a name and as the base word in a kenning.

[51] *Sygna þengill*: 'lord of Sygnir', i.e. king of Norway.

[52] *brynþings bjóðr*: 'convener of the mailcoat-assembly (battle)', warrior.

[53] *fetilstinga æsir*: 'gods of sword-belt spikes (swords)', warriors.

And at this assembly the Danes accepted Magnús Óláfsson as king over the whole realm of Danes. King Magnús stayed in Denmark for a long time during the summer, and all the people welcomed him warmly wherever he came, and submitted themselves to him. He then organised the whole country, the stewardships and prefectures, and granted revenues [36] to men of the ruling class. But when autumn was drawing to a close, he took his forces to Norway and stayed on the Elfr for a while.

CHAPTER TWENTY-TWO

There is a man called Sveinn, son of Þorgils sprakaleggr's (Break-Leg's) son Jarl Úlfr. Sveinn's mother was King Sveinn tjúguskegg's (Forkbeard's) daughter Ástríðr. She was Knútr inn ríki's (half-)sister by the same father, but she had the same mother as King Óláfr Eiríksson of the Svíar. Their mother was Skǫglar-Tósti's (Battle-) daughter Queen Sigríðr in stórláta (of the Great Undertakings).

Sveinn Úlfsson had now been staying for a long time with his relatives, the kings of the Svíar, ever since his father Jarl Úlfr had fallen, as is written in the Saga of Knútr inn gamli (the Old), [where it says] that the latter had his kinsman by marriage Jarl Úlfr killed in Hróiskelda.[54] It was for this reason that Sveinn did not stay in Denmark after that.

Sveinn Úlfson was the most handsome of all men in looks. He was also the biggest and strongest of men and a very great man for sports and a very fine speaker. It was the opinion of everyone that knew him that he had all the qualities that make a good leader.

Sveinn Úlfsson came to see Magnús Óláfsson while he was lying on the Elfr, as was written above. The king received him kindly. He had many supporters for this there too, for Sveinn was a very popular person. He also spoke well and eloquently on his own behalf before the king, and it came about that Sveinn submitted to King Magnús and became his follower. After that the king and Sveinn discussed many things in private.

[37] CHAPTER TWENTY-THREE

One day when King Magnús was sitting on his throne and there were crowds of people round him, Sveinn Úlfsson was sitting on the footstool in front of the king. Then the king began to speak:

'I wish to make known to leading men and all the people the plan that I intend to put into effect. There has come here to me a person splendid both in descent and in himself, Sveinn Úlfsson. He has now become my follower and pledged to me his troth on this. And as you know, since all Danes have

---

[54] This information is apparently not in the surviving versions of *Knýtlinga saga*.

this summer become my subjects, so the country is without a ruler, now that I have left it, though as you know it is very subject to raids there from the Vinðr and Kúrir and other eastern Baltic peoples, and likewise from Saxons. Moreover I promised to provide them with a leader for the defence and government of the country. I can see no one as well suited for this in every respect as Sveinn Úlfsson. He has the descent for being a leader. Now I am going to make him my jarl and make over to him the realm of Danes to supervise while I am in Norway, just as Knútr inn ríki appointed his father Jarl Úlfr ruler over Denmark while Knútr was in England.'

Einarr þambarskelfir says: 'Too much of a jarl, too much of a jarl, foster-son!'

The king then spoke angrily: 'You think I don't know much, but it seems to me that you think some too much of a jarl, and thus some not much of a man.'

Then the king stood up and took his sword and fastened it to Sveinn's belt. After that he took a shield and fastened it on his shoulder, after that put a helmet on his head and gave him the title of jarl and the same revenues in Denmark as his father Jarl Úlfr had had there previously. After that a shrine with holy relics was brought out. Svainn laid his hands on it [38] and swore oaths of allegiance to King Magnús. After that the king led the jarl to the throne to sit next to him. So says Þjóðólfr:

38. Úlfr's son was himself by the Elfr	*Magnússflokkr* 5
east, and made fair promises;	*Mork* I (*Flb*) 52
There Sveinn did swear them,	*Fsk* 219
set his hands on the shrine.	*Skald* II 69
For him Óleifr's son set out,	
the Skǫnungar's king, pledges—	
less long has their concord-	
lasted than it should have.	

Then Jarl Sveinn travelled to Denmark, and was warmly welcomed by the whole people there. He then chose himself a following and soon became a great ruler. In the winter he travelled widely round the country and established very good relations with the leading men. He was also popular with the common people.

CHAPTER TWENTY-FOUR

King Magnús took his forces to the north of Norway and stayed there during the winter. But when spring came, then King Magnús called out a large naval force and took it south to Denmark. And when he got there, he learned the news from Vinðland that the Vinðr in Jómsborg had departed from their allegiance to him. The kings of the Danes had commanded a great jarldom there—they had founded Jómsborg in the first place—and it had [39] become a very strong fortress. So when King Magnús heard tell of this, then he called out from Denmark a great navy and made his way to Vinðland in the summer with his whole army, and had a very large army. Arnórr jarlaskáld mentions this:

> 39. You shall hear how you carried, kinsman   *Hrynhenda* 11
> of a king,[55] the war-shield into Vinðr country—   *Skald* II 196
> fortunate, you dragged from the flat slipway
> frost-coated boards[56]—in a *stef* section.[57]
> I have never yet learned, lord, of a ruler
> launching more ships at their homeland,
> you are giving grief to the Vinðr,
> engraved by ships then was the current.

And when King Magnús got to Vinðland, then he made for Jómsborg and immediately took the fortress, killing many people in it and burning the fortress and the countryside widely round about and causing very great devastation there. So says Arnórr jarlaskáld:

> 40. Prince, you fared with fire among ill-doers;   *Hrynhenda* 12
> fated was death then to seamen.   *Skáldsk* 100 (ll. 1–4)
> A column of fire you kindled,   *Skald* II 197
> crusher of thieves,[58] south at Jóm.
> [40]   The heathen folk in the broad fortress
> to defend halls never ventured.
> King, with bright fire you afforded
> the fortress-men heart-stopping terror.

Many people in Vinðland submitted to King Magnús, but there were very many more that fled away. Then King Magnús went back to Denmark, set up his winter quarters there and dismissed his army, both the Danish one and also many of the troops that had come with him from Norway.

CHAPTER TWENTY-FIVE

The same winter that Sveinn Úlfsson had become overlord over the whole realm of Danes and he had developed good relations with very many of the

---

[55] *hilmis kundr*: 'king's descendant', i.e. Magnús.

[56] *borð*: boards, i.e. ships. Some manuscripts have *bǫrð* 'prows'.

[57] *stefjamél*: A formal *drápa* included one or more *stef* 'refrains'. A *stefjamél* or *stefjabálkr* was a group of verses appearing between refrains.

[58] *hlenna þrýstir*: 'oppressor of thieves', just king.

important men and gained good report among the common people, then he had the title of king conferred on himself, and many of the ruling class were in favour of his doing this. But in the spring, when he learnt that King Magnús was travelliing from the north from Norway bringing a great army, then Sveinn went to Skáney and from there up into Gautland and so to Svíþjóð to see his kinsman King Emund of the Svíar, and stayed there during the summer, but kept men on the watch in Denmark for King Magnús's travels and the size of his forces. And when Sveinn learnt that King Magnús had dismissed a great part of his forces, and also that he was south in Jótland, then Sveinn rode down from Svíþjóð, having now a large force that the king of the Svíar provided him with. And when Sveinn [41] came out to Skáney, then the people of Skáney welcomed him and treated him as their king. Then a large force thronged to him. After this he travelled out to Sjáland, and he was welcomed there. He subjected everywhere there to himself. Then he travelled into Fjón and subjected all the islands to himself, and the people submitted to him. Sveinn had a great army and many ships.

CHAPTER TWENTY-SIX

King Magnús heard the news of all this, and of this too, that the Vinðr had an army out. After that King Magnús summoned troops to come to him, and there soon gathered an army from all over Jótland to him. Then Duke Ótta of Saxland joined him from Brunswick. He was at this time married to Úlfhildr, the blessed King Óláfr's daughter and King Magnús's sister. The duke had a large force of men. The leaders of the Danes urged King Magnús to advance against the army of Vinðr and not allow heathen people to travel over their country there and lay it waste, and this proposal was adopted, that the king turned his army to the south on towards Heiðabýr. But when King Magnús was lying by Skotborgará on Hlýrskógsheiðr then there came to him intelligence from the army of Vinðr, which included the report that they had such a large army that no one could number it, and that [42] King Magnús had not a fraction of their numbers and the only thing for him was to flee away. King Magnús, however, wanted to fight as long as people felt he had some possibility of winning, though most were against it, and everyone agreed that the Vinðr had an invincible army, though Duke Ótta was rather in favour of fighting. The king then had a trumpet muster the whole army and had everyone put on their armour, and they lay outside during the night under their shields, because they had been told that the army of Vinðr had advanced close to them, and the king was very anxious. He felt it would be a bad thing if he had to flee, for he had never experienced that. He slept little during the night and chanted his prayers.

[43] CHAPTER TWENTY-SEVEN

The next day was the eve of Michaelmas day.[59] And when it was almost dawn, then the king fell asleep and dreamt that he saw his father the blessed King Óláfr, and he spoke to him:

'Are you very anxious and fearful now that the Vinðr are advancing against you with a large army? You must not fear heathens, even if there are a lot of them together. I will be with you in this battle. Make your attack on the Vinðr when you hear my trumpet.'

And when the king awoke, then he tells what he has dreamt. Then day began to dawn. Then all the people heard the sound of bells up in the sky, and King Magnús's men recognised, those that had been in Niðaróss, that it sounded as if it was Glǫð being rung. This bell had been given by King Óláfr to Clemenskirkja in Kaupangr.

CHAPTER TWENTY-EIGHT

Then King Magnús got up and called out that the war-trumpets should be blown. Then the army of Vinðr advanced from the south over the river against them. Then all the king's army leapt up and made for the heathens. King Magnús threw his coat of mail off himself and was wearing outermost a red silk tunic and took in his hand the axe Hel, that had been King Óláfr's. King Magnús ran ahead of all other men against the enemy army and straight away hewed with both hands at one man after another. So says Arnórr jarlaskáld:

41.	With broad axe, unwearied,	*Magnússdrápa* 10
	went forth the ruler—	*Mork* I (*Flb*) 65–66
	sword-clash happened round the Hǫrðar's	*Fsk* 223
	head[60]—and threw off his mailcoat,	*ÓH* 630
[44]	when the shaft—land was shared out by	*Skald* II 219
	the shaping guardian of Heaven,[61]	
	Hel[62] clove pallid craniums—	
	the king's two hands encircled.	

This battle was not a long one. The king's men fought like fury. And wherever they met, the Vinðr fell as thick as waves breaking on the shore, and those that were still standing turned in flight, and they were then cut down like cattle. The king himself pursued the rout eastwards across the heath, and the host fell all over the heath. So says Þjóðólfr:

[59] *Mikjálsmessuaptann*: cf. note 188 below. St Michael's day (Michaelmas or the Feast of St Michael and all Angels) is 29th September.

[60] *Hǫrða hilmir*: 'ruler of the Hǫrðar', king of Norway (Magnús).

[61] *himins skapvǫrðr*: 'the shaping-guardian of Heaven', God.

[62] *Hel*: the axe owned by St Óláfr, named after the goddess of the underworld.

42. I hold that in a troop of a hundred
Haraldr's brother's son[63] was standing—
the raven saw his hunger-ban
soon coming[64]—in the army's forefront.
Far-flung was the path of
fleeing Vinðr; where Magnús battled
hewn corpses came to hide the
heath a league broadly.

Magnússflokkr 10
Mork I (*Flb*) 65
Fsk 222
ÓH 630
Skald II 72

It is universally held that no slaughter as great as that of the Vinðr which took place on [45] Hlýrskógsheiðr has taken place in Northern Lands in Christian times. But not many of King Magnús's troops fell, though numbers were wounded. After the battle King Magnús has his men's wounds bandaged, though there were not as many doctors in the army as were now required. So the king went up to such men as seemed suitable to him and felt their hands, and as he took hold of their palms and stroked them, then he nominated twelve men who it seemed to him must have the softest hands, saying that they were to bandage men's wounds, though none of them had ever bandaged wounds before. And all these became very good doctors. There were two Icelandic men among them, one was Þorkell Geirason of Lyngar, the other Bárðr svarti (the Black) in Selárdalr's father Atli, and many doctors were descended from them afterwards. After this battle the miracle that the blessed King Óláfr had performed became famous throughout very many lands, and it was universally said that no one had better fight against King Magnús Óláfsson, and his father King Óláfr would stand by him so closely that his enemies would not be able to offer him any resistance for that reason.

[46] CHAPTER TWENTY-NINE

King Magnús now turned his army against Sveinn, whom he referred to as his jarl, though the Danes called him king. King Magnús took to his ships and prepared his army. Then both sides increased their numbers greatly. There were now many leading men among Sveinn's troops, Skánungar, Hallandsfarar, Fjónbúar. But King Magnús had mostly Norwegians and Jótar. He then took his troops to meet with Sveinn. They clashed at Ré off Vestland. A great battle took place there, and it ended with King Magnús being victorious, while Sveinn fled and lost many troops. He then fled back to Skáney, because he had a refuge up in Gautland if he needed to have recourse to one. But King Magnús then went back to Jótland and stayed there for the winter with a large following and had a watch kept on his ships. Arnórr jarlaskáld mentions all this:

---

[63] King Magnús, whose father Óláfr helgi was half-brother of Haraldr harðráði.
[64] i.e. that its food was on its way.

43. Keen, at Ré the ruler   *Magnússdrápa* 9
     raised Glammi's strong meeting.[65]   *Mork* I (*Flb*) 54
     Frankish blades were bloodied   *Skald* II 2184
     off broad Vestland by the monarch.

[47] CHAPTER THIRTY

Sveinn Úlfsson went immediately aboard his ships when he learnt that King
Magnús had disembarked from his ships. Sveinn gathered troops to himself,
all that he could get, and then went during the winter round Sjáland and
round Fjón and round the islands, and when Yule approached, he made his
way south to Jótland, making first for Limafjǫrðr, and many people there
became his subjects, and he took tribute from some. Some went to see King
Magnús. So when King Magnús heard about this, what Sveinn was up to,
then he went to his ships, taking with him the troop of Norwegians that was
then in Denmark, and some Danish troops, then made his way from the south
along the coast. Sveinn was now in Áróss and had a large force, so when
he heard about King Magnús's army, then he brought his troops out of the
town and prepared for battle. But when King Magnús had found out where
Sveinn was, and he realised that they could not now be far away from each
other, then he had a meeting with his men and spoke to his troops, saying this:
    'Now we have learnt that the jarl with his troops will be lying here now ahead
of us. I am told that they have a large force. And I want to make you aware of
my plan. I want to go ahead to a meeting with the jarl and fight with him, though
we have rather fewer troops. We shall now place our trust again, just as before,
in God Himself and my father the blessed King Óláfr. He has granted us victory
several times before when we have fought, and we have often had fewer forces
than our enemies. Now I desire that men should be prepared for us to be looking
out for them, and when our meeting comes about, then we shall row at them and
immediately start the battle. So let all my men be ready to fight.'
    Then they put on their armour and each one got himself and his position
ready. King Magnús and his men advanced until they saw the jarl's force,
immediately launching an attack. So [48] Sveinn's men armed themselves
and fastened their ships together. Immediately a fierce battle commenced.
So says the poet Þjóðólfr:

44.   Recently jarl and ruler   *Magnússflokkr* 8
      round shields brought together;   *Skald* II 73
      there biting blade-play[66] came over
      the billows' ember-pine-trees,[67]

---

[65] *Glamma rammþing*: 'strong meeting of Glammi (a sea-king)', battle.
[66] *brandleikr*: 'sword-play', battle.
[67] *grœðis glóða bǫrr*: 'conifer of embers of the ocean (gold)', man; here plural.

so that shirt-markers of the meeting
of the maid of Heðinn[68] remembered
no greater engagement; the army
got to make spear-tumult.[69]

They fought across the bows, and only those stationed in the forward part of
the ship could make their blows tell, but those that were in the midmost part
thrust with halberds, and all those that were further aft shot sling-spears or
javelins or war-darts, while some threw stones or casting spears, and those
that were behind the mast used bows and arrows. Þjóðólfr mentions this:

45.	I learned of flint-headed lances	*Magnússflokkr* 9
	launched, and many a spear—	*Skald* II 74
	the raven got meat—where we waged	
	war, swiftly at broad shields.	
	Men made use, as best they	
	might, in the quarrel of	
	arms,[70] of rocks and arrows,	
	ring-trees[71] then lay struck down.	
[49] 46.	Archers placed more arrows	*Magnússflokkr* 10
	on the tautened bowstring;	*Skald* II 75
	that day the Þrœndir would not	
	get short of missiles earlier.	
	Then sling-darts so thickly	
	sped over the battle,	
	a storm of arrows sent forth wildly,	
	scarce could you see between them.	

Here it says how furious was the shower of missiles. King Magnús was to
begin with at the beginning of the battle behind a shield wall, but when he
found they were not making much progress, then he leapt forward out of
the shield wall and so along the ship and shouted loudly, urging his men
on and going right forward to the prow into the hand-to-hand fighting. And
when his men saw this, then they all urged each other. Now there was a great
shouting throughout his host. So says Þjóðólfr:

[68] *Heðins manþinga serkjar merkjendr*: 'markers of the shirt (mailcoat) of the
assembly (battle) of Heðinn's maiden (Hildr)', warriors, who stain mailcoats with
blood. Hildr, daughter of King Hǫgni, was carried off by the legendary hero Heðinn,
which led to the Hjaðningavíg battle (*Skáldsk* 72); her assembly is battle.

[69] *geira gný*: 'din of spears', battle.

[70] *vápna senna*: 'quarrel of weapons', battle.

[71] *baugs bǫrvar*: 'conifers of the (arm)-ring', men.

47.   Among Magnús's[72] warriors   *Magnússflokkr* 11
      men urged each other boldly   *Skald* II 77
      onwards with stout war-clouds;[73]
      the urging worked, where they battled.

[50] Then a most furious battle took place. In that storm Sveinn's ship was cleared from the front across the stem and bows. Then King Magnús himself went with his troop up onto Sveinn's ship and after that one after another of his men, making then such a fierce attack that Sveinn's men gave way, and King Magnús cleared that ship and after that one after another [of the rest]. Then Sveinn fled and a great part of his forces, but a large number of his men fell and many were given quarter. So says Þjóðólfr:

48.   Further into carnage went the keeper   *Magnússflokkr* 12
      of keel-wagons,[74] Magnús—   *Skald* II 78
      that was famous—in the fair
      forestem of the landing-stage-Hrafn.[75]
      We caused there, king, booty
      to increase, and the troop of
      the jarl's housecarls to dwindle;
      the army cleared the vessels.

49.   Until the splendid destroyer   *Magnússflokkr* 13
      of sun of the swan's ground[76] granted   *Skald* II 80
      —the jarl's troop took to flight—
      truce for life to sword-staves.[77]

[51] This battle was on the Sunday next before Yule. So says Þjóðólfr:

50.   Fierce warfare, waged by   *Magnússflokkr* 14
      woods of the harsh storm of Hrammi[78]—   *Skald* II 81
      the army went eager to battle—
      on a Sunday was engaged in.

[72] This translation follows *Hkr* III 49. Diana Whaley, in *Skald* II, takes 'Magnús' as well as 'mannr' to be nominative; thus, Magnús exhorts his men, who also urge on each other. This matches Snorri's account of Magnús plunging into the fray to encourage his men, but the syntax is awkward.

[73] *bǫðský*: 'battle-cloud', shield.

[74] *kjalar vagna vǫrðr*: 'guardian of wagons of the keel (ships)', seafarer.

[75] *varar Hrafn*: 'Hrafn (horse of the legendary king Áli) of the landing stage', ship.

[76] *svanfoldar sólrýrandi*: 'destroyer of the sun (gold) of the swan's land (sea)', generous man.

[77] *hjǫrva stafir*: 'staves of swords', men.

[78] *Hramma harðéls viðir*: 'trees of the harsh storm (battle) of Hrammi (Óðinn)', warriors.

As staves of sword-uproar[79]
ceded their lives, fated—
folk sank down perforce—a body
floated on each billow.

King Magnús captured in it seven ships containing Sveinn's men. So says
Þjóðólfr:

51. He stripped, the son of Óleifr   Sts about King Magnús
     the Stout, seven ships earlier;   in Danaveldi 1
     the king won; Sogn's women   *Skald* II 88
     will learn such news without sorrow.

And again he spoke:

52. Sveinn's comrades have certainly,   Sts about King Magnús
     sword-Gautr,[80] missed out on   in Danaveldi 2
     a homecoming; rather harshly   *Skald* II 89
     has the men's venture finished.
[52]   Stirred by storm, the wave scatters
     their skulls and leg-bones—
     over the envoys of riches[81]
     the ocean roars—on the sands' bottom.

Sveinn fled straight away that night to Sjáland with those troops that had got
away and were willing to go with him, while King Magnús took his ships to
the shore and straight away that night had his men go up ashore, and early
next morning they came back down with a great deal of cattle for slaughter.
Þjóðólfr mentions this:

53. I saw great stones yesterday—   Sts about King Magnús
     skull gaped before boulder—   in Danaveldi 3
     hurled strongly; not speedily   *Skald* II 90
     proceeded their company.
     We drove down—not with words only
     will Sveinn defend the country—
     cattle; halfway along the coastline
     came the ship to anchor.

---

[79] *hjǫrva gnýstafir*: 'staves of the din of swords (battle)', warriors.
[80] *sverð-Gautr*: 'sword-Óðinn', warrior.
[81] *auðs ærir*: 'messengers of wealth', generous men.

CHAPTER THIRTY-ONE

King Magnús immediately took his forces from the south to Sjáland in pursuit
of Sveinn. But as soon as King Magnús's troops approached, then Sveinn
immediately fled up inland with all his troops, but King Magnús made after
them and pursued the rout, killing any that they caught. So says Þjóðólfr:

[53]   54.   One word told the Selund   Sts about King Magnús
             woman who bore the standard;   in Danaveldi 4
             it's true, moreover, that many   *Skald* II 91
             men bore shields blood-reddened.
             The treasure-twig[82] was fated
             to tiptoe through the forest;
             many who fled footed it
             fast to Hringstadir.

       55.   Mired to the neck was the manly   Sts about King Magnús
             monarch of Skǫnungar;[83]   in Danaveldi 5
             For Lund's overlord[84] not to prevail, *Skald* II 92
             life-proud, would be a wonder.
             Over bogs yesterday
             and earth, hurled spears flew; over
             mounds the mighty jarl's standard
             made tracks down to the sea.

[54] Sveinn then fled across to Fjón, but King Magnús then went harrying
over Sjáland, burning widely the property of the people that in the autumn
had joined Sveinn's troop. So says Þjóðólfr:

       56.   The jarl succeeded in destroying   *Magnússflokkr* 15
             the seats of princes in winter;   *Skald* II 82
             a land-defence not little
             you let issue from you.
             Generous Magnús, you managed
             to make risky war behind a shield;
             it was then, for Knútr's able nephew,
             almost as if he were finished.

       57.   You had houses, Þrœndr's ruler[85] —   *Magnússflokkr* 16
             homesteads you dared harm, angry —   *Skald* II 83
             destroyed by fire; each structure
             consigned to flame and cinders.

[82] *auðtroða*: 'stick of wealth', woman.
[83] *Skǫnunga harri*: 'lord of the Skánungar', king of Denmark.
[84] *Lundar allvaldr*: 'overlord of Lund', king of Denmark.
[85] *Þrœnda rœsir*: 'ruler of Þrœndr', i.e. king of Norway.

The jarl's followers fiercely,
friend of chieftains, you wanted
to repay—they ran away promptly—
for their perilous enmity.

[55] CHAPTER THIRTY-TWO

As soon as King Magnús got news of Sveinn, then he took his troops across
to Fjón. And as soon as Sveinn knew of this, then he went aboard ship and
sailed, coming out in Skáni, went from there to Gautland and after that to
see the king of the Svíar. But King Magnús went up onto Fjón, having many
people's property there plundered and burned. All Sveinn's men that were
there fled away in all directions. So says Þjóðólfr:

58.	Up in the air the storm tosses	Sts about King Magnús
	embers from oaken walls,	in Danaveldi 6
	south, in cormorants' country;[86]	*Skald* II 93
	kindled, fire plays wildly.	
	Dwellings burn higher by half	
	near the households on Fjón.	
	Roofs and shingles are ruined;	
	razed are halls by Northmen.[87]	
59.	Men must, Freyr of battles,[88]	Sts about King Magnús
	remember to get to know	in Danaveldi 7
	the weaving-Gefn[89] of Sveinn's soldiers,	*Skald* II 94
	since there were three encounters.	
	On Fjón one may look forward	
	to a fair girl; it's good to redden	
[56]	blades; let's join the forefront	
	of the force in weapons' tumult.[90]	

After this all the people in Denmark submitted to King Magnús. Then there
was uninterrupted peace there in the latter part of winter. Then King Magnús
appointed his men to the government over all the land there in Denmark.
And when spring drew to a close, then he took his army north to Norway
and stayed there for a very long time over the summer.

[86] *hróka land*: 'land of cormorants', the sea; here, a play on words for Sjáland (*sjár* means 'sea'). This follows the interpretation of *Hkr* III 55, which adopts the reading of some manuscripts *á hróka landi*; others have *af* instead of *á*. Diana Whaley in *Skald* II follows the latter reading and takes *hróka land* as a kenning for the sea, thus 'a storm from the sea'.

[87] *Norðmenn*: Norwegians.

[88] *viga Freyr*: 'god of battles', warrior (vocative, addressed to Magnús's soldiers).

[89] *vef-Gefn*: 'weaving-Gefn (Freyja; goddess)', woman, wife (sg. for pl.).

[90] *vápna glamm*: 'din of weapons', battle.

CHAPTER THIRTY-THREE

So when Sveinn learnt about this, then he rode straight out to Skáni, taking a large force from Svíaveldi. The Skánungar welcomed him. He then gathered troops, went after that out to Sjáland and subjected those there to himself, similarly Fjón and all the islands. So when King Magnús learnt of this, then he gathered troops and ships and after that laid his course south to Denmark. He learnt where Sveinn was lying with his army. King Magnús then advanced against him. Their meeting was in the place known as Helganes, and it was in the evening of the day. And when the battle commenced, King Magnús had a smaller force and larger ships and better manned. So says Arnórr:

	60.	I have heard it called widely	*Magnússdrápa* 12
		Helganes, where many	*Mork* I (*Flb*) 75 (ll. 1–4)
		elks of the wave[91] the well-known	*Fsk* 224
		wolf-gladdener[92] emptied.	*Skald* II 221
[57]		At early twilight, the ship-tree[93]	*Skáldsk* 65 (ll. 5–8)
		ordered shields be set together.	
		All the autumn night the rain of	
		the ogress of strife-clouds[94] lasted.	

The battle was of the fiercest, and as the night drew to an end, there came to be many casualties. King Magnús was all night throwing missiles with his hands. Þjóðólfr mentions this:

	61.	Sveinn's host bowed before halberds	*Magnússflokkr* 17
		at Helganes, as it is called;	*Mork* I (*Flb*) 70
		there wounded warriors,	*Skald* II 84
		worthy of death, sank down.	
		Many a slinged spear the Mœrir's	
		magnificent lord[95] wielded;	
		with darts the keen ruler	
		reddened the point, ash-mounted.	

To tell of this battle in the fewest words, King Magnús was victorious, and Sveinn fled. His ship was cleared from stem to stern, and all Sveinn's other ships were cleared. So says Þjóðólfr:

---

[91] *vágs elgr*: 'elk of the wave', ship.

[92] *vargteitir*: 'wolf-cheerer', warrior.

[93] *reggbúss*: 'box-tree of the ship', seafarer.

[94] *rógskýja rýgjar regn*: 'rain of the troll-wife of strife-clouds'; strife-clouds are shields; the troll-wife of shields is the axe; rain of the axe is battle.

[95] *Mœra gramr*: 'king of the Mœrir', king of Norway.

62. Firm, the jarl fled the killing *Magnússflokkr* 18
    from his empty vessel, *Mork* I (*Flb*) 73
[58] where Magnús made perilous *Fsk* 223
    the movement of Sveinn from there. *Skald* II 85
    The army's king coloured
    the cutter's blade crimson;
    blood spurted on the sharpened
    sword; for lands the king battled.

And again Arnórr says:

63. The king, scourge of Skǫnungar, *Magnússdrápa* 14
    seized all Bjǫrn's brother's[96] *Mork* I (*Flb*) 75
    warships; men rowed there *Fsk* 224
    at the right moment. *Skald* II 223

A great number of Sveinn's men fell there. King Magnús and his men got a great deal of plunder. So says Þjóðólfr:

64. I bore back from battle Sts about King Magnús
    my booty, a shield from Gautland— in Danaveldi 8
    south in summer the sword-din *Skald* II 96
    was strong—and more, a mailcoat.
    Fine weapons I got, as before I
    informed the calm lady.
[59] I gained a helmet, where the ruler,
    hardy, the Danes hammered.

Sveinn then fled up onto Skáni and all those of his troops that got away, but King Magnús and his troops drove the rout far up into the land, and there was then little resistance from Sveinn's men or the farmers. So says Þjóðólfr:

65. Ǫleifr's son had earlier Sts about King Magnús
    ordered the advance onto land; in Danaveldi 9
    Magnús, with much splendour, *Skald* II 97
    marched wrathful from the warships.
    The hardy king ordered harrying—
    here is tumult—in Denmark.
    Across the hills speeds hastily
    the horse, over the west of Skáney.

After this King Magnús went harrying all over the area. So says Þjóðólfr:

---

[96] Bjǫrn's brother is Sveinn. See *Anglo–Saxon Chronicle* C 1049.

66.　Now Northmen start to urge on—　　Sts about King Magnús
　　　near the poles we are marching—　　　in Danaveldi 10
　　　Magnús's standards; not seldom　　*Skald* II 98
　　　by my side my shield I carry.
[60]　　Not skew-footed across Skáney
　　　the scraggy one rushes,[97]
　　　few paths that are fairer
　　　I've found, to Lund southwards.

After that they began to burn the area. Then the people fled away in all directions. So says Þjóðólfr:

67.　We bore ice-cold irons　　　　Sts about King Magnús
　　　amply, in the lord's army.　　　　in Danaveldi 11
　　　Swiftly the bright hopes of Skǫnungar　*Skald* II 98
　　　for success are now failing.
　　　Briskly, through the broad settlement
　　　blazes red fire, by our
　　　enforcing; keen fire-raisers
　　　fashioned that hardship.

68.　Bright fire burns over people's　　Sts about King Magnús
　　　buildings the realm of Danes;　　　in Danaveldi 12
　　　the king destroys most swiftly　　*Skald* II 99
　　　the settlement, with a great army.
[61]　　Over a heath men weary
　　　of holding Denmark carry
　　　shields; we won victory; wounded
　　　warriors of Sveinn run from us.

69.　Last year on Fjón the leader　　Sts about King Magnús
　　　let once-used ways be trodden,　　　in Danaveldi 13
　　　I hardly hide myself in　　　　*Skald* II 101
　　　the heart of the princes' army.
　　　Mighty deeds of Magnús
　　　the men of Sveinn will not challenge—
　　　many standards this morning
　　　mount high—who now are fleeing.

Sveinn then fled east to Skáni. King Magnús then went to his ships and laid his course after that east past the coast of Skáney, and had only made very hasty preparations. Then Þjóðólfr spoke this:

[97] That is, he runs straight ahead. *Sláni* 'gangling, lanky man' could refer to the people of Skáney (cf. *Hkr* III 60). Diana Whaley takes it to refer to the poet (*Skald* II 98).

70. Other than this ocean   Sts about King Magnús
   I have nothing to drink;   in Danaveldi 14
   I suck a gulp from the salty   *Skald* II 102
   sea, as the king I follow.
[62] Before us lies—but full little
   fear we have of Svíar,
   we swear—Skáney's wide coast.
   Suffered ill we have for the ruler.

Sveinn fled up into Gautland and after that made his way to see the king of the Svíar and stayed there the winter in high honour.

CHAPTER THIRTY-FOUR

King Magnús turned back from his expedition when he had subjected Skáni to himself, making then first for Falstr, going up ashore there and harrying there, killing many troops that had previously submitted to Sveinn. Arnórr mentions this:

71. For deceit not sparingly   *Magnússdrápa* 17
   the sovereign repaid the Danish. *Mork* I (*Flb*) 76 (ll. 1–4)
   He made fall, full of courage, *Fsk* 225 (ll. 1–4)
   the Falstr-dwellers' army.   *Skald* II 226
   He heaped, the young wealth-hawthorn,[98] *Skáldsk* 66 (ll. 5–8)
   heavy corpse-piles for eagles,
   and certainly retainers
   served the eagle's feeder.[99]

After that King Magnús took his troops to Fjón and harried and caused much damage there. So says Arnórr:

[63] 72. Further, on Fjón he reddened— *Magnússdrápa* 18
   the force's lord[100] fought for land, *Mork* I (*Flb*) 76
   people paid for robbing him— *Fsk* 225
   painter of mail,[101] bright banners. *Skald* II 227
   Let men remember which other
   master of troops[102] has reached twenty
   so unstinting to the swarthy raven.
   The sovereign was granted spirit.

[98] *auðar þorn*: 'thorn-tree of wealth', man.
[99] *ara grennir*: 'feeder of eagles', warrior.
[100] *dróttar gramr*: 'lord of the retinue', king.
[101] *hringserks lituðr*: 'colourer of the mailshirt', warrior.
[102] *herskyldir*: 'army-leader', king.

CHAPTER THIRTY-FIVE

King Magnús remained that winter in Denmark, and there was then uninterrupted peace. He had had many battles in Denmark and been victorious in all of them. Oddr Kíkinaskáld (Poet of the people of Kíkin?) says this: [103]

73.	Before Michaelmas was fought	Poem about Magnús
	a metal-grim battle.	góði 1
	Vinðr fell, and folk grew very	*Mork* I (*Flb*) 74
	familiar with noise of weapons.	*Skald* II 32
[64]	And nearing Yule another,	
	not at all minor, happened—	
	among men fierce fighting	
	befell—south of Áróss.	

Again Arnórr says:

74.	Óleifr's avenger,[104] you provided matter	*Hrynhenda* 14
	for verse; this into words I fashion.	*Skald* II 200
	You cause Hlǫkk's hawks[105] to quaff the ocean	
	of carrion.[106] Now will the poem enlarge.	
	In one year you have, lessener	
	of the shield-reed's base,[107] daring—	
	great king, you are called invincible—	
	carried out four arrow-blizzards.[108]	

King Magnús had three battles with Sveinn Úlfsson. So says Þjóðólfr:

75.	The fray with good fortune	*Magnússflokkr* 19
	was fought, as Magnús wanted.	*Skald* II 86
[65]	The strife-sweller[109] gives me occasion	
	to recite about victory.	

[103] In *Morkinskinna* (or the part of *Flateyjarbók* preserving the text missing from the lacuna in *Morkinskinna*) this verse (and the only other known stanza credited to Oddr) is attributed to Þjóðólfr. Nothing is known of Oddr kíkinaskáld. His nickname may derive from the common Norwegian farm name *Kíkin*. Those who lived in these farms could be known as *Kíkinar,* and Oddr may have composed for them.

[104] *Óleifs hefnir:* 'avenger (i.e. son) of Óláfr', i.e. Magnús.

[105] *Hlakkar haukar:* 'hawks of Hlǫkkr (valkyrie)', ravens or eagles.

[106] *hrælǫgr:* 'sea of carrion', blood.

[107] *randa reyrar setrs rýrir:* 'diminisher (generous giver or damager) of the resting place (shield) of the reed of the shield (sword)', warrior or ruler.

[108] *ǫrvar hríðir:* 'storms of arrows', battles.

[109] *sóknstœrir:* 'increaser of battle', warrior.

The sovereign of Þrœndr[110] stained red
the sword; after three pitched battles
he holds ever after
the higher shield, in payment.

CHAPTER THIRTY-SIX

King Magnús was now ruling over both Denmark and Norway. So after he had gained possession of the realm of the Danes, then he sent messengers west to England. They went to see King Játvarðr and delivered to him the letters and the seal of King Magnús. And this is what was included in the letters along wih King Magnús's greetings:

'You will have heard of the special agreements that Hǫrða-Knútr and I made between ourselves, that whichever of us survived the other who had no sons, then he was to take over the lands and subjects that the other had possessed. Now it has come about, as I know that you have heard, that I have received the whole realm of the Danes as inheritance after Hǫrða-Knútr. He possessed, when he died, England no whit less than Denmark. I am claiming now to possess England in accordance with valid agreements. I wish you to give up your rule for me, or otherwise I shall come to get it with force of arms from both Denmark and Norway. The one that is granted victory will then rule the lands.'

[66] CHAPTER THIRTY-SEVEN

So when King Játvarðr had read these letters, then he replied as follows:

'It is known to everyone in this country that my father Aðalráðr was entitled by birth to this kingdom both from earlier times and from more recently. There were four of us sons of his. And when he died leaving his lands, then my brother Eatmundr took the rule and kingdom, since he was the eldest of us brothers. I was then quite happy with this, as long as he was alive. But after him, my stepfather King Knútr took the kingdom. It was not easy to claim it then, as long as he was alive. And after him my brother Haraldr[111] was king, as long as he was granted life. And when he died, then my brother Hǫrða-Knútr was ruling the realm of the Danes, and that then seemed the only fair division of the inheritance between us brothers, that he should be king over both England and Denmark. But I had no kingdom to rule over. Now he died. It was then the decision of all the people of this country to take me as king here in England. But as long as I had no royal title, I served my superiors while having no higher rank than the men who had no birthright

---

[110] *Þrœnda buðlungr*: 'king of Þrœndr', i.e. of Norway.
[111] Cf. note 43 above.

to the rule in this country. I have now received consecration to the kingship here, and the kingdom, with no less validity than my father had before me. I am not now going to give up this title as long as I am alive. But if King Magnús comes to this country with his army, then I shall not gather troops against him. He will have the opportunity to gain possession of England and deprive me first of my life. Tell him just what I have said.'

The messengers then went back and came to see King Magnús and told him the whole result of their mission. The king took his time in replying, and yet spoke as follows:

'I feel, however, that this will be the fairest and most proper thing to do, to let King Eatvarðr possess [67] his kingdom in peace as far as I am concerned, and keep this kingdom which God has let me gain possession of.'

[68] Haralds saga Sigurðarsonar

CHAPTER ONE

Sigurðr sýr's (Pig's) son Haraldr, King Óláfr the Saint's [half-] brother by the same mother, he was in the battle at Stiklarstaðir when the blessed King Óláfr fell. Haraldr was then wounded and got away with the others that took to flight. So says Þjóðólfr:

76.	By Haugr, I heard, a shield-shower,[112]	*Sexstefja* 1
	sharp, drove at the ruler;	*ÓH* 580
	but the burner of Bolgars[113]	*Skald* II 112
	his brother well supported.	
	Lifeless Ǫleifr, reluctant	*Fsk* 199 (ll. 5–8)
	he left, the princeling	
	at the age of twelve and three	
	years, helmet-stand[114] hiding.	

Rǫgnvaldr Brúsason got Haraldr out of the battle and brought him to a certain farmer who lived in a forest far from other people. Haraldr was treated there until he was cured. After that the farmer's son accompanied him east over Kjǫlr, [69] and they went the whole way by forest tracks as far as possible, and not by the normal route. The farmer's son did not realise whom he was conducting. And as they were riding between some uninhabited woods, then Haraldr uttered this:

77.	Now, with scant fame, from forest	*Mork* I (*Flb*) 83
	to forest I am slinking.	*Orkn* 53
	Who knows if I'll not be widely	*ÓH* 580
	renowned in the future?	*Skald* II 44

He travelled east across Jamtaland and Helsingjaland and so to Svíþjóð. There he found Jarl Rǫgnvaldr Brúsason and very many others of the men that had escaped from the battle, King Óláfr's men.

CHAPTER TWO

The following spring they got themselves places on a ship and travelled in the summer east to Garðaríki to visit King Jarizleifr and stayed there the winter. So says Bǫlverkr:[115]

[112] *hlífél*: 'shield-shower', battle.

[113] *Bolgara brennir*: 'burner of Bolgars', i.e. Haraldr.

[114] *hjalmsetr*: 'seat, support of the helmet', head.

[115] According to *Fsk* 245 and *Skáldatal*, Bǫlverkr was the brother of Þjóðólfr Arnórsson, but nothing else is known of him. Eight stanzas survive of his poem on Haraldr harðráði.

78. You wiped, when you had finished   *Drápa* about Haraldr
     warring, the sword's mouth,[116] ruler;   harðráði 1
     you rendered the raven full of   *Fsk* 227 (attrib. to
     raw meat; wolves howled on hillsides.   Valgarðr at Vǫllr)
     And, harsh prince—I've not heard of   *ÓH* 581
     a harmer of peace[117] advancing   *Skald* II 286
[70] more than you—the year following
     you were east in Garðar.

King Jarizleifr welcomed Haraldr and his companions. Haraldr then became leader over the king's national defence force, together with Jarl Rǫgnvaldr's son Eilífr. So says Þjóðólfr:

79. Where Eilífr held sway   *Runhent* poem about
     in a single fray   Haraldr 1
     two chiefs did group   *Mork* I (*Flb*) 85
     their wedge-formed troop.   *Fsk* 228 (1st half)
     East-Vinðr were caught   *Skald* II 103
     in a tight spot.
     For the Læsir not light
     was the liegemen's right.

Haraldr stayed in Garðaríki for some winters and travelled widely round the eastern Baltic lands. After that he set out for Grikland taking a large body of men. Then he made for Mikligarðr. So says Bǫlverkr:

[71] 80. Along the shore the cool shower   *Drápa* about Haraldr
          shoved the black prow of the warship   harðráði 2
          strongly, and the shielded[118] vessels *Mork* I (*Flb*) 87
          splendidly bore their tackle.   *Skald* II 288
          The mighty prince saw Mikligarðr's
          metal roofs before the forestem.
          Many fair-sided ships headed
          to the high city rampart.

CHAPTER THREE

At this time Queen Zoë in ríka (the Great) was ruling over Grikland, along with Michael kátalaktús (Moneychanger). And when Haraldr got to Mikligarðr and to see the queen, then he became a mercenary there and immediately in the autumn went aboard a galley with the soldiers that were

---

[116] i.e. edge.

[117] *friðskerðir*: 'peace-damager', warrior.

[118] *brynjaðr*: either covered with protective metal, or lined with shields.

going out onto the Griklandshaf. Haraldr kept his own company of men. At this time the leader over the army was a man whose name is Gyrgir. He was a kinsman of the queen. And when Haraldr had been in the army for only a little time before the Væringjar became very attached to him, then they all kept together [72] when battles took place. So then it came about that Haraldr became leader over all the Væringjar. He and Gyrgir travelled widely round the Greek islands, carrying out many raids there on pirates.

CHAPTER FOUR

It happened on one occasion when they had been travelling round the country and were about to get themselves a night's lodging by some woods, that the Væringjar arrived first at the place for their night quarters, and they picked themselves the sites for their tents that they considered the best and were on the highest ground, for there the lie of the land is such that the ground is wet, and when rain comes there, then it is not pleasant to lie where it is low down. Then Gyrgir, the leader of the army, arrived, and when he saw where the Væringjar had pitched their tents, he told them to go away and pitch them elsewhere, saying that he wished to pitch his tents there. Haraldr says as follows:

'If you arrive first at the night's lodging, then you take yourself night quarters, and we shall pitch our tents there in a different place, wherever we please. [73] You do the same now, pitch your tent wherever you like, somewhere else. I had thought that it was the right of the Væringjar here in the realm of the king of the Greeks that they should be independent and free in all respects in their relations to everyone, and be bound in service to the king alone and the queen.'

They disputed this matter ardently, until both took up weapons. Then they were on the very point of resorting to a fight. Then the most sensible men came up and parted them. They said this, that it would be more seemly that they should come to an agreement on this matter and make clear regulations between themselves, so that there would be no need for any such disputes about this in the future. Then a meeting was fixed between them, and the best and most sensible men made the arrangements. And at this meeting they decided it so that everyone was in agreement that they should cast lots and decide by lot between the Greeks and the Væringjar which of them were to ride ahead or row or enter the harbour and make their choice of camping sites first. Then both sides were to be content with what the lot said. Then the lots were made and marked. Then Haraldr said to Gyrgir:

'I want to see how you mark your lot, so that we do not both make the same marks.'

He did so. Then Haraldr marked his lot and threw it into the sheet, as did they both. Now the man who was to pick up the lot, then he picked up one of them and held it between his fingers and and raised his hand and said:

'These are the ones that are to ride ahead and row and enter the harbour and choose their camping sites first.'

Haraldr grasped the man's hand and took the lot and threw it out into the sea. After that he said:

'That was our lot.'

Gyrgir says: 'Why did you not let more men see it?'

'See here,' says Haraldr, 'the one that is left. You will recognise your mark on that one.'

Then that lot was examined, and they all recognised Gyrgir's mark on it. It was declared that the Væringjar were to have their preferred choices on everything they had been disputing.

There were other things [74] that led to disagreements between them, and it always turned out that Haraldr got his way.

CHAPTER FIVE

They all travelled together during the summer and made raids. When the whole army was together, Haraldr put his men outside the battle or else where there was least danger to life, saying he wanted to avoid losing his troops. But when he was on his own with his men, then he engaged so energetically in the fighting that he could only achieve either victory or death. It often happened, when Haraldr was leader of the troop, that he was victorious when Gyrgir was not. The soldiers noticed this and declared they would be better off if Haraldr was sole leader over the whole army, and criticised the commander because he and his troops got nowhere. Gyrgir says that the Væringjar would never give him any help, told them to go off somewhere else, and he would go with the rest of the army and let each get on as best they could. Then Haraldr left the army, and the Væringjar with him, and the Romance speakers.[119] Gyrgir went with the army of Greeks. Then it became clear what each could do. Haraldr always won victory and wealth, but the Greeks went back to Mikligarðr, except that the young men that wanted to get themselves riches attached themselves to Haraldr and took him now as their leader. Then he made his way with his army west to Africa, which the Væringjar refer to as Serkland. He then greatly added to his troops. In Serkland he won eighty cities. Some were surrendered, but [75] some he took by force. After that he went to Sicily. So says Þjóðólfr:

[119] Probably Normans.

81.   One may say eighty strongholds   *Sexstefja* 2
       in Serkland were taken,   *Mork* I (*Flb*) 93
       the young foe of the fire-red   *Fsk* 230
       field of the snake[120] risked himself, *Skald* II 113
       before the host-upholder,[121]
       hazardous to Serkir,
       went, shield-holding, to wage Hildr's
       harsh sport[122] in level Sicily.

So says Illugi Bryndœlaskáld (poet of the people of Brynjudalr):

82.   With the shield you, under splendid Mikjáll—   Poem about
       the son of Buðli, as we have heard,   Haraldr harðráði 4
[76]   bade home his brothers-in-law—[123]   *Fsk* 230
       brought Southern Lands, Haraldr.   *Skald* II 285

Here it says that now at this time Mikjáll was king of the Greeks.

Haraldr stayed for many winters in Africa, acquiring a lot of portable wealth, gold and all kinds of precious objects. But all the wealth that he acquired and did not need to keep for his expenses, he sent by means of reliable men of his north to Hólmgarðr into the care and keeping of King Jarizleifr, and a huge quantity of wealth was amassed there, which is not surprising should happen, when he was raiding the part of the world that was richest in gold and and precious objects, when he achieved as much as was truly said above, that he would have won eighty cities.

CHAPTER SIX

So when Haraldr got to Sicily, then he raided there and made his way there with his men to a certain large and populous city. He surrounded the city, as there were strong walls there, so that he thought it was uncertain that they could be broken down. The citizens had plenty of food and other supplies that they needed for defence. Then Haraldr tried this expedient, that his fowlers caught small birds that nested in the city and flew to the forest in the daytime to find food for themselves. Haraldr had pine shavings tied to the backs of the birds and poured wax and sulphur on them and had [77] them set on fire.

---

[120] *ormtorgs hǫtuðr*: 'enemy of the serpent's market-place (treasure)', generous man.

[121] *herskǫrðudr*: 'army supporter', king.

[122] *Hildrs leikr*: 'game of Hildr (valkyrie)', battle.

[123] In the poems *Atlakviða* and *Atlamál*, Atli treacherously invites his brothers-in-law Gunnarr and Hǫgni to visit him and puts them to death. In Illugi's poem, of which four stanzas survive, references to legendary stories are intercalated in each stanza in this way, in a technique like that called *stæltr* 'inlaid' in *Snorra Edda* (*Háttatal* 12).

The birds flew, as soon as they were freed, all into the city at once to see their young and their homes, which they had in the thatches of houses, where they were thatched with reeds or straw. Then the fire from the birds got into the thatches of the houses. And though each one was carrying a small amount of fire, it soon grew into a large fire, when a lot of birds carried it to the thatches in many parts of the city, and the next thing was that one building after another caught fire until the city was in flames. Then all the people went out of the city and begged for mercy, the very same ones that previously on many a day had spoken haughtily and scornfully of the army of Greeks and their leader. Haraldr gave everyone quarter that asked for it, after that gaining control over this city.

CHAPTER SEVEN

There was another city that Haraldr took his men to. It was both populous and strongly built, so that there was no likelihood that they would be able to storm it, there being level and hard ground around the city. Then Haraldr had them set to work to dig a hole, starting where a stream was flowing and there was a deep gully so that they could not be seen from the city. They carried the earth out to the water and let the stream carry it away. They were engaged on this work both day and night. They worked in shifts. But the army made attacks round the city every day, and the citizens went to the battlements, and they shot at each other and at night both sides slept. And when Haraldr decided that the underground passage was long enough to have got in past the city wall, then he had his men armed. It was towards daybreak when they entered the underground passage. And when they reached the end, they dug up above their heads until they came to stones set in mortar. This was the floor of the stone-built city hall. After that they broke up the floor and got up into the hall. There they found many of the citizens sitting [78] eating there and drinking, and they were surprised in a very awkward situation, for the Væringjar came in with drawn swords and straightway killed some, while some fled, those that were able to. The Væringjar made after them, while some took the city gates and threw them open. The whole host of the army entered by them. And when they got into the city, then the people of the city fled, though many begged for mercy, and all were granted this who gave themselves up. Haraldr took the city in this way and with it a huge amount of wealth.

CHAPTER EIGHT

They found a third city, which was the largest of all these and the strongest built and richest in wealth and inhabitants. Around this city there were great ditches, so they realised that they could not win here with the same kind of stratagems as they did the previous cities. They lay there a very long time without managing to achieve anything. So when the citizens saw this, then they got bold. They put their lines of soldiers up on the city wall, after that they opened their gates and shouted to the Væringjar, egging them on and telling them to come into the city now and taunting them for lack of courage, saying they were no better at fighting than chickens. Haraldr told his men to behave as though they had not noticed what they were saying.

'We will get nowhere,' he said, 'by rushing up to the city. They will use their weapons on us down beneath their feet.[124] And even if we get into the city with a few men, they will then be able to shut those they want to inside, and some of us outside, for they have set guards on all the city gates. We shall make just as much fun of them and we shall let them see that we are not afraid of them. Our men shall advance over the ground as close as they can to the city, taking care, however, [79] not to go within range of their missiles. Our men shall all go unarmed and play games, and let the citizens see that we do not care about their lines of soldiers.'

So it went on after that for a few days.

CHAPTER NINE

There are Icelandic men named that were on this expedition with Haraldr, Snorri goði's (the priest/chieftain's) son Halldórr (he brought this story back to this country), secondly there was Úlfr, son of Óspakr, son of Ósvífr inn spaki (the Wise). They were both the strongest of men and very bold fighters and most dear to Haraldr. They both took part in the games. And when this procedure had gone on for some days, then the citizens wanted to display even greater daring. They did not now go up armed onto the city walls, but still let the city gates stand open. And when the Væringjar saw this, then they went one day to their games with swords under their cloaks and helmets under their hoods. And when they had been playing for a while, then they found that the citizens were not reacting. Then they quickly grasped their weapons, after that running to the city gates. And when the citizens saw this, they fought back well and were fully armed. A battle took place there at the city gates. The Væringjar had no shields, except that they wrapped their cloaks round their left arms. They were wounded, and some fell, and all were in a poor way. Haraldr and the men that were with him that were in the camp came up to help their comrades. But the citizens had now got up onto the city walls, and were shooting missiles and stones onto them. Then there was a fierce battle. Those that were at the city gates felt that help was slower in coming to them than they wished. And when Haraldr got to the city gates, then his standard bearer fell. Then he spoke:

[124] i.e. presumably from the battlements.

'Halldórr, pick up the standard!'

Halldórr replied, picking up [80] the pole and speaking unwisely:

'Who is going to carry a standard before you, if you follow it in as cowardly a fashion as you have been doing for a while now?'

This was spoken more in anger than in truth, for Haraldr was the boldest fighter. Then they fought their way into the city. The battle was fierce and ended with Haraldr being victorious and winning the city. Halldórr was badly wounded, having a great gash in his face, and he had this disfigurement all his life, as long as he lived.

CHAPTER TEN

It was the fourth city that Haraldr came to with his army that was the largest of all those that have already been described. It was also so strongly built that they could see no hope of being able to storm it. After that they surrounded the city and blockaded it, so that no supplies could be carried to the city. And when they had waited a short while, then Haraldr got an illness, so that he took to his bed. He had his tent pitched away from the rest of the camp, for he felt it would be restful for him not to hear the noise and laughter of the troops. His men came frequently with their troops to see him and back again to ask him for instructions. The citizens saw this, that there was something unusual with the Væringjar. They sent out spies to find out what this could mean. And when the spies returned to the city, they were able to report the news that the leader of the Væringjar was sick and this was why there were no attacks on the city. And when this had gone on for a while, then Haraldr became weaker. His men then got very anxious and downcast. The citizens learnt of all this. It reached the point where the sickness was so afflicting Haraldr that his death was spoken of throughout the army. After this the Væringjar went to talk with the citizens, telling them of their leader's death, asking that clerics should give him burial in the city. And when the citizens learned this news, then [81] there were many that were in charge of the monasteries or other great Church establishments there in the city; then they were each keen to take this corpse to their church, for they knew that a great offering would come in with it. Then a whole multitude of clerics put on vestments and went out from the city with shrines and holy relics and made a fine procession. And the Væringjar also made a great funeral cortège. Then the coffin was carried high and covered over with fine silk cloth, with many banners carried above it. But when all this had been carried in past the entrance to the city, then they threw down the coffin across the city gateway in front of the gates. Then the Væringjar blew a war signal in all their trumpets and drew their swords. Then the whole army of the Væringjar rushed from the camp fully armed and ran then to the city with shouts and cries. But the monks and other clerics that had gone out on this funeral procession competing with each other, wanting to be first and foremost to be out there to receive the offering, now they showed twice as much zeal in getting as far away as possible from the Væringjar, for they were killing everyone that was closest to them, whether he was cleric or lay. The Væringjar went through this whole city killing the people and plundering all the establishments in the city, taking a huge amount of wealth from it.

CHAPTER ELEVEN

Haraldr was many winters on this raiding expedition that has just been described, both in Serkland and Sicily. After that he took this army back to Mikligarðr and stayed there a little while before setting out on his journey to [82] Jórsalaheimr. He then left behind the gold for the salaries of the king of the Greeks' army and all the Væringjar that had joined up with him for this expedition. It is said that on all these expeditions Haraldr had fought eighteen major battles. So says Þjóðólfr:

83.	It is known that eighteen—	*Sexstefja* 6
	often truce has been riven	*Skald* II 117
	on the king's behalf—harsh battles	
	Haraldr has conducted.	
[83]	Sharp claws with blood you coloured,	
	king triumphant, of the grey eagle—	
	the wolf won a morsel wherever	
	you went—before you came hither.	

CHAPTER TWELVE

Haraldr went out to Jórsalaland with his followers, then continuing after that over to Jórsalaborg. And wherever he went over Jórsalaland, all the cities and strongholds were surrendered to his power. So says the poet Stúfr, who had heard the king himself tell about these events:[125]

[125] Stúfr blindi ('the Blind') Þórðarson was an Icelandic poet, the grandson, as *Laxdœla saga* tells us, of Guðrún Ósvífrsdóttir (*ÍF* V 100) and, according to *Stúfs þáttr*, the great-grandson of Glúmr Geirason (see Vol. I, note 178). The *þáttr* survives in two versions: one tells of Stúfr reciting to King Haraldr in Norway a poem called *Stúfsdrápa*; according to the other version, preserved in *Morkinskinna*, it was a memorial poem for the king that was called *Stúfsdrápa* or *Stúfa*. Whether Stúfr composed one poem or two in honour of Haraldr, it seems that the surviving four full and four half-stanzas attributed to him are from the memorial poem, since they refer to Haraldr in the past tense rather than addressing him. The poem has a *klofastef* 'split refrain' of three lines, distributed as the final lines of three separate stanzas (84, 85 and 108 below): *Hafi ríks þars vel líkar / vist of aldr með Kristi / Haralds ǫnd ofarr lǫndum* 'Let the powerful Haraldr's spirit have residence with Christ forever above lands, where it is pleasant'.

84.   The very bold one, prevailing,[126]   *Stúfsdrápa* 2
         advanced from the Greeks,   *Mork* I 107
         blade-brave—the land bowed to the raiser   *Fsk* 233
         of battles[127]—to win Jórsalir.   *Skald* II 352
         And for his ample power
         as his due to the battle-strengthener[128]
         the land unburned was delivered.
         Let the powerful have, where it is pleasant . . .

[84] Here it tells how that land came unburned and unplundered into Haraldr's power. Then he went out to the Jórðán and washed himself there, as the custom is among other pilgrims to the Holy Land. Haraldr deposited a great amount of wealth at the Lord's sepulchre and the Holy Cross and at other holy relics in Jórsalaland. He then restored to peace the whole route out to the Jórðán, killing robbers and other plunderers. So says Stúfr:

85.   The angry speech and the actions   *Stúfsdrápa* 3
         of Egðir's king[129] prevailed   *Mork* I 108
         on both banks of the Jórðán;   *Fsk* 234
         that banished men's crimes.   *Skald* II 353
         People got sure punishment
         for proven misdemeanours,
         unruliness, from the ruler
         . . . residence with Christ forever.

Then he went back to Mikligarðr.

[85] CHAPTER THIRTEEN

When Haraldr was come to Mikligarðr from out in Jórsalaland, he was keen to travel to Northern Lands for his patrimony. He had now heard that his brother's son Magnús Óláfsson had become king in Norway and also in Denmark. He then left the service of the king of the Greeks. And when Queen Zoë got to know of this, she got very angry and raised charges against Haraldr, reckoning that he had acted dishonestly with the king of the Greeks' wealth that had been gained in raiding expeditions while Haraldr had been leader over the army. There was a girl called Maria, young and fair. She was Queen Zoë's brother's daughter. Haraldr had asked for this girl's hand in marriage, but the queen had refused. Væringjar that have been in Mikligarðr as mercenaries have come back

[126] *enn øfri*: 'the one who had the upper hand'.
[127] *víga valdir*: 'cause, controller of battles', warrior.
[128] *gunnar herðir*: 'hardener of warfare', warrior.
[129] *Egða gramr*: 'king of the Egðir', i.e. of Norway.

here to the north saying that the story had gone around among well-informed people there that Queen Zoë herself wanted to have Haraldr as her husband, and that this was really her main complaint against Haraldr when he wanted to leave Mikligarðr, though this was not the one made public to the ordinary people. The king of the Greeks at this time was the one called Konstantinus Monomakus. He was ruling the kingdom along with Queen Zoë. For these reasons the king of the Greeks had Haraldr taken prisoner and put in a dungeon.

CHAPTER FOURTEEN

Now when Haraldr had nearly reached the dungeon, then the blessed King Óláfr appeared to him, saying that he was going to help him. There on that street a chapel was later built and dedicated to King Óláfr, and this chapel [86] has stood there ever since.

The dungeon was built in such a way that there is on it a high tower, open to the sky, and a doorway from the street to get into it. Haraldr was put into it, and with him Halldórr and Úlfr. The following night a rich woman came down into the dungeon, having got up by means of some ladders, together with two of her serving men. They let down a rope into the dungeon and drew them up. This woman had previously been granted a cure by the blessed King Óláfr and he had then appeared to her in a dream, instructing her to free his brother from prison. Then Haraldr went straight to the Væringjar, and they all stood up to receive him and welcomed him. After that the whole troop armed themselves and went to where the king was sleeping. They took the king prisoner and put out both his eyes. So says Þórarinn Skeggjason in his *drápa*:[130]

86.	The king got even more embers	*Haraldsdrápa* 1
	of arms;[131] the emperor	*Mork* I 112
	of Gríkland got stone-blind from	*Fsk* 235
	a grave major injury.	*Skald* II 294

So says the poet Þjóðólfr too:

87.	Both eyes of the emperor	*Sexstefja* 7
	the ender of the heath-goer's	*Mork* I 112
	sorrow[132] had stabbed out—	*Fsk* 235 (ll.1–4)
	strife then had started.	*Skald* II 118

[130] Þórarinn Skeggjason is named in *Skáldatal* (604-05) as a poet of Haraldr, but is otherwise unknown, and this half-stanza is the only verse attributed to him. He may be the brother of another Icelandic poet and lawspeaker, Markús Skeggjason, named in *Íslendingabók* (22). In *Morkinskinna* and *Fagrskinna* the verse is attributed simply to 'Þórarinn'. A *drápa* is usually a fairly lengthy formal poem with refrains.

[131] *handa glæðr*: 'arm-embers', gold arm-rings.

[132] *heiðingja sútar eyðir*: 'destroyer of sorrow (hunger) of heath-goer (wolf)', warrior.

[87]   In the east the overlord
         of Egðir[133] on the bold ruler
         made a nasty mark; the Greeks'
         monarch took an ill journey.

In these two *drápa*s about Haraldr and many other poems about him it is
mentioned that Haraldr blinded the actual king of the Greeks. They could
have named for this role commanders or counts or any other men of high
rank if they were certain that that would be more accurate, for it was Haraldr
himself that transmitted this story, together with the other men that were
there with him.

[88] CHAPTER FIFTEEN

During that same night Haraldr and his men went to the apartments that Maria
slept in and took her away by force. After that they went to the Væringjar's
galleys and took two of the galleys, rowing after that in to Sjáviðarsund.
And when they got to where iron chains were lying across the channel, then
Haraldr said that the men were to sit at the oars on each galley, while the men
that were not rowing were all to run to the rear of the galley and each one was
to hold his sleeping bag in his arms. So the galleys ran up onto the chains.
As soon as they stuck and they lost way, then Haraldr told all the men to run
forward. Then the galley that Haraldr was on tipped forward and it leapt off
the chains with its momentum, but the other one broke when it balanced on
the chains, and there were many perished there, though some were rescued
from the water. Thus Haraldr got out from Mikligarðr and so sailed into
Svartahaf. And before he sailed away from the land, he set the young lady
up ashore and provided her with a good retinue back to Mikligarðr, telling
her now to tell her kinswoman Zoë how much power she had over Haraldr
and asking whether the queen's authority had in any way [89] prevented him
from being able to get the young lady.

Then Haraldr sailed north to Ellipaltar, going from there all the way across
Austrríki. On these travels Haraldr composed some entertaining verses, and they
are sixteen altogether and they all end in the same way.[134] This is one of them:

88.	Boards[135] sliced, past broad Sicily,	*Gamanvísur* 2
	the sea; then we were splendid.	*Mork* I 114
	The stag of the cabin[136] swiftly	*Fsk* 237
	slid under men, as expected.	*Skáldsk* 75 (ll. 1–4)

[133] *Egða allvaldr*: 'ruler of Egðir', king of Norway.
[134] Each of the five surviving verses ends with the same couplet.
[135] *súð*: riveted boards, i.e. ship.
[136] *vengis hjǫrtr*: 'hart, stag of the roofed cabin or raised deck in the stern', ship.

I little think a laggard   *Skald* II 36
likely to go thither;
yet the Gerðr of gold rings[137]
in Garðar keeps aloof from me.

In this he refers to King Jarizleifr in Hólmgarðr's daughter Ellisif.

CHAPTER SIXTEEN

So when Haraldr got to Hólmgarðr, King Jarizleifr welcomed him extremely warmly. He stayed there for the winter, taking now into his own keeping all the gold that he had previously sent there from out in Mikligarðr, and many kinds of valuable objects. It was so much wealth that no [90] one in northern countries had seen so much in the possession of one man. Haraldr had three times been involved in palace plundering[138] while he was in Mikligarðr. It is the law there that every time a king of the Greeks dies, then the Væringjar shall hold a palace plundering. They shall then go through all the king's palaces where his treasuries are, and everyone shall then be free to keep whatever he gets his hands on.

CHAPTER SEVENTEEN

That winter King Jarizleifr gave his daughter to Haraldr in marriage. She was called Elisabeth; northern people call her Ellisif. Stúfr blindi (the Blind) reports this:

89.   He made, the monarch of Egðir,[139]   *Stúfsdrápa* 4
       the match he wanted, prolific battler;   *Mork* I 118
       the people's confidant[140] took plenty   *Fsk* 238
       of gold and the prince's daughter.   *Skald* II 354

[91] So in the spring he set out from Hólmgarðr and went during the spring to Aldeigjuborg, getting himself a ship there and sailing from the east during the summer, making first for Svíþjóð and laying his course towards Sigtúnir. So says Valgarðr at Vǫllr:[141]

---

[137] *gollhrings Gerðr*: 'goddess of the gold ring', lady.

[138] This practice is not referred to elsewhere either in Norse or Greek sources, and it is unlikely ever to have taken place in Constantinople.

[139] *Egða allvaldr*: 'king of Egðir', i.e. of Norway.

[140] *gumna spjalli*: 'confidant of men', ruler, king.

[141] Valgarðr is listed in *Skáldatal* as a poet of Haraldr harðráði, but he is otherwise unknown, apart from seven full and four half-stanzas, apparently all from this same poem addressed to Haraldr. His nickname 'at Vǫllr' may refer to an origin in Völlur in Rangárvallasýsla in southern Iceland.

90.   You launched with the fairest freight—   Poem about Haraldr
      fame is granted you—a vessel.   harðráði 5
      Gold from Garðar, doubtless,   *Mork* I 118
      you got from the east, Haraldr.   *Fsk* 238
      You steered stoutly in raging   *Skald* II 304
      storm, all-trusty ruler—
      you saw, when the sea-spray slackened,
      Sigtún—while the ships wallowed.

CHAPTER EIGHTEEN

There Haraldr met Sveinn Úlfsson. He had that autumn fled in the face of
King Magnús off Helganes. And when they met, they welcomed each other.
King Óláfr sœnski (the Swedish) of the Svíar was father of Haraldr's wife
Ellisif's mother, while Sveinn's mother Ástríðr was King Óláfr's sister.[142]
Haraldr and Sveinn became close friends and confirmed their friendship
with promises. All the Svíar were friends of Sveinn, for he belonged to
the foremost family in the land. Now all the Svíar also became friends and
supporters of Haraldr. Many important people there were connected with
him by marriage. So says Þjóðólfr:

[92]   91.   The oaken keel carved westward   *Sexstefja* 9
             the climbing water from Garðar.   *Skald* II 121
             After that all the Svíar
             aided you, bold land-ruler.
             Haraldr's waterlogged warship
             went, with much gold, under
             the broad sail, listing to leeward—
             over the lord broke a furious tempest.

CHAPTER NINETEEN

After that they got themselves ships, Haraldr and Sveinn, and soon a large
army gathered round them, and when this force was ready, then they sail
from the east to Denmark. So says Valgarðr:

92.   Then into the ocean, war-glad ruler,   Poem about Haraldr
      the oak sped under you—   harðráði 6
      your proper patrimony   *Mork* I 120
      was prepared for you—from Svíþjóð.   *Fsk* 239
      The ship had sail hoisted   *Skald* II 305
      high against stay where you ran it

---

[142] Cf. *Magnúss saga ins góða* ch. XXII above.

[93]   past flat Skáney; ladies
             you scared, close kin to Danes.

First they took the army to Sjáland and made raids there and carried out
burnings in many places there. After that they made for Fjón, going ashore
there and making raids. So says Valgarðr:

93.   Haraldr, you totally ravaged   Poem about Haraldr
      the whole—lord, foes you conquer;   harðráði 7
      to call on fallen carrion   *Mork* I 121
      quickly the wolf ran—of Selund.   *Fsk* 240
      The king made with many   *Skald* II 306
      men for Fjón, inflicted
      no small hardship on helmets.
      The highly carved shield shattered.

94.   A bright blaze in the settlement   Poem about Haraldr
      burned, south of Hróiskelda.   harðráði 8
      The bold ruler had buildings   *Mork* I 122
      brought down by burning.   *Fsk* 241
      Many landsmen low were lying,   *Skald* II 307
      liberty Hel stole from some,
[94] families to the forest silent
      fled, grief-stricken.

95.   The crowd, sadly scattered—   Poem about Haraldr
      Danes still living were fleeing—   harðráði 9
      loitered, and lovely   *Mork* I 122
      ladies were captured.   *Fsk* 241
      A lock held the lass's body,   *Skald* II 307
      lots of women to the warships
      passed before you; bright fetters
      into flesh bit greedily.

CHAPTER TWENTY

King Magnús Óláfsson made his way north in Norway in the autumn after
the Battle of Helganes. Then he learnt the news that his kinsman Haraldr
Sigurðarson was come to Svíþjóð, and this too, that he and Sveinn Úlfsson
had become close friends and had a great army out, planning again to subject
the realm of the Danes to themselves, and after that Norway. King Magnús
calls out a levy from Norway, and soon a great army gathers round him. He
then learnt that Haraldr and Sveinn were come to Denmark, [95] burning

everything there and destroying it by fire, and the people of the country were in many places submitting to them. It was also said as well, that Haraldr was bigger than other men and stronger and so intelligent that nothing was impossible to him and he was always victorious when he fought battles; he was also so wealthy in gold that people knew of no precedent. So says Þjóðólfr:

> 96.   Now for trees of sea-stallions—[143]   *Skald* II 159
> serious fear the troop suffers;
> the host takes ships offshore—
> sure peace is a risky prospect.
> Splendid Magnús means to
> move slipway-steeds[144] south, lavish
> with war,[145] while Haraldr fits out other
> wave-steeds[146] to go northwards.

CHAPTER TWENTY-ONE

King Magnús's men, those that took part in his making policies, reckon that they would be in a hopeless situation if the kinsmen, he and Haraldr, were going to be after each other's lives. Many people offered to go and seek for a settlement between them, and in the light of these arguments the king agreed to this. Some men were then put onto a swift vessel and they went as fast as they could south to Denmark, getting there some Danish men that were reliable friends of King Magnús to take this offer to Haraldr. This business was conducted [96] in the greatest secrecy. And when Haraldr heard this said, that his kinsman King Magnús was going to offer him a settlement and friendship, and Haraldr was to have a half share of Norway along with King Magnús, while the wealth of both of them was to be shared half and half between the two of them,[147] this private agreement then went back to King Magnús.

CHAPTER TWENTY-TWO

It was a little later on that Haraldr and Sveinn were talking one evening over their drink. Sveinn asked which were the valuable objects Haraldr had that he was most fond of. He answered that it was his standard, Landeyðan

[143] *vídis valmeiðar*: 'trees of the horse of the sea (ship)', seafarers.

[144] *hlunngotar*: 'horses of the slipway', ships.

[145] *mildr morðs*: 'generous with war, slaughter', referring to Magnús.

[146] *unnvigg*: 'wave-horse(s)', ship(s).

[147] Something is missing here. Hulda (and Hrokkinskinna) have: 'then Haraldr agreed to these terms for his own part'.

(Land Waster). Then Sveinn asked what it was about the standard that made it such a great treasure. Haraldr says that it was held that he before whom the standard was carried would be victorious, saying that so it had turned out ever since he had had it. Sveinn replies:

'I will believe that this power is in the standard if you fight three battles against your kinsman King Magnús and you are victorious in them all.'

Then says Haraldr crossly: 'I am aware of the kinship between me and Magnús without your reminding me of it, and it is not for that reason the case that should we proceed against each other in hostile fashion, other meetings between us would not be more suitable.'

Sveinn then changed colour and spoke:

'Some people say, Haraldr, that you have done this before, keeping only those of your private agreements that you feel are advantageous to you.'

Haraldr replies: 'Rather fewer occasions will you be able to quote on which I have not kept my private agreements, than I know that King Magnús will assert that you have kept with him.'

Then each proceeded on his own way. In the evening, when Haraldr was going to bed on the raised deck of his ship, then he spoke to his servant:

[97] 'Now I am not going to lie in the bed tonight, because I have a suspicion that everything is not going to be free from treachery. I noticed this evening that my kinsman-in-law Sveinn was very angry at my plain speaking. You must keep watch in case anything unexpected should take place here tonight.'

Then Haraldr went elsewhere to sleep, and put there in his bed a log of wood. And during the night a boat was rowed up to the raised deck, and a man went on board there and ripped open the awning over the raised deck, after that stepped up just by it and struck at Haraldr's bed with a great axe so that it stuck fast in the log. This man immediately leapt out into the boat, though it was pitch-dark, immediately rowing away, but the axe remained behind to show what had happened. It was stuck fast in the log.

After this Haraldr woke up his men and made them aware what treachery they were up against.

'We can see,' he says, 'that we are getting no kind of support from Sveinn here when he engages in treachery against us. That will be the best course to get away from here while there is a chance. Let us now untie our ships and row secretly away.'

This they did, rowing during the night northwards along the coast, travelling day and night until they got to King Magnús where he was lying with his army. Then Haraldr went to see his kinsman King Magnús and a joyful meeting took place, as Þjóðólfr says:

97.   You caused water, king known widely,   *Sexstefja* 10
       to be cut above thin planking—   *Skald* II 122
       fine ships split the flood—where you
       fared from the east to Denmark.
[98]   Then Óleifr's son offered
       you half shares with himself
       of lands and liegemen; the kinsmen,
       I believe, met there most joyfully.

Then these kinsmen had a talk between themselves. It all went in conciliatory fashion.

CHAPTER TWENTY-THREE

King Magnús was lying by the coast and had a tent up ashore. He then invited his kinsman Haraldr to his table and Haraldr went to the banquet with sixty men. There was a very fine banquet there. And as the day drew to a close, King Magnús went into the tent where Haraldr was sitting. Some men went with him carrying loads consisting of weapons and clothing. Now the king went to the man at the bottom of the table and gave him a good sword, to the next a shield, then clothing or weapons or gold, something bigger to those that were of higher rank. Finally he came to face his kinsman Haraldr with two canes in his hand, saying this:

'Which of the canes here do you wish to have?'

Then Haraldr replies: 'The one that is nearer to me.'

Then spoke King Magnús: 'With this cane I give you half the realm of Norway with all its dues and taxes and all the possessions that belong to it on this condition, that you shall be as lawfully king as I everywhere in Norway. But when we are all together, I shall have precedence in greetings and service and in seating. If there are three of us of this rank, I shall sit in the middle. I shall occupy the royal berth and dock. You shall also stand by [99] and support our rule in the role in which we have set you as the person in Norway that we had thought no one would have been as long as our skull had remained up above the ground.'

Then Haraldr stood up and thanked him warmly for the rank and honour. Then they both sit down and were very merry that day. In the evening Haraldr and his men went to their ship.

CHAPTER TWENTY-FOUR

The next morning King Magnús had trumpets blown for an assembly of the whole army. And when the assembly was in session, then King Magnús announced in the presence of them all the gift that he had given his kinsman

Haraldr. Þórir of Steig gave Haraldr the title of king at this assembly. On that day King Haraldr invited King Magnús to his table, and he went with sixty men during the day to King Haraldr's tents where he had prepared a banquet. Then both the kings were present there sitting together, and there was a fine feast [100] and it was served splendidly. The kings were merry and happy. So when the day drew to a close, then King Haraldr had a very large number of bags carried into the tent. The men also carried in clothing and weapons and other kinds of precious objects. He shared out this wealth, giving it and dealing it out among the followers of King Magnús who were present at the banquet there. After that he had the bags opened, saying then to King Magnús:

'Yesterday you gave us a great deal of power that you had previously won from your enemies and ours, and took us into fellowship with yourself. That was well done, for you have worked hard for it. Now on our side there is this, that we have been abroad and moreover have been through some dangers as a result of which I have amassed this gold, which you will now be able to see. I wish to contribute this to the fellowship with you. We shall have all this wealth in equal shares, just as each of us has half the power in Norway. I realise that our characters are different. You are a much more liberal man than I. We shall divide this wealth equally between us. Then each of us can do what he wants with his share.'

After that Haraldr had a great oxhide spread out on the ground and the gold from the bags poured onto it. Then scales and weights were got out and the wealth was weighed out in parts, everything divided by weight, and it seemed to everyone that was looking on a most amazing thing that so much gold should have been brought together in one place in Northern Lands. It was, however, really the property and wealth of the king of the Greeks, since everyone says that there are housefuls of red gold there. The kings were now very merry. Then a nugget came up. It was as big as a man's head. King Haraldr picked up the nugget and spoke:

'Where is now the gold, kinsman Magnús, that you can bring out to equal this nugget-head?'

Then Magnús replies: [101] 'There has been such warfare and great military expeditions that I am giving you nearly all the gold and silver that is in my keeping. There is now no more gold than this ring in my possession.'

He took the ring and gave it to Haraldr. He looked at it and spoke:

'This is not much gold, kinsman, for a king who has two kingdoms, and yet there are some who would doubt whether you own this ring.'

Then King Magnús replied gravely: 'If I do not rightly own that ring, then I do not know what I have got rightfully, for my father the blessed King Óláfr gave me this ring at our final parting.'

Then King Haraldr replies with a laugh: 'You are telling the truth, King Magnús: your father gave you the ring. This ring he took from my father for no very good reason. Moreover, it is true that at that time things were not good for petty kings in Norway when your father's power was at its maximum.'

King Haraldr gave Steigar-Þórir there at the banquet a mazer bowl.[148] It had a silver band round it and a silver handle on top, both gilded, and was completely filled with pure silver coins. With it there were two gold rings that together weighed a mark. He also gave him his cloak, it was fine cloth dyed brown, trimmed with white fur, and promised him great honour and his friendship. Þorgils Snorrason said this, that he saw an altar-cloth that was made from this mantle, and Guthormr Steigar-Þórir's son's daughter Guðríðr said that she claimed her father Guthormr had the bowl in his possession, as she saw with her own eyes. So says Bǫlverkr:

98.	To you, as I heard, harmer	*Drápa* about Haraldr
	of hoards,[149] was later granted	harðráði 7
[102]	the green ground, and you offered	*Mork* I (*Flb*) 129
	him gold when you met Magnús.	*Fsk* 246
	The accord between you kinsmen	*Skald* II 292
	was kept most peacefully,	
	and Sveinn after that	
	only an age of war expected.	

CHAPTER TWENTY-FIVE

King Magnús and King Haraldr both ruled Norway the next winter after their settlement, and each of them had his own following. During the winter they travelled round Upplǫnd receiving banquets and were sometimes both together, and sometimes each on his own. They travelled all the way north to Þrándheimr and to Niðaróss. King Magnús had been looking after the holy relics of King Óláfr since he came into the country, cutting his hair and nails every twelve months, and he himself kept the key with which the shrine could be opened. Then many kinds of miracles took place at the holy relics of King Óláfr. There soon came to be rifts in the harmony between the kings, and many people were so malicious as to encourage ill-will between them.

CHAPTER TWENTY-SIX

Sveinn Úlfsson remained behind asleep after Haraldr had gone away. After that Sveinn made enquiries about Haraldr's movements. So when he learnt

---

[148] A bowl hollowed from a burr on a maple.

[149] *hoddstríðir*: 'hoard-damager', generous man.

that Haraldr and [103] Magnús had come to an agreement and that they now had a single army between them, then he took his troops east along the coast of Skáney and stayed there until he learnt in the winter that Magnús and Haraldr had taken their force north to Norway. After that Sveinn took his troops south to Denmark and he received all the royal dues there that winter.

CHAPTER TWENTY-SEVEN

So when spring began, they called out a levy from Norway, King Magnús and King Haraldr. It so happened on one occasion, that King Magnús and King Haraldr were lying one night in a certain harbour, and the following day Haraldr was ready first, and he sailed straight away, and in the evening he sailed into the harbour that he and King Magnús had intended to stay in that night. Haraldr berthed his ship in the royal berth and put up his awning there. King Magnús sailed later in the day, and they arrived in the harbour when Haraldr and his men had already put up their awnings. They see that Haraldr and his men had berthed in the royal berth and that he intended to lie there. So when King Magnús and his men had furled their sails, then King Magnús said:

'Let men now pull on their oars and position themselves all along the sides of the ship, let some get out their weapons and arm themselves. And since they are unwilling to move away, we shall fight.'

But when King Haraldr sees that Magnús was going to start a battle with them, then he spoke to his men:

'Cut the cables and let the ships slip out of the berth. Kinsman Magnús is angry!'

They did so, they sailed their ships out of the berth, King Magnús sailed his ships into the berth. When both parties had berthed their ships, King Haraldr went with some of his men aboard King Magnús's ship. The king received him warmly, bidding him welcome. Then King Haraldr replies:

[104] 'I thought we were come among friends, though I was a little doubtful for a while whether you were going to let it be so. But it is true what they say, childhood is hasty. I do not want to take it in any other way than as a characteristic of childhood.'

Then says King Magnús: 'It was a characteristic of my family, not of my childhood, though I cannot but bear in mind what it is that I have granted, and what I have retained. If this small matter were now taken as our deliberate policy, then it would soon arise again. But we want to keep all the agreements that have been entered into, and we expect the same from you, as we have stipulated.'

Then Haraldr replied: 'It is indeed the traditional thing for the wiser one to give way.'

And he then went back to his ship. From such exchanges between the kings it could be seen that it was difficult to avoid problems between them. King Magnús's men reckoned that he was in the right in what he said, while those that were less sensible reckoned that Haraldr had been rather put to shame. But King Haraldr's men said that nothing had been stipulated other than that King Magnús was to have the berth if they both arrived at the same time, and that Haraldr was not obliged to vacate the berth if he had got there first, reckoning that Haraldr had behaved sensibly and well. But those that wanted to express the more hostile view reckoned that King Magnús was trying to upset the agreement, and reckoned that he had done wrong and brought shame on King Haraldr. In such disagreements there soon came to be talk among less sensible people of there being discord between the kings. There were many indications now that the kings differed in their attitudes, though there is little of it written here.

CHAPTER TWENTY-EIGHT

King Magnús and King Haraldr took this army south to Denmark. And when Sveinn learnt this, then he fled away east to Skáni. The kings Magnús [105] and Haraldr stayed in Denmark for a long time during the summer, subjecting the whole country to themselves. They were in Jótland in the autumn. It happened one night when King Magnús was lying in his bed, that he had a dream and dreamt he was in the presence of his father the blessed King Óláfr, and he dreamt he spoke to him:

'Which would you rather, my son, go with me now or become the most powerful of all kings and live a long time and commit a misdeed that you will scarcely or not at all be able to put right?'

And he dreamt he replied: 'I want you to make the choice for me.'

Then he dreamt the king replied to him: 'Then you shall go with me.'

King Magnús tells this dream to his men. And a little later he caught a sickness and lay there in a place called Súðaþorp. And when he was come close to death, then he sent his brother Þórir to Sveinn Úlfsson, to say that he was to stand by Þórir when he needed it. This was also in the message, that King Magnús gave the realm of Denmark to Sveinn when his life was over, saying that it was right that Haraldr should rule over Norway and Sveinn over Denmark. After that King Magnús góði died, and his death was very greatly mourned by all the common people. So says Oddr Kíkinaskáld:

[106]	99.	Men shed many tears bearing	Poem about Magnús góði 2
		the munificent king to the grave;	*Mork* I (*Flb*) 176
		that was a weighty burden	*Fsk* 249
		for the ones he had given gold to.	*Skald* II 33

The lord's housecarls could hardly
hold back, the mind troubled —
and the king's company sat often
cast down thereafter — from weeping.

CHAPTER TWENTY-NINE

After these events King Haraldr held an assembly with the troops, telling people his intention of taking the army to Vébjargaþing and having himself accepted as king over the realm of the Danes, afterwards winning the country, reckoning it to be as much his patrimony as the realm of Norway after his kinsman King Magnús, then bidding the troops put out all their strength, declaring that then the Norwegians [107] would for ever be the masters of the Danes. Then Einarr þambarskelfir replies, declaring himself to be under a greater obligation to convey his foster-son King Magnús to his burial and bring him to his father King Óláfr than to fight abroad and covet another king's realm and possessions, ending his speech by saying that he thought it better to follow King Magnús dead than any other king alive, afterwards having the corpse taken and laid out decently so that his lying in state on the royal ship could be seen. Then all the Prœndir and Norwegians set out on their journey home with King Magnús's body, and the levy broke up. Then King Haraldr realised that his best course was to go back to Norway and first of all take possession of that realm, and from there reinforce his troops. King Haraldr now went back to Norway with the whole force. And as soon as he got to Norway, then he held an assembly with the people of the country and had himself accepted as king over the whole land. Thus he went on all the way from the east through the Vík, being accepted as king in every district of Norway.

CHAPTER THIRTY

Einarr þambarskelfir and with him the whole host of Prœndir took Magnús Óláfsson's body and conveyed it to Niðaróss, and he was buried there at Clemenskirkja. The blessed King Óláfr's shrine was there at that time. King Magnús had been an average person in size, with regular features and a fresh complexion, light-coloured hair, well-spoken and decisive, noble in character, most liberal with his wealth, a great warrior and a most bold fighter. He was the most popular of all kings, praised by both friends and foes.

[108] CHAPTER THIRTY-ONE

That autumn Sveinn Úlfsson was located in Skáni and was preparing to set out east into Svíaveldi, intending to give up the title he had assumed in

Denmark. But when he had got to his horse, then there rode up to him there some men to tell him the news, to begin with that King Magnús Óláfsson is dead, and also this, that the whole army of Norwegians was gone away from Denmark. Sveinn replies to this swiftly, saying:

'I call God to witness that never again shall I flee the realm of the Danes as long as I live.'

He then mounts his horse and then rides south to Skáni. Then immediately a great troop flocked to him. That winter he subjected the whole realm of Danes to himself. All the Danes now accepted him as king. King Magnús's brother Þórir came to Sveinn in the autumn with the message from King Magnús, as was witten above. Sveinn welcomed him, and Þórir stayed with him after that for a long time in high honour.

CHAPTER THIRTY-TWO

King Haraldr Sigurðarson took the kingship over the whole of Norway after King Magnús Óláfsson's death. Now when he had ruled Norway for one winter, and when spring came, then he called out a levy from the whole country, [109] a half-levy[150] in troops and ships, and made his way south to Jótland. He made raids in many places during the summer and burned, and sailed into Goðnarfjǫrðr. Then King Haraldr composed this:[151]

100.	We'll let, while the linen-oak[152]	*Mork* I 188
	lulls her husband, the anchor	*Fsk* 250–51
	grip in Goðnarfjǫrðr,	*Skald* II 46
	the Gerðr of incantation.[153]	

Then he spoke to the poet Þjóðólfr, telling him to cap it. He said:

101.	Further south next summer—	*Mork* I 188
	I speak a prophecy—cold-nose[154]	*Fsk* 251
	shall fix with its fluke the vessel	*Skald* II 165
	of fir; we add a hook to the ocean.	

Bǫlverkr alludes in his *drápa* to Haraldr travelling to Denmark the next summer after King Magnús's death:

102.	From the fair land you fitted out	*Drápa* about Haraldr
	a fleet—sea washed over vessels;	harðráði 8

[150] According to lawbooks this was one man in fourteen.

[151] In *Morkinskinna* this and the following half-stanza form a single stanza attributed to Haraldr; one version of *Fagrskinna* attributes the whole stanza to Þjóðólfr, the other, like *Heimskringla*, divides it between Haraldr and Þjóðólfr.

[152] *líneik*: 'oak-tree of linen', woman.

[153] *galdrs Gerðr*: 'Gerðr (goddess) of chant', woman.

[154] *kaldnefr*: the anchor.

	the next year, with splendid stud-horses	*Mork* I 189
	of the surge,[155] you carved the ocean.	*Fsk* 251
[110]	On dark wave the fine hull—[156]	*Skáldsk* 94 (ll. 1–4)
	Danes were then in trouble—	*Skald* II 293
	lay; people looked on	
	laden warships offshore.	

Then they burned Þorkell geysa's (Dash's) estate. He was an important leader. Then his daughters were led to the ships as captives. They had made a great joke the winter before about King Haraldr travelling to Denmark with warships. They had carved an anchor in cheese, saying that it might well serve to hold back the king of Norway's ships. Then this was composed:

	103.	Island-ring objects,[157]	*Mork* I 190
		anchor-rings, Danish maidens	*Fsk* 252
		carved out of yeast-cheese;	*Skald* II 815
		that irked the ruler.	
		Now in the morning many	
		a maid sees—fewer are laughing—	
[111]		a hefty hook of iron	
		holding the overlord's vessels.	

People say that an informant who had seen King Haraldr's fleet said to Þorkell geysa's daughters:

'You said, daughters of Geysa, that Haraldr would not be coming to Denmark.'

Dótta replied: 'That was true yesterday.'

Þorkell ransomed his daughters with a huge amount of money. So says Grani:[158]

	104.	Never did the dogged one	Poem about Haraldr
		let dry her eyelashes[159]	harðráði 1
		in heavily dense Hornskógr	*Mork* I 192
		the Hlǫkk of Kraki's snowdrift.[160]	*Fsk* 252

---

[155] *gjalfrstóð*: 'stud-horses of the surge', ships.

[156] *skokkr*: 'hull'; Kari Ellen Gade in *Skald* II translates 'bottom boards'. Here, it represents 'the ship(s)'.

[157] *eybaugs þing*: 'thing of the island-ring (sea, which encircles islands)' something belonging to the sea, or equipment used in the sea, (here) anchor.

[158] *Skáldatal* names Grani among Haraldr's poets, but his only surviving works are this stanza, another in *Morkinskinna* and in part in *Snorra Edda*, and a further couplet in *Snorra Edda*.

[159] that is, allow her to stop weeping.

[160] *Kraka drífu Hlǫkk*: 'valkyrie of the (snow-)drift of Kraki (gold)', woman (here, one of Þorkell's daughters, perhaps the Dótta of line 7, if not a generic singular).

> The lord of Filir[161] drove the fleeing   *Skald* II 296
> of the chieftain's foes to the shore.
> Very fast Dótta's father
> was forced to pay out riches.

King Haraldr made raids all that summer in the realm of the Danes and got a huge amount of wealth, but he was not resident in Denmark that summer, going back to Norway in the autumn and staying there during the winter.

[112] CHAPTER THIRTY-THREE

King Haraldr married Þorbergr Árnason's daughter Þóra the next winter after King Magnús inn góði died.[162] They had two sons. The elder was called Magnús and the second Óláfr. King Haraldr and Queen Ellisif had two daughters. One was called Maria and the other Ingigerðr.

Now the next spring after this military expedition that has just been told about, King Haraldr called out a force and went in the summer to Denmark and made raids and after that every summer in succession. So says the poet Stúfr:

> 105.   Falstr, it is said, was laid waste;   *Stúfsdrápa* 5
>   fear lay heavy on people.   *Mork* I 194
>   The raven was fed; the Danish   *Fsk* 253
>   were frightened every year.   *Skald* II 355

CHAPTER THIRTY-FOUR

King Sveinn ruled over the whole of Denmark after King Magnús died. He stayed put in the winters, but lay out with a levy in the summers and threatened to go north into Norway with an army of Danes and cause no less damage there than King Haraldr had done in the realm of the Danes. One winter King Sveinn challenged King Haraldr that they should meet on the Elfr the next summer and fight to the finish or else come to a settlement. Then both spent the whole winter preparing their ships, and they both called out a half levy the following summer.

[113] That summer Þorleikr fagri (the Fair) came from out in Iceland and set himself to compose a *flokkr*[163] about King Sveinn Úlfsson. He heard, when he got to the north of Norway, that King Haraldr was gone south to the Elfr against Sveinn. Then Þorleikr uttered this:[164]

---

[161] *Fila dróttinn*: 'lord of Filir (inhabitants of Fjalir)', king of Norway.

[162] Presumably Þóra was Haraldr's concubine rather than his wife.

[163] An informal series of stanzas without a refrain. See note 35 above.

[164] What we are told here is all that is known about Þorleikr (or Þorleifr) fagri, except that in *Skáldatal* he is said to have been a poet of Sveinn Úlfsson. Ten stanzas of the *flokkr* survive, and a further three fragments are attributed to Þorleikr.

106. It is likely that the Innþrœndr   *Flokkr* about Sveinn Úlfsson 2
      army, active in point-onslaught,[165]   *Mork* I 195
      will meet on the road of Rakni[166]   *Fsk* 254
      the ruler expert in battle.   *Skald* II 314
      Of the two, God can determine
      which takes life from the other,
      or lands; Sveinn cares little
      for lightly kept covenants.

And again he uttered this:

107. Haraldr, who often raises   *Flokkr* about Sveinn Úlfsson 3
      red shield off land, angrily   *Mork* I 196
      steers broad board-oxen[167] southwards   *Fsk* 254
      onto Buðli's pathways,[168]   *Skald* II 315
      while glorious leek-beasts,[169] gold-mouthed,
      gaily covered with colour,
      of Sveinn, who reddens spears,
      sailed across the sea northwards.

[114] King Haraldr came to the arranged meeting with his army. Then he learnt that King Sveinn was lying south off Sjáland with his fleet. Then King Haraldr divided his forces, letting most of the troop of farmers go back. He went with his following and landed men and his favourite troops and all those of the troop of farmers who were closest to the Danes. They went south to Jótland to the south of Vendilskagi, and so south round Þjóð, laying everywhere they went waste. So says the poet Stúfr:

108. Those at Þjóð fled forthwith   *Stúfsdrápa* 6
      from the prince's meeting.   *Mork* I 197
      High-hearted, he dared boldly.   *Fsk* 256
      . . . Haraldr's spirit above lands . . .[170]   *Skald* II 355

They went all the way south to Heiðabýr, took the market town and burnt it. King Haraldr's men then composed this:

109. All Heiðabœr in anger   *Mork* I 197
      from end to end was ravaged   *Fsk* 256
      with fire; that can be called *Skald* II 816
      a courageous deed, I consider.

---

[165] *odda snerta*: 'onslaught of spear-points', battle.
[166] *Rakna stígr*: 'path of Rakni (a sea-king)', the sea.
[167] *borðraukn*: 'draught-animal(s) of the board', ship(s).
[168] *Buðla slóðir*: 'tracks of Buðli (sea-king)', the sea.
[169] *gullmunnuð*: with gold figureheads; *lauks dýr*: 'beast(s) of the leek (mast)', ship(s).
[170] For the split refrain, see note 125 above.

[115]   There is hope we bring harm to—
             high flame spewed from buildings—
             Sveinn; I stood last night on the rampart
             of the stronghold before dawning.

Þorleikr also mentions this in his *flokkr* when he had heard that no battle had taken place on the Elfr:

110.   How the king hoping for battle   *Flokkr* about Sveinn Úlfsson 6
       to Heiðabœr travelled   *Mork* I 199
       the war-Rǫgnir[171] can enquire of   *Fsk* 257
       the king's troop, if he knows not,   *Skald* II 317
       when Haraldr took westward
       once to the king's town, that year
       that never should have been,
       needlessly, skis of fair weather.[172]

CHAPTER THIRTY-FIVE

Then Haraldr travelled north taking sixty ships, most of them being large ones and heavily loaded with plunder that they had captured during the summer. And when they got north past Þjóð, then King Sveinn came down to the shore with a large army. He then challenged King Haraldr to fight and go ashore. King Haraldr had a force that was less than half their number. [116] Yet he challenged King Sveinn to fight with him on ships. So says Þorleikr fagri:

111.   Sveinn bade—he was born at   *Flokkr* about Sveinn Úlfsson 7
       the best time under Miðgarðr—[173]   *Mork* I 200
       the powerful ranks redden   *Fsk* 257
       rimmed shields on land.   *Skald* II 319
       But Haraldr, shy of hesitation,
       held he would, if the land was
       defended by the rash king, fight on
       the fair-weather horse[174] rather.

After that Haraldr sailed north past Vendilskagi. Then the wind blew them off course and they took shelter under Hlésey and lay there during the night. Then a dense fog came down upon the sea. And when morning came and the sun rose, then they saw to one side on the sea what looked like some fires burning. King Haraldr was now told of this. Then he looked and straightway said:

[171] *folk-Rǫgnir*: 'battle-god' (*Rǫgnir* is a name for Óðinn), warrior.
[172] *byrskíð*: 'ski(s) of fair wind', ship(s).
[173] *und Miðgarði*: i.e. in the world.
[174] *byrjar val*: 'horse of fair wind', ship.

'Take the awnings off the ships, and let men start rowing. The army of Danes must be come upon us. The fog must have cleared where they are, the sun must be shining on their dragon heads that are gilded.'

So it was as Haraldr said. Now was come there King Sveinn of the Danes with an invincible army. Both parties then rowed as fast as they could. The Danes had ships that were faster to row, but the Norwegians' ships were both swollen and deep in the water. Now the distance between them grew less. Then Haraldr realised that it would not do to leave things as they were. Haraldr's dragon ship was sailing in the rear of all his ships. Then King Haraldr said that they were to throw planks of wood overboard and put on them [117] clothing and things of value. There was such a complete calm that this was carried along by the current. So when the Danes saw their wealth drifting on the sea, then those that were ahead turned after it, thinking it easier to take what was floating free than to get it on board from the Norwegians. Now the pursuit was delayed. Now when King Sveinn came up behind them with his ship, he urged them on and said it was a great disgrace, having such a large army, that they should not manage to catch them and gain power over them, when they had a small force. Then the Danes set to and worked hard at the rowing a second time. So when King Haraldr realised that the Danes' ships were gaining on them, then he told his men to lighten the ships and carry overboard malt and wheat and bacon and chop out their drink.[175] This worked for a while. Then King Haraldr had the bulwarks and casks and barrels that were empty taken and thrown overboard, and prisoners of war as well. So when all this was tossing about together on the sea, then King Sveinn ordered the men to be helped, and this was done. With this delay they drew apart. Then the Danes turned back and the Norwegians went on their way. So says Þorleikr fagri:

112.	I have heard it all, how	*Flokkr about Sveinn Úlfsson* 8
	on the ships' path[176] Norwegians	*Mork* I 203
	were pursued by Sveinn, while	*Fsk* 260
	the second king escaped, keen-spirited.	*Skald* II 320
	The loot of the lord of Þrœndr[177] —	
	they lost more vessels —	
	was all set on storm-swollen	
	sea of Jótland floating.	

[118] King Sveinn turned his fleet back under Hlésey, meeting there seven of the Norwegians' ships. This was troops from the levy and just farmers. So when King Sveinn got up to them, then they begged for quarter for themselves and offered ransom for themselves. So says Þorleikr fagri:

---

[175] i.e. from their wooden containers fastened in the ships.

[176] *flausta vegr:* 'way of ships', sea.

[177] *Þrœnda þengill:* 'lord of Þrœndr', i.e. king of Norway.

113. To the lord of men a large ransom	*Flokkr* about Sveinn Úlfss. 9
the leader's friends offered.	*Mork* I 203
They soothed the fight, stern-minded,	*Fsk* 260
whose force was smaller.	*Skald* II 321

113.   To the lord of men a large ransom   *Flokkr* about Sveinn Úlfss. 9
         the leader's friends offered.   *Mork* I 203
         They soothed the fight, stern-minded,   *Fsk* 260
         whose force was smaller.   *Skald* II 321
         And swiftly deciding farmers
         stayed then, when they started
         exchanging words—life was cherished
         by children of men[178]—the onset.

CHAPTER THIRTY-SIX

King Haraldr was a powerful man and a firm ruler within his own country, very intelligent in his thinking, so that it is universally held that there has been no ruler in Northern Lands that has been as profoundly wise as Haraldr or as clever in his decisions. He was a great warrior and of the very boldest in fighting. He was strong and better able to use weapons than any other man, as has been written above. And yet there are many more of his famous achievements that have not been recorded. The reason for this is our ignorance, and this too, that we are unwilling to write down in books unattested stories. Though [119] we have heard talk or mention of other things, still it seems to us better from now on that material should be added than that the same should have to be removed. There is much material about King Haraldr recorded in poems that Icelandic men presented to him or to his sons. He was for that reason a great friend to them. He was also a very great friend to all the people here in this country.[179] And when there was a great famine in Iceland, then King Haraldr allowed four ships licence to export meal to Iceland and stipulated that no pound of a ship's cargo was to be dearer than the cost of a hundred ells of homespun. He licensed all poor people who could provide their own food for the voyage to travel out of Iceland. And as a result this land was able to eke out its sustenance until there was harvest and recovery. King Haraldr sent out here a bell for the church that the blessed King Óláfr sent the timber for, which was raised at the Alþingi. Such memorials have people here of King Haraldr, and many others in the noble gifts that he presented to people who visited him.

Halldórr Snorrason and Úlfr Óspaksson, who were mentioned above, came to Norway with King Haraldr. Their natures were different in many ways. Halldórr was one of the biggest and strongest and handsomest of men. King Haraldr bore this testimony of him, that he has been the one of the men that had been with him that was least taken aback by sudden events. Whether it was deadly danger or welcome news or whatever might turn up in the way

---

[178] *ýta kindr*: 'offspring of men', people.
[179] i.e. in Iceland. These are Snorri Sturluson's thoughts.

of danger, then he was no happier and no sadder, [120] he slept and drank and enjoyed food neither more nor less than was his custom. Halldórr was a man of few words and not of ready speech, outspoken and severe in character and uncompromising; and that was unpleasant for the king, when he had plenty of other decent and compliant men around him. Halldórr stayed a short time with the king. He went to Iceland, set up house in Hjarðarholt, lived there until his old age and became an old man.

CHAPTER THIRTY-SEVEN

Úlfr Óspaksson stayed with King Haraldr on very friendly terms. He was a most intelligent person, well-spoken, a most outstanding person, reliable and straightforward. King Haraldr made Úlfr his marshal and gave him in marriage Jórunn Þorbergsdóttir, sister of Þóra, who was married to King Haraldr. Úlfr and Jórunn's children were Jóan sterki (the Strong) at Rásvǫllr and Brígiða, mother of Sauða-Úlfr (Sheep-), father of Pétr byrðarsveinn (Load-Carrying Lad),[180] father of Úlfr flý (Speck) and his brothers. Jóan sterki's son was Erlendr hímaldi (Slowcoach), father of Archbishop Eysteinn and his brothers. King Haraldr gave Úlfr stallari (Marshal) the privileges of a landed man and revenues of twelve marks and in addition half a district in Þrándheimr. So says Steinn Herdísarson in *Úlfsflokkr*.[181]

[121] CHAPTER THIRTY-EIGHT

King Magnús Óláfsson had Óláfskirkja built in Kaupangr. It was in the place where the king's body had been kept the night before its burial. It was at that time above the town. He also had the royal palace raised there. The church was still not fully finished before the king died. King Haraldr had that completed that was still lacking. He also provided materials for building himself a stone hall there in the palace grounds, and it was not fully finished before he had Máríukirkja built from its foundations up on the gravel bank near where the holy relics of the king lay in the ground the first winter after his fall. It was a great minster strongly built with mortar, so that it could hardly be demolished when Archbishop Eysteinn had it pulled down. The holy relics of King Óláfr were kept in Óláfskirkja while Máríukirkja was

---

[180] Cf. ch. 9 of *Haraldssona saga* below.

[181] Steinn Herdísarson was great-grandson of the Icelandic poet Einarr skálaglamm Helgason (Vol. I, note 315), and a distant cousin of Stúfr blindi and of Úlfr himself. Kari Ellen Gade in *Skald* II (366) and other editors assign stanza 130 below to *Úlfsflokkr*, of which nothing else survives. Seven stanzas are preserved of his *Nizarvísur* on the Battle of the Niz in 1062, in which he is said to have been present on Úlfr's ship (see p. 147, st. 130 below), and sixteen stanzas of his *Óláfsdrápa* for Haraldr's son Óláfr kyrri.

being built. King Haraldr had the buildings of the royal palace placed below Máríukirkja by the river, where they are now. But the building he had had erected as his hall he had consecrated as Gregoriuskirkja.

CHAPTER THIRTY-NINE

There is a man called Ívarr hvíti (the White) who was an important landed man. He had an estate in Upplǫnd. He was Jarl Hákon inn ríki's (the Great's) grandson. Ívarr was of all men the most handsome in looks. Ívarr's son was called Hákon. It is said of him that he was superior to all men living at that time in Norway in valour and strength and abilities. He was already in his youth on warlike expeditions and won great honour for himself on them, and Hákon became a most excellent person.[182]

[122] CHAPTER FORTY

Einarr þambarskelfir was the most powerful of the landed men in Þrándheimr. He and King Haraldr were not on very good terms. Yet Einarr still had the revenues that he had had while King Magnús was alive. Einarr was most extremely wealthy. He was married to Jarl Hákon's daughter Bergljót, as was written above. Their son Eindriði was now fully grown up. He was now married to Sigríðr, daughter of Ketill kálfr (Calf) and King Haraldr's niece Gunnhildr. Eindriði inherited handsomeness and fairness from his mother's family, Jarl Hákon or his sons, but got his size and strength from his father Einarr, and all the abilities in which Einarr surpassed other men. He was a most popular person.

CHAPTER FORTY-ONE

There was a jarl named Ormr in Upplǫnd at this time. His mother was Jarl Hákon inn ríki's daughter Ragnhildr. Ormr was a most excellent man. At this time Áslákr Erlingsson was east at Sóli in Jaðarr. He was married to Jarl Sveinn Hákonarson's daughter Sigríðr. Jarl Sveinn's other daughter, Gunnhildr, was married to King Sveinn Úlfsson of the Danes. These were descendants of Jarl Hákon now in Norway, as well as many other fine people, and this line was all much handsomer than other folk and most were people of very great ability, and all of them fine people.

[123] CHAPTER FORTY-TWO

King Haraldr was an imperious person. And this became more marked as he strengthened his hold on the land, and it reached the point that it was no good for most people to cross him in speech or to bring forward any matter other than what he wished to have done. So says the poet Þjóðólfr:

[182] There is a separate saga about Hákon Ívarsson, which was one of Snorrri's sources.

114. The trusty troop of the battle-   *Sexstefja* 11
attender[183] must, at the pleasure   *Mork* I 226 (ll. 5–8)
of the splendid strife-grower,[184]   *Fsk* 273 (ll. 5–8))
sit and stand, lord-dutiful.   *Hákonar saga Ívarss.* 7
The whole nation kneels to   *Skald* II 123
the nourisher of the war-starling,[185]
the only choice is to say yea to
all that the king bids people.

CHAPTER FORTY-THREE

Einarr þambarskelfir was the most prominent leader of the landowners out over all Þrándheimr. He was the spokesman for them at assemblies attended by the king's men. Einarr had a good knowledge of the laws. He was not lacking in boldness in invoking them at assemblies, even if the king himself was present. All the landowners supported him. This made the king very angry, and eventually it came about that they quarrelled with each other openly. Einarr said that the landowners would not put up with injustice from him if he contravened the law of the land with them. And this went on between them on a number of occasions. [124] Then Einarr took to having a large number of men about him in his residence, but many more when he went to the town if the king was going to be present there. It happened one time that Einarr went in to the town and had a large following, eight or nine longships and nearly five hundred men. And when he got to the town, he went ashore with this troop. King Haraldr was in his palace and was standing out on a balcony and saw Einarr's troop disembarking, and it is said that Haraldr then spoke:

115. Here I see the active Einarr,   *Mork* I (*Flb*) 207
able, þambarskelmir,   *Fsk* 263
to cut the kelp-halter,[186]   *Hákonar saga Ívarss.* 47
come ashore well-attended.   *Skáldsk* 80 (ll. 5–8)
With full force he is waiting   *Skald* II 47
to fill the king's throne; often
at a jarl's heels a smaller host
of housecarls surges, I notice.

116. The reddener of radiance   *Mork* I (*Flb*) 207
of rims[187] from the country   *Fsk* 262

---

[183] *hjaldrvitjaðr*: 'battle-visitor', warrior.

[184] *dolgstœrandi*: 'increaser of battle', warrior.

[185] *folkstara feitir*: 'fattener of the war-starling (raven)', warrior.

[186] *þangs þjalmi*: 'noose of seaweed', the sea; to cut this is to sail.

[187] *randa bliks rjóðandi*: 'reddener of the gleam (sword) of shields', warrior.

will oust us, unless Einarr   *Hákonar saga Ívarssonar* 47
the axe's thin mouth kisses.   *Skald* II 48

Einarr stayed some days in the town.

[125] CHAPTER FORTY-FOUR

One day a meeting was being held, and the king himself was at the meeting. A thief had been taken in the town and was brought to the meeting. The man had previously been with Einarr, and he had been well pleased with the man. Einarr was told. Now he felt sure that the king would not let the man off even if Einarr thought it important. So Einarr had his troop arm themselves and after that go to the meeting. Einarr took the man from the meeting by force. After this friends of both came up and negotiated a settlement between them. So it came about that a meeting was arranged; they were to meet face to face. There was an audience chamber in the royal palace down by the river. The king went into this chamber with a few men, while the rest of his following was out in the courtyard. The king had a board placed across the roof-hole, and this left a very small opening. Then Einarr came into the courtyard with his troop. He said to his son Eindriði:

'You stay ouside with our troop, then I shall be in no danger.'

Eindriði stood outside by the entrance. And when Einarr came into the hall, he said:

'It is dark in the king's audience chamber.'

At that moment men leapt at him, some were thrusting and some cutting. So when Eindriði heard this, he drew his sword and ran into the chamber. He was immediately cut down, as were both of them. Then the king's men ran to the chamber and in front of the entrance, and the landowners were at a loss what to do, for they now had no leader. They egged each other on, saying it was disgraceful that they should fail to avenge their chief, and yet nothing came of any attack. The king went out to his troops and he put them in battle order and raised his standard, but there was no attack made by the landowners. Then the king went out onto his ship, and all his troops, after that rowing out along the river and so on his way out into the fiord. Einarr's wife Bergljót heard about his death. She was then in the lodging that [126] she and Einarr had previously used out in the town. She immediately went up into the king's palace where the troop of landowners was. She urged them hard to battle, but at that moment the king rowed out along the river. Then said Bergljót:

'It is a pity that my kinsman Hákon Ívarsson is not here now. The slayers of Eindriði would not be rowing out here along the river if Hákon was standing here on the river bank.'

After that Bergljót had Einarr and Eindriði's bodies laid out. They were buried at Óláfskirkja by the tomb of King Magnús Óláfsson. After the fall of Einarr Haraldr was hated so much for what he had done there that the only reason why the landed men and landowners made no attack and fought no battle against him was that no leader came forward to raise a standard at the head of the army of landowners.

CHAPTER FORTY-FIVE

At this time Finnr Árnason was living at Yrjar in Austrátt. He was now one of King Haraldr's landed men. Finnr was married to Hálfdan son of Sigurðr sýr's daughter Bergljót. Hálfdan was King Óláfr inn helgi and King Haraldr's brother. King Haraldr's wife Þóra was Finnr Árnason's niece. Finnr was on very good terms with the king, as were all his brothers. Finnr Árnason had been for some summers on raids in the west. They had at this time all been together raiding, Finnr and Guthormr Gunnhildarson and Hákon Ívarsson. King Haraldr travelled out through Þrándheimr and out to Austrátt. He was welcomed there. After that they spoke together, the king and Finnr, and discussed between themselves these events that had now taken place a very short time before, the killing of Einarr and his son, and also the grumbling and unrest that the Þrœndir were directing at the king. Finnr replies instantly:

'You have [127] managed everything in the worst possible way. You do all sorts of bad things, and afterwards you are so frightened that you don't know where you are.'

The king answers with a laugh: 'Kinsman-in-law, I shall now send you into the town. I want you to reconcile the landowners to me. If that does not work, I want you to go to Upplǫnd and see to it with Hákon Ívarsson that he is not against me.'

Finnr replies: 'What will you offer me if I undertake this dangerous mission, for both the Þrœndir and the Upplendingar are such great enemies of yours, that it is impossible for any messengers of yours to travel there unless they can rely on their own resources?'

The king replies: 'Go, kinsman-in-law, on this mission, for I know that you will be successful, if anyone can be, in making us reconciled, so choose a favour from me.'

Finnr says: 'Keep your word then, and this is the favour I choose: I choose a truce and the right to stay in the country for my brother Kálfr, and [that he may keep] all his possessions, and also this, that he may have all his titles and all his power, such as he had before he left the country.'

The king spoke and agreed to all this that Finnr said: they had witnesses and confirmed it by shaking hands. After that Finnr said:

'What shall I promise Hákon for agreeing to a truce with you? He has now most say with the Þrœndir.'

The king says: 'What you must hear first, is what Hákon demands on his part for a settlement. After that promote my interests as far as you can, but ultimately refuse nothing except only the kingdom.'

After this King Haraldr travelled south to Mœrr and and gathered troops to himself and got a large following.

CHAPTER FORTY-SIX

Finnr Árnason went in to the town, taking with him his personal following, nearly eighty men. And when he got into the town, then he had a meeting with the townspeople. Finnr spoke long and eloquently at the meeting, telling the townspeople [128] and the farmers to adopt quite another course than hostility towards their king and driving him out, reminding them of how much evil had come upon them after they had done that before with the blessed King Óláfr, saying that the king would atone for this slaying in accordance with the judgment the noblest and wisest men would be willing to pass. By the time Finnr had ended his speech, people were willing to leave this matter as it was until the messengers returned that Bergljót had sent to Upplǫnd to see Hákon Ívarsson. After that Finnr went out to Orkadalr with the men that had accompanied him to the town. After that he went up to Dofrafjall and east across the mountain. Finnr went first to his kinsman-in-law Jarl Ormr — the jarl was married to Finnr's daughter Sigríðr — and told him about his mission.

CHAPTER FORTY-SEVEN

After that they arranged a meeting with Hákon Ívarsson. And when they met, then Finnr presented his message to Hákon that King Haraldr had sent to him. It was soon apparent from what Hákon said that he felt himself under a deep obligation to avenge his kinsman Einarr, saying that word had come to him from Þrándheimr that he would be getting plenty of support from there for an uprising against the king. After that Finnr put it to Hákon how much difference it would make to him, that it would be better to accept from the king honours as great as he could ask for rather than risk starting warfare against the king to whom he was in the past bound in service, saying that he would suffer defeat.

'And you will then have forfeited both wealth and security. But if you defeat King Haraldr, then you will be named a traitor to your lord.'

The jarl[188] supported what Finnr said too. So when Hákon had considered this business then he revealed what was in his mind, saying as follows:

[188] i.e. Ormr.

'I will come to terms with [129] King Haraldr if he will give me in marriage his kinswoman King Magnús Óláfsson's daughter Ragnhildr, with as great a dowry as befits her and pleases her.'

Finnr says that he will agree to this on behalf of the king. They confirm these terms between themselves. After that Finnr travels back north to Þrándheimr. Then this unrest and disturbance was settled, so that the king still held his kingdom in peace within the country, since now all the banding together that Eindriði's kinsmen had started in opposition to King Haraldr was put an end to.

CHAPTER FORTY-EIGHT

So when the appointed time for Hákon to claim the fulfilment of the particular promises made to him came, then he went to see King Haraldr. And when they start their discussion, then the king says that he is willing for his part to stand by all the terms of the settlement agreed between Finnr and Hákon.

'You, Hákon,' says the king, 'must discuss this matter with Ragnhildr, to see whether she is willing to accept this match. But neither you nor anyone else has the power to decide on marrying Ragnhildr unless she is in agreement.'

After this Hákon went to see Ragnhildr and raised the matter of this proposal with her. She replies as follows:

'I frequently realise that my father King Magnús is truly dead and gone as far as I am concerned, if I must give myself in marriage to just a farmer, even if you are a fine man and endowed with many skills. If King Magnús were alive, then he would not marry me to any man of lower rank than king. So it is not to be expected that I should be willing to marry a man of no rank.'

After this Hákon went to see King Haraldr and tells him what had passed between him and Ragnhildr, then brings up the special agreement between him and Finnr. Finnr was also present, and other men who had been there at the conversation between him and Finnr. Hákon calls them all to witness, that it had been stipulated that the king was to [130] endow Ragnhildr with whatever she wished.

'Now if she is unwilling to marry a man with no rank, then you can give me a title. I have the descent that makes me entitled to be a jarl, and some other qualifications, according to what people say.'

The king says: 'My brother King Óláfr and his son King Magnús, when they were ruling the kingdom, they had one jarl at a time in the country. I have also done the same since I became king. I do not want to take the title from Jarl Ormr that I have previously given him.'

Then Hákon realised in regard to his petition, that it would not be successful. He was now greatly displeased. Finnr was very angry too. They said that the king was not keeping his word, and parted with matters thus.

Hákon straightway left the country taking a well-manned longship. He reached the south of Denmark and went straight to see his kinsman-in-law King Sveinn.[189] The king welcomed him warmly and gave him large revenues there. Hákon became defender of the land there against vikings who were raiding the realm of the Danes a great deal, Vinðr and other people from the eastern Baltic, including Kúrir. He lay out on warships winter and summer.

CHAPTER FORTY-NINE

There is a man named Ásmundr, of whom it is said that he was King Sveinn's nephew and his foster-son. Ásmundr was the most accomplished of all men. The king was very fond of him. But when Ásmundr grew up, he was soon a very overbearing person, and he became a fighter. The king was displeased at this, and made him go away from him, giving him a good estate on which he could well maintain himself and his followers too. [131] So when Asmundr got this property of the king's, he gathered a large troop around himself. But the wealth the king had given him was not sufficient for his maintenance. Then he took over another one, much larger, that belonged to the king. And when the king learnt this, then he summoned Ásmundr to see him. And when they met, then the king says that Ásmundr was to stay in his court and have no following, and it had to be as the king wished. But when Ásmundr had been a short time with the king, then he could not stand it there and ran away during the night and got back to his following and now did even more wickedness than before. And as the king was riding round the country and got to where Ásmundr was, then he sent a troop to take Ásmundr prisoner by force. After that the king had him put in irons and kept like that for a while, thinking he might settle down. But when Ásmundr got out of his irons, then he immediately ran away and got himself a troop and warship, taking it then and raiding both abroad and at home and caused a very great deal of damage, killing many men and plundering widely. But the people that were the victims of this warfare came to the king and complained to him about their losses at his hands. He replies:

'What's the point of telling me about this? Why don't you go to Hákon Ívarsson? He is my land-protector and appointed to protect you farmers from warfare and punish vikings. I was told that Hákon was a bold man and valiant, but now it seems to me he does not want to get involved anywhere that he thinks there will be any danger.'

These words of the king's were conveyed to Hákon and were greatly expanded on. After this Hákon went with his troop to search for Ásmundr.

[189] Hákon's father Ívarr hvíti was grandson of Jarl Hákon inn ríki Sigurðarson (see p. 121 above, ch. 39); Sveinn Úlfsson married Gunnhildr daughter of Jarl Hákon's son Sveinn.

Their meeting was at sea. Hákon immediately engaged in battle. A fierce and great battle took place there. Hákon boarded Ásmundr's ship and cleared the ship. So it came about that he and Ásmundr engaged in hand to hand fighting and exchanged blows in person. Ásmundr fell there. Hákon cut off his head. After that Hákon went [132] straightway to see King Sveinn and came before him while the king was sitting at table. Hákon went in front of the table and laid Ásmundr's head on the table before the king and asked if he recognised it. The king made no reply and his face went red as blood. After that Hákon went away. A little later the king sent men to him and ordered him to leave his service.

'Say that I will do him no harm, but I cannot be responsible for all our kinsmen.'

CHAPTER FIFTY

After this Hákon left Denmark and went to the north of Norway to his properties. His kinsman Jarl Ormr was now dead. People were very pleased to see Hákon, his relatives and friends. Then many high-ranking people came forward to negotiate terms of a settlement between King Haraldr and Hákon. It came about that they reached agreement on these terms, that Hákon married the king's daughter Ragnhildr and King Haraldr gave Hákon a jarldom and the same power as Jarl Ormr had had. Hákon swore oaths of allegiance to King Haraldr for the service that he was bound to perform.

CHAPTER FIFTY-ONE

Kálfr Árnason had been on viking raids in the west after he left Norway, but in the winters he often stayed in Orkney with his kinsman-in-law Jarl Þorfinnr. His brother Finnr Árnason sent word to Kálfr, and had him told of the private agreement that he and King Haraldr had entered into together, that Kálfr should have the right to live in Norway and [keep] his possessions and the same revenues as he had had from King Magnús. And when this message reached Kálfr, then he immediately set out, travelling east to Norway, first of all to see his brother Finnr. After that Finnr secured a truce for Kálfr, and they met face to face, the king and Kálfr, then made their peace in accordance with what [133] the king and Finnr had previously agreed privately between themselves. Kálfr pledged himself to the king and all the undertakings such as he had previously entered into with King Magnús, so that Kálfr was duty bound to carry out all the tasks that King Haraldr wished [to have done] and that he felt his realm would be benefitted by. Then Kálfr took over all his possessions and revenues that he had previously had.

CHAPTER FIFTY-TWO

So the next summer following, King Haraldr called out a levy, going south to Denmark and raiding there during the summer. But when he got south to Fjón, then he found himself faced with a great gathering of troops. Then the king made his troops disembark from their ships and prepared to go ashore. He drew up his troops, putting Kálfr Árnason at the head of one company and ordering them to go ashore first and telling them which direction they were to take, while he said he would go ashore after them and come to their support. Kálfr and his men went ashore, and soon they were met by troops. Kálfr immediately engaged in battle, and this battle did not last long, since Kálfr was soon overpowered, and he took to flight along with his men, and the Danes pursued them. Many of the Norwegians fell. There fell Kálfr Árnason. Haraldr went up inland with his host. There it soon turned out to be in their path that they found the slain before them, and soon found Kálfr's body. It was carried down to the ships. But the king went up inland and made raids and slew many men there. So says Arnórr:

> 117.   The flashing blade on Fjón—   *Haraldsdrápa 1*
>   fire ran through men's houses—   *Skald II 261*
>   the king crimsoned; the Fjón-dwellers'
>   company grew smaller.

[134] CHAPTER FIFTY-THREE

After this Finnr Árnason expressed his feeling of hatred towards the king in respect of his brother Kálfr's fall, declaring that the king had engineered Kálfr's death and that Finnr had just been the victim of a fraud when he persuaded his brother Kálfr to return over the sea from the west into the power and trust of King Haraldr. And when this talk got about, then many people said that it seemed foolish of Finnr to believe that Kálfr would gain the trust of King Haraldr, it being evident that the king would be revengeful about lesser offences than those that Kálfr had committed against King Haraldr. The king let anyone say what they pleased about this, not admitting anything, also not denying anything. The only thing that was clear was that the king felt it had turned out well. King Haraldr spoke this verse:

> 118.   Now, urged to enmity,   *Skald II 49*
>   of eleven and two in all
>   I've caused the killing;
>   I recall still those men's slaying.
>   spoilers of gold[190] still pay back
>   deceptions with malice,

---

[190] *golls lýtendr:* 'spoilers of gold', (generous) men.

which goes with guile; little
gets the leek, they say, growing.

Finnr Árnason took this affair so much to heart [135] that he left the country
and turned up in the south in Denmark, went to see King Sveinn and was
welcomed warmly there, and they spoke in private for long periods, and it
turned out in the end that Finnr became subject to King Sveinn and became
his follower, and King Sveinn gave Finnr a jarldom and Halland to govern,
and he stayed there as defender of the land from the Norwegians.

CHAPTER FIFTY-FOUR

Ketill kálfr (Calf) and Gunnhildr at Hringunes's son was called Guthormr,
nephew of King Óláfr and King Haraldr. Guthormr was an able and manly-
looking person at an early age. Guthormr frequently stayed with King Haraldr
and was there on very friendly terms and took part in the king's policy-
making, for Guthormr was an intelligent person. He was a very popular
person. Guthormr frequently went raiding and raided a great deal in the
British Isles. He had a large troop of men. He had a retreat and winter quarters
in Dublin in Ireland and was on very friendly terms with King Margaðr.

CHAPTER FIFTY-FIVE

The following summer King Margaðr and Guthormr with him went and
raided in Bretland and they gained a huge amount of wealth there. After
that they made their way into Ǫngulseyjarsund. There they were going to
share out their booty. But when that great pile of silver was brought out and
the king saw it, then he wanted to have all the wealth for himself alone and
paid little regard to his friendship with Guthormr. Guthormr was ill pleased
with this, that he and his men should be denied their share. The king says
that he [136] should have two alternatives available:
    'The first, to put up with what we wish to have done, the second, to engage
in battle with us, and the one that is victorious shall have the wealth, and
this besides, that you must leave your ships, and I shall have them.'
    It seemed to Guthormr that there were great objections to both courses,
feeling he could not with honour abandon his ships and wealth without having
done anything to deserve it. It was also very perilous to fight with the king
and the great force that he had with him. But the odds between their forces
were so great, that the king had sixteen longships, and Guthormr five. Then
Guthormr asked the king to grant him three nights' respite on this matter for
him to have discussions with his men. He imagined that he might be able to
soften the king's attitude during this time and put his friendship with the king
on a better footing by means of his men's representations. But nothing that

he asked for could be got from the king. This was the eve of St Óláfr's day.[191]
Now Guthormr chose rather to die bravely or win victory rather than the other
course, to suffer disgrace and dishonour and get a name for cowardice from
such a great loss. Then he invoked God and his kinsman the blessed King
Óláfr, praying for their support and help, and vowing to give a tenth part of
all the booty they got if they won the victory to that blessed person's house.
After that he organised his troops and drew them up in battle order against
that great host and set to and fought them. And with the help of God and the
blessed King Óláfr, Guthormr won the victory. Margaðr fell there and every
man, young and old, that was in his following. And after this sublime victory
Guthormr wends his way happily home with all the wealth they had won in
battle. Then from the silver that they had won there was taken every tenth
coin, as had been promised to the blessed King Óláfr, and this was an immense
amount of money, so that of this silver Guthormr had a crucifix made of the
same height as himself or his forecastle man, and that [137] image is seven
ells high.[192] Guthormr gave this crucifix made like that to the foundation of
the blessed King Óláfr. It has stayed there since as a memorial of Guthormr's
victory and the miracle performed by the blessed King Óláfr.

CHAPTER FIFTY-SIX

There was a count in Denmark, evil and envious. He had a Norwegian servant
girl whose family was from Þrœndalǫg. She worshipped the blessed King
Óláfr and firmly believed in his sainthood. But this count, whom I mentioned
just now, did not believe all that he was told about that holy man's miracles,
saying it was nothing but just rumour and gossip, making mock and fun of
the praise and glory that all the people of the country accorded the good
king. So now came the feast day on which the gracious king lost his life
and which all Norwegians observed. Then this foolish count did not wish
to keep it holy, and gave his servant girl orders to bake and heat the oven
for bread on that day. She knew for certain the nature of the count, that he
would harshly punish her if she did not comply with what he had ordered
her to do. She goes unwillingly to her task and heated the oven, lamenting
bitterly as she worked and vowing to King Óláfr, saying she would never
believe in him unless he avenged this monstrous behaviour by some sign.
Now here you may hear the fitting punishments and just miracles: it all
happened straight away and at the same time, that the count went blind in

[191] *Óláfsvǫkuaptann*: St Óláfr's day, Óláfsmass (*Óláfsmessa*) below, end of
ch. 56, is 29th July. The vigil (*Óláfsvaka*) would be held the preceding night, at the
end of the eve of St Óláfr's day.

[192] The standard ell varied in the Middle Ages between approximately 48 and 57 cm. The
viking ell is said to have been 46 cm. This would make the image at least 10 ft 6 in. high.

both eyes and the bread that she had put in the oven turned to stone. Pieces
of this stone reached the foundation of the blessed [138] King Óláfr and
many other places. After that Óláfsmessa has always been kept in Denmark.

CHAPTER FIFTY-SEVEN

West in Valland there was a man that was disabled so that he was a cripple,
walking on knees and knuckles. He had been out on the road during the day,
and was now asleep. He dreamt that a noble-looking man came to him and
asked where he was bound for, and he mentioned a certain town. So this
noble person spoke to him:

'Go to the church of St Óláfr that stands in London, and you will then be
made whole.'

And after that he awoke and went straight to seek St Óláfr's church. And
eventually he came to London Bridge and asked the citizens there if they
could tell him where St Óláfr's church was, but they replied that there were
many more churches there than they could tell to which person each of them
was dedicated. So a little later a man went up to him there and asked where
he was bound for. He told him, and this person then spoke:

'We shall both go together to St Óláfr's church, and I know the way there.'

After that they went across the bridge and went up the street that led to
St Óláfr's church. And when they got to the gateway into the churchyard,
then this person stepped over the threshold that was in the gateway, and the
cripple rolled himself in over it and immediately stood up cured. But when
he looked around, then his companion had disappeared.

[139] CHAPTER FIFTY-EIGHT

King Haraldr had a market town built east in Oslo, and often stayed there,
for it was a good place for getting supplies, the land around being very
productive. Staying there was very convenient for guarding the land from the
Danes, and also for incursions into Denmark. He was accustomed to doing
this frequently, even when he did not have a large army out. It happened
one summer that King Haraldr was travelling with some light ships and
did not have a large force of men. He made his way south into the Vík, and
when he got a favourable wind, he sails across to the coast of Jótland, then
set to and made raids, but the people of the country gathered together and
defended their land. Then King Haraldr made his way to Limafjǫrðr and
sailed into the fiord. Limafjǫrðr is so shaped that the entrance there is like
a narrow river channel, but when you get in along the fiord, then it is like a
huge sea there. Harald made raids there on both shores, while the Danes had
hosts gathered everywhere. Then King Haraldr took his ships up to a certain

island. It was a small and uninhabited place. And when they searched, then they found no water, so told the king about it. He had a search made for if any heather-snake[193] was to be found on the island, and when one was found, they brought it to the king. He had the snake brought to a fire and heated up and made exhausted so that it should get as thirsty as possible. After that a thread was tied to its tail and the snake released. Then it soon wriggled off, and the thread unwound itelf from the ball of thread. Men followed the snake until it dived down into the ground. The king told them to dig for water there. This was done; they found water there so that there was no lack.

King Haraldr learnt from his informants the news that [140] King Sveinn was come with a large naval force before the entrance to the fiord. He took a long time to get in, since only one ship could go at a time. King Haraldr took his ships further in to the fiord. And where it is broadest it is called Lúsbreið, and there from the inner bay there is a narrow isthmus across to the open sea to the west. Haraldr and his men rowed over to it in the evening. And during the night, when it had got dark, they cleared the ships and dragged them over the isthmus and had completed the whole job before dawn and put the ships to rights once more, making their way north past Jótland. Then they said:

> 119.　　Haraldr slipped out of　　　　　　*Skald* II 818
> 　　　　the hands of the Danes.

Then the king said that the next time he came to Denmark, he would have more troops with him and larger ships. Then the king travelled north to Þrándheimr.

[141] CHAPTER FIFTY-NINE

King Haraldr stayed the winter in Niðaróss. He had a ship built during the winter out on Eyrar. It was a buss-type ship.[194] This ship was built after the style of Ormr inn langi and finished with the finest craftsmanship. There was a dragon head at the prow, and in the rear a curved tail, and the necks of both were all decorated with gold. It numbered thirty-five rowing benches, and was of a proportionate size, and was a most handsome vessel. The king had all the equipment for the ship carefully made, both sail and rigging, anchor and cables. King Haraldr issued a challenge during the winter south to Denmark to King Sveinn that he should the next spring come from the south to the Elbr and meet him and fight to reassign the lands and let one or the other have both kingdoms.

---

[193] An adder (cf. *Óláfs saga Tryggvasonar* (Vol. I), ch. 80).

[194] *búza* was a large transport ship. The word appears in twelfth-century Latin in connection with the Crusades. In Middle High German sources it meant a kind of warship.

CHAPTER SIXTY

That winter King Haraldr called out a levy, a full one, from Norway. And when spring came, a great army gathered. Then King Haraldr had the great ship launched on the river Nið. After that he had the dragon heads set up. Then spoke the poet Þjóðólfr:

120.	Launched forth, fair lady, from river	Stanzas about
	to flood I saw the warship;	Haraldr's *leiðangr* 1
	look where long linked planks	*Skald* II 150
	lie offshore, of the splendid dragon.	
	The bright snake's[195] manes, since it was	
	sent out from the slipway,	
[142]	glow—garnished necks bear pure	
	gold—over the cargo.	

After that King Haraldr prepares the ship and his journey. And when he was ready, he sailed the ship out of the river. It was very skilfully rowed. So says Þjóðólfr:

121.	The squad-Baldr[196] on a Saturday	Stanzas about
	slings off the long awning	Haraldr's *leiðangr* 2
	where at the linked planks of the serpent	*Hákonar s. Ívarss.* 2
	splendid ladies gaze from town.	*Skald* II 151
	The young lord set about steering	
	the spanking-new warship	
	out of the Nið; in the ocean	
	the oars of men dip, westward.	

122.	Straight from the stroke the king's army	Stanzas about
	slices the oar expertly.	Haraldr's *leiðangr* 3
	At the oars' motion maiden	*Hákonar s. Ívarss.* 25
	marvels as she stands amazed.	*1GT* (ll. 1–2)
[143]	Rowing there'll be, till into two	*Skald* II 152
	the tarred sea-gear[197] breaks, lady.	
	The fir, four-sided,[198] to that gives	
	in full peacetime its sanction.	

[195] *ormr*: 'serpent, dragon', dragon-ship.

[196] *lið-Baldr*: 'troops-god', battle-leader.

[197] *sæfǫng*: 'sea-gear', oars.

[198] *þǫll*: 'fir-tree', is taken here to refer to oars made of fir-wood; *ferkleyf* 'four-cleaved' probably refers to their square cross section. Kari Ellen Gade in *Skald* II takes *þǫll* as an incomplete kenning for a woman, and *ferkleyf* as referring to the 'sea-gear' (oars) mentioned in l. 6.

123. There is strain for troops before slicing
     sea-gear from the strong ocean,
     where in readiness for rowing
     the rowlock holds seventy oars.
     Northmen row out the iron-nailed
     adder[199] on the hail-dashed—
     it is like seeing from beneath
     an eagle's wing—current.

Stanzas about
Haraldr's *leiðangr* 4
Hákonar saga
Ívarssonar 25
Skald II 154

King Haraldr took the army south along the coast, having a full levy of troops and ships out. And when they make their way eastwards into the Vík, they met a strong headwind, and the host lay in harbours far apart from each other, both off the outlying islands and within the fiords. So says Þjóðólfr:

124. The ship's shaven prows have
     shelter under the forest.
     The lord of the fleet locks in
     lands with stems of warships.
[144] All the host is anchored—
     the isthmus for shelter
     is used by armoured[200] warships—
     in each bay in the skerries.

Stanzas about
Haraldr's *leiðangr* 5
Skald II 155

But in the great storm that arose, the great ship needed good anchoring. So says Þjóðólfr:

125. The king hits high crashing
     Hlésey's fence[201] with the forestem.
     Then the prince uses to the utmost
     the anchor-ropes of the warship.
     Not gentle to the bowed iron[202]
     is the scathe of the lime-tree.[203]
     The thick fluke is fretted
     by foul weather and rocks.

Stanzas about
Haraldr's *leiðangr* 6
Skald II 156

And when they got a favourable wind King Haraldr took the army east to the Elfr and arrived there in the evening of the day. So says Þjóðólfr:

---

[199] *naðr*: 'snake', dragon ship.

[200] *hábrynjaðr*: 'high-armoured', a reference to shields lined along the sides of the ship.

[201] *Hléseyar hryngarðr*: 'crashing fence round the island of Hlésey', the sea.

[202] *bjúgt járn*: 'bowed iron', the anchor fluke.

[203] *lindis skaði*: 'harmer of the lime-tree', wind, storm.

126.   Haraldr has now hastened   Stanzas about
         halfway to Elfr, valiantly.   Haraldr's *leiðangr* 7
         The lord of Norway overnights   *Skald* II 157
         near to the lands' border.
[145]   The king has a þing[204] at Þumli:
         there for Sveinn is appointed—
         if the Danes do not run—a meeting
         due to the raven[205] with him.

CHAPTER SIXTY-ONE

And when the Danes learn that the army of Norwegians was come, then they all flee that are able to do so. The Norwegians learn that the king of the Danes also has his army out and that it is lying south round Fjón and round Smálǫnd. And when King Haraldr learnt that King Sveinn was unwilling to hold a meeting with him or a battle, as had been arranged, then he adopted this course again like the previous time, let the force of farmers go back and manned a hundred and fifty ships. After that he took this force south past Halland and raided widely. He sailed the army into Lófufjǫrðr and made raids inland there. A little later King Sveinn came upon them there with his army of Danes. He had three hundred ships. And when the Norwegians saw the army, then King Haraldr had the army called together by trumpets. Many said that they should flee, saying that it was impracticable to fight. The king replied as follows:

'Each man of us shall fall one on top of another before we flee.'

So says Steinn Herdísarson:

127.   This he said, what, hawk-minded,   *Nizarvísur* 1
         he thought would happen: *Mork* I 244
         The king held there was hardly   *Fsk* 264
         hope from him there of mercy.   *Skald* II 360
[146]   Rather than surrender,
         the ruler, famous, said we must
         each fall crossways on top of
         the other; men readied all weapons.

After that King Haraldr placed his host in position for an attack. He placed his great dragon forward in the middle of the force. So says Þjóðólfr:

128.   Giver of friendly gifts, eager,   *Sexstefja* 13
         gracious to wolves, he made hover   *Hákonar saga Ívarss.* 27

---

[204] i.e. a hostile meeting, a battle with Sveinn.
[205] *fundr skyldr hrafni*: 'a meeting owed to the raven', i.e. a battle.

his dragon in the fleet's forefront,   *Skald* II 125
in the force's vanguard, at the middle.

This ship was very well manned and had a large complement. So says
Þjóðólfr:

129. To stand firm the prince, peace-choosy,[206]   *Sexstefja* 14
     instructed the bold company;   *Skald* II 126
     the ruler's friends over rowlocks
     raised a shield-wall, as I saw it.
     He closed in the strong-swimming
     serpent[207] with shields beyond Niz,
     the able man of action,
     so that each touched the other.

[147] Úlfr stallari placed his ship to one side of the king's ship. He spoke to
his men, saying that they were to sail the ship forward energetically. Steinn
Herdísarson was on Úlfr's ship. He spoke:

130. Úlfr urged us all, the king's marshal,   *Úlfsflokkr* 1
     when out at sea were shaken   *Mork* I 245
     long-hafted halberds;[208] rowing   *Fsk* 266
     was hastened on the ocean.   *Hákonar saga*
     He bade, brisk confidant,   *Ívarssonar* 27
     of the bold king, that the ship properly   *Skald* II 366
     advance—and men assented—
     side by side with the ruler.

Jarl Hákon Ívarsson lay furthest out on one wing, and many ships
accompanied him, and this force was very well equipped. But outermost on
the other wing lay the leaders of the Prœndir. There too there was a large
army and a fine one.

CHAPTER SIXTY-TWO

King Sveinn also drew up his forces. He placed his ship to face King
Haraldr's ship in the middle of the force, and next to him Finnr Árnason
brought forward his ship. The Danes positioned all the troops next to them
that were boldest and best equipped. After that each side tied their ships
together right [148] across the middle of the fleet. But because the army was

---

[206] *friðvandr*: perhaps 'careful about peace'?

[207] *ramsyndr naðr*: 'strong-swimming snake', dragon ship.

[208] *hôkesjur*: 'high (i.e. long-shafted) halberds', shaken in battles at sea. Kari Ellen
Gade in *Skald* II chooses to take the first syllable as *hár* 'rowlock', and reads this as
a kenning for oars, which are shaken in the motion of rowing.

so huge, there was a very large number of ships that were not tied in, and so each one brought his ship forward whenever he felt like it, and this happened all at very different times. And though there was a great unevenness in the odds, yet each side had an invincible army. King Sveinn had six jarls with him in his force. Sveinn Herdísarason said this:

131.   The hersir's lord[209] faced hazard,   *Nizarvísur* 2
       who awaited with longships,   *Mork* I 244
       half the second hundred,[210]   *Fsk* 265
       heart-strong, a Danish meeting.   *Skald* II 361
       Next it came about that the country
       of kelp[211] was carved by the angry
       Hleiðr-dweller,[212] with three hundred
       horses of the sea,[213] thither.

CHAPTER SIXTY-THREE

King Haraldr had a blast of trumpets sounded as soon has he had got his ships ready, and let his men hasten forward to the attack. So says Steinn Herdísarson:

132.   Before the river's mouth Haraldr   *Nizarvísur* 3
       hindered Sveinn's access.   *Skald* II 362
       Resistance ensued, for no peace
       the sovereign would beg for.
[149]   The king's confidants
       increased the rowing, sword-girt,
       outside Halland; hot wounds
       splashed blood on the water.

After that the battle began and it was of the fiercest. Each of them urges his troops on. So says Steinn Herdísarson:

133.   Shy of shields, each ruler—   *Nizarvísur* 4
       short the distance between armies— *Skald* II 362
       capable, bade the company
       of combatants shoot and strike.
       Both flew, when red blood
       the blade discharged—
       that snapped the span of fated
       sailors—rocks and arrows.

---

[209] *hersa dróttinn*: 'lord of hersir (lords)', king.

[210] i.e. a hundred and fifty.

[211] *þangs láð*: 'land of seaweed', the sea.

[212] *Hleiðrar atseti*: 'resident of Hleiðr (ancient seat of Danish kings)', king of the Danes.

[213] *sunda marir*: 'horses of sounds (of the sea)', ships.

It was late in the day when battle was joined, and so it continued all night.
King Haraldr shot from a bow for a long time. So says Þjóðólfr:

134. All night the king of Upplǫnd²¹⁴   *Sexstefja* 15
    his elm-bow drew, valiant.   *Mork* I 246 (ll.1–4)
    Onto white shields showered   *Fsk* 266 (ll.1–4)
    shafts sent by the ruler.   *Skald* II 127
[150]   The bloodied point broke wounds on
    byrnie-wearers,²¹⁵ where—
    flight of Fáfnir's spears²¹⁶ thickened—
    Finns' payment pierced shields.²¹⁷

Jarl Hákon and the troops that accompanied him did not tie their ships
together, and rowed at the ships of the Danes that were going free, and every
ship that he grappled with, he cleared. And when the Danes realised this,
then each of them moved their ship away from where the jarl was sailing.
He pursued the Danes as they backed away, and they were then on the point
of fleeing. Then a small boat rowed up to the jarl's ship and someone called
to him, saying that one wing of the formation was giving way and many of
their troops were fallen. After that the jarl rowed over there and launched a
strong attack there, so that the Danes were now again in retreat. So the jarl
went on all night, pushing forward where there was the greatest need, and
wherever he turned up, then there was no resistance to him. Hákon rowed
round the fringes of the battle. In the latter part of the night there was a
general flight of Danes, for now King Haraldr had gone up with his men
aboard King Sveinn's ship. This was then so completely cleared that all the
men on the ship had fallen except those that had leapt into the water. So
says Arnórr jarlaskáld:

135. Sveinn went from his warship   *Haraldsdrápa* 4
    with reason, most valiant—   *Mork* I 249
    steel struck hard on helmets—   *Skald* II 264
    such is my opinion.
[151]   The ship of the fluent-speaking
    friend of Jótar²¹⁸ had to

²¹⁴ *upplenzkr hilmir*: 'king of Upplǫnd', i.e. of Norway.

²¹⁵ *brynmenn*: men wearing mailcoats.

²¹⁶ *Fáfnir's vigrar*: 'Fáfnir's spears', spears of (thrown from) the ship, where the
dragon name Fáfnir refers to a dragon-ship. The reading *Fáfnir* occurs in only one
manuscript, Eirspennill; others have the obscure *famnings* or *fannings*.

²¹⁷ *Finna gjǫld*: 'payment of Finns (Lapps)', arrows. The reference is to the three
magic arrows of Gusi, king of the Finns (Lapps), mentioned in *Ǫrvar-Odds saga*.

²¹⁸ *Jótar vinr*: 'friend of Jótar', king of Denmark.

float empty before the ruler
fled from his dead followers.

So when King Sveinn's standard had fallen and his ship emptied, then all his men fled, though some fell. But on the ships that were tied together, the men there leapt into the water, though some got onto other ships that were not tied. But all Sveinn's men now rowed away, those that managed to. There was a very great loss of life. And where the kings themselves had been fighting and most of the ships were tied together, there were left behind empty more than seventy of King Sveinn's ships. So says Þjóðólfr:

136.	They said Sogn's able ruler[219]	*Sexstefja* 17
	stripped at least seventy	*Mork* I 248
	splendid ships of Sveinn's people	*Fsk* 268
	all in a single moment.	*Skald* II 130

King Haraldr was rowing after the Danes and pursuing them, but that was not easy, for the fleet of ships in front was so tightly packed that one could hardly move forward. Jarl Finnr refused to flee, and he was captured. He also had poor sight. So says Þjóðólfr:

137.	Six Danish jarls for success	*Sexstefja* 18
	Sveinn need not reward,	*Mork* I 250
	who increase in one conflict	*Fsk* 268
	courage in arrow-play.[220]	*Skald* II 131
[152]	He who was not willing,	
	war-bright, to save his valiant	
	heart, was captured in the company's	
	kernel, Fiðr Árnason.	

CHAPTER SIXTY-FOUR

Jarl Hákon lay behind with his ship, while the king and other troops pursued the rout, since the jarl's ship could not move forward there because of the ships that lay in the way. Then a man rowed to the jarl's ship on a boat and made for the raised deck. This was a big man and he had a broad hood. He called up onto the ship:

'Where is the jarl?'

He was in the part of the ship in front of the raised deck, and was staunching some man's blood. The jarl looked at the man with the hood and asked him his name. He says:

[219] *Sogns gramr*: 'king of Sogn', i.e. of Norway.

[220] *ǫrleikr*: 'arrow-play', battle. For a contrary interpretation, see Kari Ellen Gade in *Skald* II.

'This is Vandráðr ([One in] Trouble). Talk with me, jarl.'

The jarl leant out to him over the side of the ship. Then the man in the boat said:

'I would receive life from you, if you will grant it.'

The jarl straightened up and called over two of his men by name that were both dear to him, saying:

'Step into the boat and convey Vandráðr to land. Take him to my friend, Farmer Karl. Say this to him as a token, that he should give Vandráðr the horse that I gave Karl the other day and his saddle and his son to accompany him.'

After that they stepped into the boat and take to the oars, while Vandráðr steered. This was when day was just breaking. There was then the maximum of ships moving about, [153] some were rowing to land, some out to sea, both on small ships and large ones. Vandráðr steered where he thought there was the greatest space between the ships. And where the Norwegians' ships were rowing close to them, then the jarl's men announced themselves, and everyone let them pass wherever they wanted to go. Vandráðr steered on along the shore and did not go in to land until they had got beyond where the crowd of ships was. After that they went up to Karl's dwelling, and it began to get light. They went into the living room. Karl was there and had just got dressed. The jarl's men told him their errand. Karl spoke, saying that they should have something to eat first, and had a table set up for them and let them have a wash. Then the housewife came into the room and immediately said:

'It is a very strange thing that we never get any sleep or peace in the night for the shouting and racket.'

Karl replies: 'Did you not know that the king has been fighting in the night?'

She asked: 'Which side came off best?'

Karl replies: 'The Norwegians won.'

'Our king must have fled again,' she says.

Karl replies: 'People are not sure of that, whether he has fallen or fled.'

She said: 'We are unfortunate in our king. He is both a cripple and a coward.'[221]

Then Vandráðr spoke: 'The king will not be a coward, but he is not blessed with victories.'

Vandráðr was the last to take a wash, and when he took the towel, then he wiped himelf on the middle of it.[222] The housewife took hold of the towel and snatched it from him. She said:

---

[221] Examination of King Sveinn's skeleton has revealed that he had a poor gait, being bow-legged, was slightly wounded in one foot, and waddled.

[222] A normal guest would use only the edge of the communal towel. Vandráðr betrays his rank by his behaviour, as he does again when he takes the highest-ranking seat at table .

'You haven't much idea how to behave. It is boorish to wet the whole of the towel at once.'

After this Karl set the table up before them, and Vandráðr sat in the middle. They ate for a while, and after that they went out. Now a horse was ready and the old man's son was ready to [154] accompany him, and he had another horse. They ride away to the forest, and the jarl's men went to their boat and row out to the jarl's ship.

CHAPTER SIXTY-FIVE

King Haraldr and his men pursued the rout a short way, after that rowed back to the ships that were empty. They then searched the slain. A large number of dead men were found on the king's ship, but the king's body was not found, and yet they felt sure that he was fallen. Then King Haraldr had the bodies of his own men prepared for burial, and the wounds of those that needed it bandaged. After that he had the bodies of Sveinn's men conveyed to land and sent messages to the farmers that they were to bury the dead. After that he had the plunder shared out. He waited there some time. Then he learnt the news that King Sveinn was come to Sjáland, and the whole of his army that had fled from the battle was now come to him, and many other troops, and he had got a huge army.

CHAPTER SIXTY-SIX

Jarl Finnr Árnason was captured in the battle, as was written above. He was taken to the king. King Haraldr was now very cheerful and said:

'We have now met here, Finnr, but the last time was in Norway. The Danish court has not stood by you very well, and Norwegians will have a thankless task dragging you about with them, a blind man, and so keeping you alive.'

Then the jarl replies: 'Norwegians have many thankless tasks to perform, and that worst of all everything you make them do.'

Then said King Haraldr: 'Will you accept quarter, though you do not deserve it?'

Then the jarl replies: 'Not from a hound like you.'

The king said: 'Then do you want your kinsman Magnús to give you quarter?'

King Haraldr's son Magnús was now captain of a ship.

[155] Then the jarl replies: 'What say does that puppy have in the giving of quarter?'

Then the king laughed, finding it fun to taunt him, and said:

'Will you accept quarter from your kinswoman Þóra?'

Then says the jarl: 'Is she here?'

'She is so,' says the king.

Then jarl Finnr spoke this nasty speech when he could not control what he said, which has since been quoted to show how angry he was:

'It is not surprising that you have done well in horsefights, since the mare is behind you.'

Jarl Finnr was given quarter, and King Haraldr kept him with him for a while. Finnr was rather gloomy and abrupt in what he said. Then said King Haraldr:

'I can see, Finnr, that you will not now be friends with me and with your kinsmen. I will now give you leave to go to your king, Sveinn.'

The jarl replies: 'I will accept that, and all the more thankfully in that I may the sooner get away from here.'

After that the king had the jarl's party conveyed ashore. The Hallandsfarar welcomed him. King Haraldr now took his troops to the north of Norway, going first in to Oslo, then giving leave to return home to all those of his troops that wished to go.

CHAPTER SIXTY-SEVEN

People say that King Sveinn stayed in Denmark that winter and continued his rule as before. During the winter he sent men north to Halland for Karl and his wife. And when they came to where the king was, then he summons Karl to him. After that the king asked if Karl recognised him or felt he had seen him before. Karl replied:

'I recognise you now, king, and I recognised you before when I saw you, and it is thanks to God that the little service I was able to do you was of benefit to you.'

The king replies: 'All the days that I live henceforward I have to reward you for. Now [156] in the first place, I will give you whatever dwelling in Sjáland you choose for yourself, and in addition I shall make you a great man, if you know how to cope with that.'

Karl thanked the king warmly for what he said, and added:

'There still remains a boon that I wish to ask for.'

The king asked what it was. Karl says:

'I would ask this, that you, king, let me take my wife with me.'

The king says as follows: 'This I will not grant you, for I shall provide you with a much better and wiser woman. But your wife can keep the cottage that you have both had previously. That will provide a maintenance for her.'

The king gave Karl a large and splendid estate and arranged a good marriage for him, and then he became an important person. This got to be well known and was reported widely. It reached north to Norway.

CHAPTER SIXTY-EIGHT

King Haraldr stayed the winter after the Battle of the Niz in Oslo. In the autumn, when the troops returned from the south, there were many discussions and stories told about this battle that had taken place in the autumn by the Niz. Everyone that had been there felt he had something to tell about it. It happened on one occasion that some men were sitting in a lower room and were drinking and were full of talk. They were discussing the Battle of the Niz, and also who had left it with the greatest renown. They were all agreed on one thing, that there had been no one there like Jarl Hákon:

'He was the boldest fighter, and he was the most skilful, and he was the most successful, and everything that he did was of the greatest help, and it was he that won the victory.'

King Haraldr was out there in the yard and was talking with some people. After this he went to the entrance to the room and said:

'Everyone here would like to be called Hákon.'

And he went on his way.

[157] CHAPTER SIXTY-NINE

Jarl Hákon travelled in the autumn to Upplǫnd and stayed there in his realm during the winter. He was very popular among the Upplendingar. It happened during the spring, towards its end, that on one occasion when people were sitting drinking, there was again discussion of the Battle of the Niz, and people were loud in their praise of Jarl Hákon, but even so there were some who preferred others. So when they had been discussing this for a while, then some man or other puts in:

'It may be that other men fought boldly by the Niz besides Jarl Hákon, and yet there can have been no one there that I think can have achieved such success as he did.'

They say that his greatest success was in having forced into flight many of the Danes. The same man replies:

'It was a greater success when he gave King Sveinn his life.'

Someone replies to him: 'You cannot know what you are saying.'

He replies: 'I have very precise knowledge of this, for it was the man that conveyed the king to land himself that told me.'

And then it was, as is often said, that 'many are the ears of the king'. The king was told of this, and he immediately had many horses brought out and rode straight away during the night with two hundred men. He rode all that night and during the following day. Then there came riding towards them some men that were on their way out to the town with meal and malt. There was a man called Gamall that was in the king's party. He rode up to one of the farmers. He was an acquaintance of his. They spoke in private. Gamall says:

'I will pay you to ride as fast as you can along the shortest secret routes that you know, and get to Jarl Hákon. Tell him that the king is going to kill him, for the king now knows that the jarl put King Sveinn ashore by the Niz.'

They agree on the terms. This farmer rode and got to the jarl, he was at the time sitting drinking and was not gone to bed. So when the farmer had delivered his message, the jarl stood up straight away, and all his men.The jarl had [158] all his movable wealth taken away from the dwelling into the forest. All the men too were away from the dwelling during the night when the king arrived. He stayed there during the night, and Jarl Hákon rode on his way and turned up east in Svíaveldi at King Steinkell's and stayed with him during the summer. King Haraldr after that turned back out to the town. The king went in the summer north to Þrándheimr. They stayed there during the summer, and in the autumn went back east into Vík.

CHAPTER SEVENTY

Jarl Hákon travelled straight away in the summer back to Upplǫnd when he heard that the king was gone north, remaining there until the king came from the north. After that the jarl travelled east into Vermaland and stayed there for a long time during the winter. King Steinkell gave the jarl the governorship there. He went during the winter, towards its end, west into Raumaríki, and he had a large troop that the Gautar and Vermir had provided him with. Then he took up his land dues and the taxes that he was entitled to from the Upplendingar. After that he travelled back east to Gautland and remained there during the spring. King Haraldr stayed during the winter in Oslo and sent men of his into Upplǫnd to collect the taxes and land dues and the fines payable to the king. But the Upplendingar say this, that they were going to pay all the dues that they were bound to pay and hand them over to Jarl Hákon as long as he was alive and had not forfeited his rights or his realm, and the king got no land dues from there that winter.

CHAPTER SEVENTY-ONE

That winter there passed dispatches and messengers between Norway and Denmark, and these involved the desire of both sides, the Norwegians and the Danes, to make peace between themselves and a settlement, [159] and they called upon the kings to undertake this, and these embassies seemed to be getting close to coming to terms; and it came about eventually that a peace conference was arranged on the Elfr between King Haraldr and King Sveinn. So when spring came, both the kings gathered large numbers of forces and ships together for this expedition, and the poet tells in a *flokkr*[223] about the travels of these kings:[224]

138. The lord, land-encircling,[225]   *Halli stirði, flokkr* 1
    locks it north of Eyrarsund   *Skald* II 338
    with ship's stems. The raven-soother[226]
    spurned with his heel[227] the harbour.
    Gold-encrusted prows keenly
    carve—and the washboards[228] quiver—
    the ocean ahead under
    the army west of Halland.

139. Oath-firm Haraldr often   *Halli stirði, flokkr* 2
    encloses land with warships.   *Skald* II 338
    Sveinn cuts, to encounter the other
    king, island-sounds[229] also.
    He has out no small army
    of all the Danes, the praise-winning
    raven-feeder,[230] all bays enfolding
    in the south with prows.

Here it says that these kings keep the appointment that [160] has been made between them, and they both come to the frontier, as it says here:

140. You set out south, whither,   *Halli stirði, flokkr* 3
    sage king, all the Danes requested.   *Skald* II 340
    Still for a set meeting
    is seen no less matter.
    Sveinn starts northwards
    to strive, nearly to the frontier,
    off the wide land it waxed
    windy—to meet Haraldr.

[223] See note 35 above.

[224] The poet of stanzas 138–43 is anonymous, but in *Skald* II they are atributed to Halli stirði, mentioned in *Skáldatal* as one of Haraldr's poets but otherwise unknown. Johan Peringskiöld's 1697 edition of *Heimskringla* includes an attribution of stanza 140 to 'Halli stríði' (II, 143), probably basing it on a misreading of his text.

[225] i.e., who surrounds territory with ships.

[226] *hrafngœlir*: 'raven-comforter', warrior.

[227] *hæll*, i.e. *kjalarhæll*, 'heel of the keel', the rear end of the keel, with word-play on the metaphor of the ship as horse?

[228] *hlýða*: 'washboard', 'mounted on the uppermost strake . . . to provide extra protection from the waves' (Jesch 2001, 141).

[229] *eysund*: 'island-sounds', sea.

[230] *hrafngrennir*: 'raven-feeder', warrior (here, Sveinn).

So when the kings met, people began to discuss the settlement between
the kings, and when the topic turned to this, then there were many that
complained of the losses they had suffered from the raiding, plundering and
killing. This went on for a long time, as it says here:

141.　On both sides eloquent farmers　　　　*Halli stirði, *flokkr* 4
　　　　utter very loudly　　　　　　　　　 *Skald* II 341
　　　　words that much worry people
　　　　when the men encounter.
[161]　　Not quick are men who quarrel
　　　　constantly throughout—
　　　　stubbornness swells in the princes—
　　　　settlement terms to approve.

142.　Rulers' great rage grows very　　　　*Halli stirði, *flokkr* 5
　　　　risky, if they must settle.　　　　　 *Skald* II 342
　　　　Men who can mediate
　　　　measure the weight of issues.
　　　　All that pleases the people
　　　　princes must be told of.
　　　　If men must part less friendly,
　　　　malice[231] is the reason.

After this the best men and those that had most sense got involved. Then the
terms of peace between the kings were concluded in this way, that Haraldr
was to have Norway, and Sveinn Denmark as far as the frontier that had been
of old between Norway and Denmark. Neither was to compensate the other.
The raiding that had been started was to stop, and whoever had been lucky
in what he had gained was to keep it. This peace was to remain in force as
long as they were kings. This settlement was confirmed by oaths. After that
the kings exchanged hostages. As it says here:

143.　This I have heard, that hostages　　　*Halli stirði, *flokkr* 6
　　　　Haraldr and Sveinn allotted　　　　 *Skald* II 342
　　　　against trouble—God arranges that—
　　　　gladly, each with the other.
[162]　　Their oaths may they honour
　　　　and all the peace terms—with witnesses
　　　　sealed was the settlement there—so that
　　　　neither side may blemish it.

King Haraldr took his troops north into Norway, and King Sveinn went
south to Denmark.

---

[231] *vili grandar* (so the best manuscript)s): 'a will to injury'. *Hkr* III 161 follows
the reading of *Eirspennill*: *vili girndar*: 'a will for greed', avarice.

CHAPTER SEVENTY-TWO

King Haraldr was in the Vík during the summer, and he sent his men to Upplǫnd for the dues and taxes that he was entitled to there. Then the farmers carried out no payments, saying they would let everything there wait for Jarl Hákon, in case he should come to them. Jarl Hákon was now up in Gautland and had a large force. And when the summer was coming to an end, King Haraldr made his way south to Konungahella. Then he took all the light ships he could get hold of and made his way up along the Elfr. He had the ships dragged out [of the water] past the waterfalls and conveyed them up into Lake Vænir. After that he rowed east across the lake to where he had heard Jarl Hákon was. So when the jarl got intelligence of the king's travels, then he made his way down towards the sea, not wanting the king to make raids on them. Jarl Hákon had a large force that the Gautar had provided him with. King Haraldr sailed his ships up into a certain large river. After that he took to land marches, but left behind some of his troops to guard the ships. The king himself rode and some of his men, but many more were on foot. They had to pass through a certain wood and there lay ahead of them some marshland with brushwood on it and then again a wooded ridge. And when they got up on the ridge, then they saw [163] the jarl's troops. There was now only marsh between them. Then both sides drew up their troops. Then the king said that his troops were to sit up on the ridge.

'Let us see first if they want to attack. Hákon is impetuous,' he says.

The weather was frosty and there was some drifting of snow. Haraldr and his men sat under their shields, but the Gautar had not put much clothing on and they got cold. The jarl told them to wait until the king attacked and they were all standing on the same level. Jarl Hákon had the standards that King Magnús Óláfsson had had. The Gautar's lawman was called Þorviðr. He was sitting on a horse and the reins were tied to a peg that was stuck in the marsh. He spoke, saying:

'God knows that we have a large troop here and pretty bold men. Let us ensure that King Steinkell hears that we are giving proper support to this good jarl. I am sure that if the Norwegians attack us, we shall resist them dauntlessly. But if the young ones squeal and will not stand firm, then let us run no further than here to this brook. And if the young ones squeal more, as I am sure will never happen, then let us run no further than to this mound.'

At that moment the army of Norwegians leapt up and shouted a war cry and beat on their shields. Then the army of Gautar began to shout, and the lawman's horse shied so violently when it was startled by the war cry that the peg came up and struck him on the head, the lawman. He said:

'The worst luck of all the Norwegians upon whoever shot that!'

The lawman then galloped away. King Haraldr had earlier said to his troops as follows:

'Though we give off a banging and shouting, yet let us not go over the ridge before they come up here at us.'

And they did as he advised. But as soon as the war cry was raised, then the jarl had his standard brought up, and when they got beneath the ridge, then the king's troops threw themselves down upon them. Then immediately [164] some of the jarl's troops fell, and some fled. The Norwegians did not pursue the rout far, because it was late in the day. They captured there Jarl Hákon's standards and such of the weapons and clothing as they could get hold of. The king had both the standards carried before him as he came down. They discussed among themselves whether the jarl must have fallen. But when they rode down through the wood, then they had to ride in single file. A man leapt across the path and thrust a halberd through the man carrying the jarl's standard. He takes hold of the standard pole and ran the opposite way into the wood with the standard. And when the king was told this, then he said:

'The jarl is alive! Give me my coat of mail!'

The king then rides through the night to his ships. Many said that the jarl had taken his vengeance. Then Þjóðólfr said this:

144.   The men who owed aid to   *Mork* I 266
the jarl battle-happy—   *Skald* II 173
the strong ruler achieved this—
Steinkell's, to death are given.
But Hǫkon swiftly, his hope of
help from there turning out badly,
retreated; he who tones down
the tale may tell it thus.

King Haraldr was that night, what was left of it, by his ships, but in the morning when it was light, then there was ice covering all round the ships so thick that one could walk round the ships. Then the king told his men that they were to cut the ice away from the ships and out into the lake. Men then went up [165] and set about the ice-cutting. King Haraldr's son Magnús was captain of the ship that lay furthest down the large river and furthest out in the lake. And when men had pretty well cut out the ice, then a man leapt out over the ice to where it was waiting to be cut and after that went at the ice-cutting as if he were mad and crazy. Then a man said:

'Now it is as often happens, that no one is as handy, wherever he joins in, as that Hallr Koðránsbani (Slayer of Koðrán). See now how he is cutting the ice!'

Now there was a man on Magnús's ship called Þormóðr Eindriðason, and when he heard Koðránsbani named, then he leapt at Hallr and struck him a mortal blow. Koðrán had been the son of Guðmundr Eyjólfsson, and Valgerðr was Guðmundr's sister and mother of Þormóðr's mother Jórunn. Þormóðr was a winter old when Koðrán was killed and had never seen Hallr Ótryggsson before now. Now the ice was also cut out as far as the lake, and Magnús sailed his ship out into the lake and immediately set sail and sailed west across the lake, while the king's ship lay furthest in in the broken ice, and he was the last to get out. Hallr had been in the king's following and was a great friend of his, and he was very angry. The king was late reaching the harbour. Magnús had now shot the killer in the wood and offered atonement for him, but the king was on the point of attacking Magnús and his men until their friends came up and made peace between them.[232]

CHAPTER SEVENTY-THREE

That winter King Haraldr travelled up into Raumaríki and had a large force. He brought charges against the farmers, accusing them of having withheld dues and taxes from him, and supported his enemies in acts of hostility against him. He had the farmers taken prisoner, some of them mutilated, some killed, and many deprived of all their possessions. They fled, those that were able to. [166] He had settlements burnt very widely and caused complete devastation. So says Þjóðólfr:

145. The humbler of island-Danes	*Sexstefja* 21
harshly bridled the Raumar.	*Mork* I 225
There, I hold, bold Haraldr's	*Fsk* 272
host advanced strongly.	*Skald* II 135
Fire was kindled for requital;	
the king prevailed, and later	
the high roof-hound[233] brought to	
heel the wretched farmers.	

After that Haraldr went up into Heiðmǫrk and burnt there and and caused damage there no less than in the previous place. From there he travelled out to Haðaland and out to Hringaríki, burning there and laying everywhere waste. So says Þjóðólfr:

146. Burned were fierce men's assets.	*Sexstefja* 22
Embers lodged in rafters.	*Mork* I 225 (ll. 5–8)
With a harsh stone the Heinir	*Fsk* 272 (ll. 5–8)
he hit, the war-leaders' shaker.[234]	*Skald* II 136

[232] This story is also told in *Ljósvetninga saga* ch. 20.
[233] *hrótgarmr*: 'roof-hound', fire.
[234] *hertoga hristir*: 'shaker of war-leaders', king.

For life people pleaded.
Fire imposed on the Hringar
harsh judgement, before the halting
of Hǫalfr's damage²³⁵ happened.

After that the farmers submitted all their affairs to the king.

[167] CHAPTER SEVENTY-FOUR

After King Magnús died, fifteen winters passed before the Battle of the
Niz took place, and after that two more before Haraldr and Sveinn were
reconciled. So says Þjóðólfr:

147. The ruler of Hǫrðar²³⁶ hung up   *Sexstefja* 23
      hostility finally;   *Fsk* 273
      peace began in the third year;   *Mork* I 261
      iron had bitten shields off the seashore. *Skald* II 137

After the settlement there was the king's dispute with the Upplendingar for
three seasons.²³⁷ So says Þjóðólfr:

148. Now of actions it is not easy   *Sexstefja* 19
      adequately to speak, whereby   *Skald* II 133
      the king taught Upplendingar
      to own a barren plough.²³⁸
      Such long-lasting fame the clever
      lord's head has won itself
      in these past three seasons
      that it will endure forever.

[168] CHAPTER SEVENTY-FIVE

Eaðvarðr Aðalráðsson was king in England after his brother Hǫrða-Knútr.
He was known as Eaðvarðr inn góði (the Good). That is what he was. King
Eaðvarðr's mother was Ríkarðr Ruðujarl's daughter Queen Emma. Her
brother was Viljálmr Bastard's father Jarl Roðbjartr,²³⁹ who was now duke in
Rúða in Normandy. King Eaðvarðr was married to Jarl Guðini Úlfnaðrsson's

²³⁵ *Hǫolfs galli*: 'flaw, destruction of Hǫalfr', fire. Hálfr was a legendary king
killed when his stepfather set fire to the hall in which he was drinking (*Hálfs saga
ok Hálfsrekka*, chs 12–13).

²³⁶ *Hǫrða fylkir*: 'ruler of Hǫrðar', i.e. king of Norway.

²³⁷ i.e. 18 months. The seasons counted were summers and winters.

²³⁸ i.e. he had so devastated the land that crops could not be sown.

²³⁹ It is actually Emma's brother's son Robert I son of Richard II that is meant,
since she was Richard I's daughter. Her brother was Richard II.

daughter Queen Gyða. Gyða's brothers were Jarl Tósti—he was the eldest—, the second Jarl Mǫrukári, the third Jarl Valþjófr, the fourth Jarl Sveinn, the fifth Haraldr—he was the youngest. He was brought up in King Eaðvarðr's court and was his foster-son, and the king loved him immensely and treated him as his son, for the king had no child.

[169] CHAPTER SEVENTY-SIX

It happened one summer that Haraldr Guðinason had a journey to make to Bretland and went by ship. And when they got out to the open sea, then a contrary wind arose and they were driven far out to sea. They reached land west in Normandy and had endured a deadly storm. They made for the city of Rúða and there met Jarl Viljálmr. He welcomed Haraldr warmly and his company. Haraldr stayed there a long time in the autumn with hospitable entertainment, for storms were raging and it was not possible to go to sea. So when it got close to winter, then they discussed this, the jarl and Haraldr, that Haraldr should stay there for the winter. Haraldr was sitting in a seat of honour on one side of the jarl, and the jarl's wife on his other side. She was fairer than any other woman that people had seen. They always all had entertaining talk together over their drinks. The jarl generally went early to bed, but Haraldr sat long in the evenings talking with the jarl's wife. So it went on for a long time during the winter. On one occasion, as they were talking, she said:

'The jarl has now spoken about it to me and asked what it is that we talk about so constantly, and he is now angry.'

Haraldr replies: 'We must now let him know as soon as possible everything that we have talked about.'

The next day Haraldr called the jarl to speak with him, and they went into the audience chamber. The jarl's wife was also there and their advisers. Then Haraldr began his speech:

'There is this that [170] you have to be informed of, jarl, that there is more to my coming here than what I have yet revealed to you. I am intending to ask for your daughter as my wife. I have spoken of this often to her mother, and she has promised me to support this suit with you.'

And as soon as Haraldr had raised this request, then everyone that heard welcomed it, and backed it with the jarl. This business was concluded in such a way that the girl was betrothed to Haraldr, but because she was so young, then some winters' delay was laid down until the marriage date.

CHAPTER SEVENTY-SEVEN

So when spring came, then Haraldr got his ship ready and prepared to be off. He and the jarl parted on very friendly terms. Then Haraldr sailed out to England to see King Eaðvarðr and did not come to Valland afterwards to fulfil this marriage agreement. King Eaðvarðr ruled England for three and twenty winters, and he died of sickness in London on the nones of January.[240] He was buried at Pálskirkja, and English people declare him to be a saint.

Jarl Guðini's sons were at this time the most powerful men in England. Tósti was appointed chief over the king of the English's army, and he was the defender of the country when the king started to get old. He was made superior to all other jarls. His brother Haraldr was always within the court the next in line [171] for all services and it was his duty to watch over all the royal treasuries. People say that when the king's death drew close, then Haraldr was nearby and few other people. Then Haraldr bent over the king and said:

'I call you all to witness that the king has just now given me the kingdom and complete power in England.'

Next the king was lifted dead from the bed. That same day there was a meeting of the leading men there. At this there was a discussion of the election of a king. Now Haraldr produced his testimony that King Eatvarðr had given him the kingdom on the day of his death. This meeting ended with Haraldr being taken as king and he was consecrated king on the thirteenth day[241] in Pólskirkja. Then all the leading men gave allegiance to him, and all the people. But when his brother Jarl Tósti heard this, he was ill pleased. He thought he had no less a claim to be king.

'I want,' he says, 'the chief men of the land to choose as king the one that they think is most suitable.'

So these words were spread around among the brothers. King Haraldr says this, that he will not give up the kingdom since he had been enthroned in the place that the king was entitled to sit, and had after that been annointed and consecrated king. All the support of the multitude came to be behind him too. He also had control of all the royal treasuries.

[172] CHAPTER SEVENTY-EIGHT

So when Haraldr realised that his brother Tósti wanted to deprive him of the kingdom, then he was mistrustful of him, for Tósti was a clever man and a great man and was on good terms with the leading men of the land. Then King Haraldr took from Jarl Tósti the control of the army and all the power that he had previously held greater than that of other jarls in that country. Jarl Tósti would by no means suffer to be the underling of a brother to whom he was equal in birth. So he went off with his following south across the sea to Flanders, stayed there a short time, then went to Frísland and on from there to Denmark to see his kinsman King Sveinn. They were siblings,

[240] 5th January 1066.
[241] i.e. of Christmas, 6th January.

King Sveinn's father Jarl Úlfr and Jarl Tósti's mother Gyða. The jarl asks King Sveinn for help and support. King Sveinn invited him to stay with him, saying that he shall get a jarldom in Denmark so that he can be a leader of fitting status there. The jarl says as follows:

'I wish to [173] go to England back to my patrimony. And if I get no support for this from you, king, then I will instead offer you to give you all the support that I have at my command in England if you will go with an army of Danes to England to win land just like your uncle Knútr.'

The king says: 'I am so far an inferior man to my kinsman King Knútr that I can hardly keep the realm of the Danes from the Norwegians. The old Knútr gained the kingdom of the Danes by inheritance, and England by warfare and battle, and yet it was for a time rather uncertain whether he might not lose his life there afterwards. He got Norway without a battle. Now I have the sense to adjust the level of my ambitions more to my weak abilities than to the achievements of my kinsman King Knútr.'

Then the jarl said: 'I have had less success in my errand here than I expected that you, such a high-ranking man, would grant me, your kinsman, in my need. It may now be that I shall look for friendship in a direction that is much less fitting, and yet it may be that I shall find a ruler that is less prone to be dismayed by the idea of very great undertakings than you are, king.'

After that the king and the jarl parted not entirely of one mind.

CHAPTER SEVENTY-NINE

Jarl Tósti changed direction in his travel, and turned up in Norway and went to see King Haraldr. He was in the Vík. And when they meet, the jarl reveals his errand to the king, telling him all about his travels since he left England and asking the king to give him support in getting back his realm in England. The king's reply is this, that Norwegians would not be keen to travel to England and lay it waste and have an English ruler over them.

'People say,' he says, 'that those English are not very reliable.'

The jarl replies: 'Is it true what I have heard people [174] say in England, that your kinsman King Magnús sent men to King Eaðvarðr, and it was in the message that King Magnús had inherited England just like Denmark from Hǫrða-Knútr, as stood in their oaths?'

The king says: 'Why did he then not get it, if he had a right to it?'

The jarl says: 'Why do you not have Denmark, as King Magnús had before you?'

The king says: 'The Danes have no reason to boast over us Norwegians. Many a burnt patch have we left for those kinsmen of yours.'

Then said the jarl: 'If you will not tell me, then I will tell you. King Magnús won Denmark because the leading men of that land helped him, and you did not get it because all the people of the country stood against you. King Magnús did not fight to conquer England because the people of the country wanted to have Eatvarðr as king. If you want to gain England, then I can bring it about that the majority of the leaders in England will be your friends and supporters. I lack nothing more in comparison with my brother Haraldr than just the name of king. Everyone knows that no such fighting man has been born in Northern Lands as you, and I find it surprising that you have been fighting for fifteen winters to win Denmark, but you will not take England, which now lies open to you.'

King Haraldr considered carefully what the jarl was saying, and realised that much of what he said was true, and on the other hand he began to get keen to have the kingdom. After this the king and the jarl spoke together long and often. They settled on this plan, that they should in the summer go to England and conquer the country. King Haraldr sent word all over Norway and called out troops for an expedition, a half levy. This now became widely known. There were many guesses about where the expedition would be going. Some said, reckoning up King Haraldr's achievements, that nothing would be impossible for him, while some said that England would be difficult to defeat, the population there being enormous and the host that is known as [175] *þingamannalið*[242] being there. These were men of such boldness that the support of one of them was better than that of two of King Haraldr's best men. Then Úlfr stallari replies:

149.	There's no call for king's marshals	*Mork* I 303
	constantly to hang about—	*Skald* II 348
	I gain[243] wealth eagerly—	
	in Haraldr's prow-area,[244]	
	if we are bound, bright linen-	
	bank,[245] to flee two before—	
	young, I learned otherwise—	
	only one *þingamaðr*.	

Úlfr stallari died that spring. King Haraldr stood over his grave and said, as he was walking away:

'There lies one now that was most faithful and most loyal to his lord.'

Jarl Tósti sailed in the spring west to Flæmingjaland to meet up with the troops that had gone with him from out in England and the others that had joined him from both England and there in Flæmingjaland.

[242] The Norse term for the king's personal following in England (literally 'the troop of men of the assembly', the king's household troops). Cf. line 8 of the next verse.

[243] *fæk* 'I get'. *Mork* has the past tense, *fekk*, a reading adopted in *Skald* II.

[244] *stafnrúm*: 'the space in the stem [occupied] by fighting men' (Jesch 2001, 145).

[245] *hǫrbrekka*: 'linen-slope', woman.

CHAPTER EIGHTY

King Haraldr's army assembled in Sólundir. And when King Haraldr was ready to sail out from Niðaróss, then he first went to King Óláfr's shrine and opened it and cut his hair and nails and afterwards locked the shrine and threw the keys out into the Nið, and [176] the blessed King Óláfr's shrine has never since been opened. There had now passed from his fall thirty-five winters. He had also lived thirty five winters in this world. King Haraldr took the troops that were following him south to meet up with his own troops. A large force was collected there, so that it is people's report that King Haraldr had nearly two hundred ships, and in addition carriers for provisions and small craft. While they were lying in Sólundir, a man that was on the king's ship who is named as Gyrðr had a dream. He dreamt he was standing on the king's ship and looking up at the island where a large troll-wife was standing with a long knife in her hand, and in the other hand a trough. He also dreamt he could see across all their ships and it seemed to him that there was a bird sitting on every ship's prow. These were all eagles and ravens. The trollwife spoke:

150.	It's sure, the eastern overlord	*Mork* I 305
	urges himself westwards	*Hemings þáttr* 45
	for a meeting with many splendid—	*Skald* II 819
	my gain is this—knucklebones.[246]	
	The corpse-grouse[247] can pick out,	
	confident of plenty,	
	steak from the sovereign's	
	stem-hawks.[248] I go along with that.	

[177] CHAPTER EIGHTY-ONE

There is a man named Þórðr, who was on a ship that was lying a short way from the king's ship. He dreamt during the night that he thought he saw King Haraldr's fleet sail to land, felt sure that it was England. He saw on the coast a great host and he dreamt that both sides were preparing for battle, and had many standards raised, but in front of the troops of people of the country rode a great trollwife mounted on a wolf, and the wolf had a man's corpse in its mouth and blood flowed over its chops, and when it had eaten it, then she flung another into its mouth, and after that one after another, and it gulped them all down. She said:

[246] *mót við knútu*: 'a meeting with knucklebones', a meeting with the dead, i.e. death.

[247] *valþiðurr*: 'capercaillie of slaughter', raven or eagle.

[248] *stafns haukr*: 'hawk of the prow', ship. It could also be a kenning for 'warrior'.

151.   The she-troll makes shine the blood-red   *Mork* I 304
       shield, when war approaches.   *Fsk* 277
       The wife of Aurnir's offspring[249]   *Hemings þáttr* 45
       sees the king's downfall fated.   *Skald* II 821
       The woman with jaws working
       worries the flesh of soldiers.
       the wolf's mouth is stained within
       with blood by the mad woman,
       and with blood by the mad woman.[250]

[178] CHAPTER EIGHTY-TWO

Moreover King Haraldr dreamed one night that he was in Niðaróss and met his brother King Óláfr, and he uttered a verse before him:

152.   The famous king, for his advancement,   *Mork* I 305
       the fat one, won most battles;   *Fsk* 277
       I had, since at home I lingered,   *Hemings þáttr* 39
       a holy fall to earth.   *Skald* II 822
       Still I dread that death is
       due, lord, to come upon you;
       the greedy troll's steeds[251] you're going
       to glut. God will not cause it.

Many other dreams were narrated at this time, and other kinds of ominous visions, most of them dismal ones. King Haraldr, before he left Þrándheimr, had his son Magnús taken as king there, and set him in charge of the kingdom in Norway while King Haraldr was away on his travels. Þóra, Þorbergr's daughter, was also left behind, but Queen Ellisif went with him, and her daughters Maria and Ingigerðr. King Haraldr's son Óláfr also left the country with him.

CHAPTER EIGHTY-THREE

So when King Haraldr was ready and there arose a favourable wind, he sailed out to sea and came to land by Hjaltland, though some of his troops came by Orkney. King Haraldr lay [179] there a short while, before he sailed to Orkney, and he took with him from there a large troop and Jarl Þorfinnr's sons, the jarls Páll and Erlendr, but left there Queen Ellisif and their daughters Maria and Ingigerðr. From there he sailed south past Scotland and on past

[249] *Aurnir's jóða brúðr*: 'woman of Aurnir's (giant's) offspring', troll-woman.
[250] The repetition of the last line is characteristic of the verse-form *galdralag* 'incantation form', appropriate to prophetic verses.
[251] The troll's horse is a wolf (cf. *Gylf* 46/26). The adjective 'greedy', grammatically agreeing with 'troll's', properly belongs with *fákum* 'horses'.

England and came to land there where it is called Kliflǫnd. There he went ashore and immediately made raids and subjected the land to himself, meeting no resistance. After that King Haraldr made for Skarðaborg and fought there with the citizens. He went up onto the cliff that is situated there and had a great fire made there and set ablaze. And when the fire was burning, they took great forks and flung the fire down into the town. Then one building after another caught fire. Then the whole place went up in flames. The Norwegians slew many people there, and took all the wealth they got hold of. There was then nothing else the English people could do, if they were to stay alive, but submit to King Haraldr. He then subjected all the land to himself wherever he went. After that King Haraldr made his way with the whole army south along the coast and landed by Hellornes. There he was met by an assembled force, and King Haraldr fought a battle there and was victorious.

CHAPTER EIGHTY-FOUR

After that King Haraldr went to the Humber and up along the river and came to land there. At this time the jarls were up in Jórvík, Mǫrukári and his brother Jarl Valþjófr, and had an invincible force. King Haraldr was lying in the Ouse when the jarls' army made their way down. Then King Haraldr went ashore and began to draw up his troops. One wing of his formation was stationed [180] forward on the bank of the river, and the other extended up inland to a certain dyke. It was a deep fen, broad and full of water. The jarls let their formation move slowly down along the river with the whole host. The king's standard was close to the river. There the formation was very deep, but it was shallowest by the dyke and those troops were the most unreliable. Then the jarls advanced down along the dyke. Then the wing of the Norwegian formation that reached to the dyke gave way, and the English men pushed forward there after them, thinking that the Norwegians must be going to flee. Mǫrukári's standard advanced there.

CHAPTER EIGHTY-FIVE

So when King Haraldr saw that the formation of English men was come down along the dyke opposite them, then he had the war trumpets blown and urged on the army vigorously, then letting the standard Landeyða be carried forward, pressing the attack so strongly that everything gave way before them. Then the casualties in the jarls' troops became heavy. Then their troops soon turned in flight, some fleeing up and down along the river, but most of the host leapt out into the dyke. The dead lay there so thickly that the Norwegians were able to walk across the dyke dry-shod. Jarl Mǫrukári perished there. So says Steinn Herdísarson:

153. Many troops perished in the river.   *Óláfsdrápa* 1
      Submerged, men drowned.   *Mork* I 307
      Soon lay no few soldiers   *Fsk* 279
      encircling young Mǫrukári.   *Skald* II 368
[181] The forward lord of men[252] pursued
      the flight; before the valiant
      ruler the host rushed headlong.
      High-spirited, knows under . . .[253]

This *drápa* was composed by Steinn Herdísarson about King Haraldr's son
Óláfr, and in it he mentions that Óláfr was in the battle with his father King
Haraldr. This is spoken of in *Haraldsstikki* too:[254]

154. There lay fallen   *Skald* II 807
      in the fen below
      the host of Valþjófr
      hewn by weapons,
      so that war-bold
      Norwegians might
      cross walking
      on corpses alone.

Jarl Valþjófr and the troops that got away fled up to the city of Jork. There
was a very great slaughter there. The battle was on Wednesday, the next day
before Matheusmass.[255]

[182] CHAPTER EIGHTY-SIX

Jarl Tósti had come from the south from Flæmingjaland to King Haraldr as
soon as he got to England, and the jarl was in all these battles. It then turned
out as he had said to Haraldr before this meeting, that multitudes of people
thronged to them in England. These were relations and friends of Jarl Tósti,
and it was a great enhancement of the king's forces. After this battle that has
just been related, troops from all round the neighbouring districts submitted to
King Haraldr, though some fled. Then King Haraldr prepared his expedition
to capture the city and stationed his army by Stamford Bridge. And [183]

---

[252] *Msk* has *Fila dróttinn* 'lord of the Filir', i.e. king of Norway (here, Óláfr Haraldsson).

[253] The last line is part of a *klofastef* 'split refrain', of which a second line is found in
st. 168. The third line is preserved in *Morkinskinna* and *Fagrskinna*. The whole can be
translated 'High-spirited Óláfr knows himself much the best king born under the sun.'

[254] This anonymous poem is mentioned only here (and in the related Hulda–
Hrokkinskinna), and this is the only surviving stanza. It is in a variant of *fornyrðislag*
metre that may have been known as *stikkalag*, Cf. *Háttatal* p. 73, note to 97/11.

[255] St Matthew's day (in the west) is 21st September.

because the king had won such a great victory against great leaders and overwhelming forces, all the people were afraid and despaired of standing up to him. Then the citizens decided to send a petition to King Haraldr and offer themselves and also the city into his power. The result of this whole petition was that on the Sunday King Haraldr went with his whole army up to the city and set up an assembly, the king and his men, outside the city, and the citizens attended the assembly. All the people accepted submission to King Haraldr, and gave him hostages, sons of high-ranking men, it being the case that Tósti knew details of all the people in that city, and in the evening the king went down to his ships with an automatic victory, and was very merry. An assembly was arranged for early on the Monday in the city. King Haraldr was then to set up the organisation of the place with men of the ruling class and hand out ranks and fiefs. That same evening after sunset there came to the city from the south King Haraldr Guðinason with an invincible army. He rode into the city with the goodwill and consent of all the citizens. All the gates of the city and all the routes in were occupied, so that no information could reach the Norwegians. This army was in the place during the night.

CHAPTER EIGHTY-SEVEN

On the Monday, when Haraldr Sigurðarson had eaten breakfast, he had the trumpets blown for going ashore, then he makes his army ready and divides the troops, which parts are to go and which are to be left behind. In every company he had two men go inland for every one left behind. Jarl Tósti got ready for going inland with King Haraldr with his company, but there were left behind to guard the ships the king's son Óláfr and [184] the Orkney jarls Páll and Erlendr and Þorbergr Árnason's son Eysteinn orri (Black Grouse), who at that time was the noblest and dearest to the king of all the landed men. King Haraldr had before this promised him his daughter Maria. The weather was now extremely good and the sun was hot. The men left behind their mailcoats, and marched up with shields and helmets and halberds and girded with swords, and many also had arrows and bows and were very merry. But when they advanced into the neighbourhood of the city, they found riding towards them a large troop. They saw the cloud of dust raised by the horses and beneath it fair shields and white mailcoats. Then the king halted his troops, had Jarl Tósti called to him and asked what troops these would be. The jarl speaks, saying he thought it more than likely that it would be hostile, saying also that it could on the other hand turn out that this would be some of his kinsmen, looking for mercy and friendship, so as to get in return the king's support and trust. Then the king said that they would first of all hold still and find out about the army. They did so, and the troop turned out to be larger the closer it got, and to look at it all seemed just like a heap of bits of ice with the glittering of their weapons.

[185] CHAPTER EIGHTY-EIGHT

King Haraldr Sigurðarson spoke then:

'Let us now take up some good and sensible plan, for there is no denying that it is hostile, and it must be the king himself.'

Then the jarl replies: 'The first thing is to turn back as quickly as we can to our ships for our troops and weapons, then face them as best we can, or alternatively let the ships look after us, and then riders will have no power over us.'

Then King Haraldr replies: 'I wish to follow a different plan, to mount three bold fellows on the swiftest horses and let them ride as fast as they can and tell our troops—then help will soon come to us—because the English men can expect a storm of the sharpest, rather than that we should get the worst of it.'

Then the jarl speaks, bidding the king have his own way in this as in everything else, saying that he too was not eager to flee. Then King Haraldr had his standard, Landeyða, set up. He was called Frírekr that was carrying the standard.

CHAPTER EIGHTY-NINE

After that King Haraldr drew up his troops, making the battle line long and not deep. Then he curved the wings round backwards so that they met. It then formed a wide circle and a thick one, and the same everywhere all round the outside, shield against shield and the same above their heads, but the king's company was within the circle and the standard was there too. It was a picked troop. In a separate place was Jarl Tósti with his company. He had a different standard. It was drawn up in this way, because the king knew that mounted men were accustomed to ride forwards in small detachments and withdraw immediately. So the king says that his company and the jarl's company should move forward to where the greatest need was.

'And our bowmen shall also be there with us, and those that are standing foremost shall set the butts of their spears [186] in the ground, and set the points before the breasts of the riders, if they ride at us, and those that are standing closest, they are to set their spear points before the breasts of the horses.'

CHAPTER NINETY

King Haraldr Guðinason was come there with an invincible army, both horsemen and men on foot. King Haraldr Sigurðarson then rode round his formation and examined how they were drawn up. He was sitting on a black horse with a white blaze on its head. The horse fell under him and the king forward off it. He stood up straight away and said:

'A fall is a good omen for a journey.'

Then King Haraldr of the English spoke to the Norwegians that were with him:

'Did you recognise that big man that fell off his horse there, with the dark tunic and the fair helmet?'

'That is the king himself,' they said.

The king of the English says: 'A big man and he has a stately air, and it is more than likely that he has run out of luck.'

CHAPTER NINETY-ONE

Twenty horsemen rode forward from the *þingmannalið*[256] out in front of the Norwegians' battle line and they were fully mailcoated and their horses too. Then spoke one of the horsemen:

'Is Jarl Tósti among the troops?'

He answers:'That is not to be denied, you will find him here.'

Then spoke one of the horsemen: 'Your brother Haraldr sends you a greeting and has this to say too, that you should have pardon and the whole of Northumberland, and rather than that you should not be willing to pay homage to him, then he will give you a third of the whole kingdom alongside him.'

Then answers the jarl: 'Then there is something on offer other than hostility and dishonour like last winter. If this had been offered then, then there would be many a man still alive that is now dead, and the kingdom in England would then have been in a better state. [187] Now if I accept this offer, what will he offer King Haraldr Sigurðarson for his trouble then?'

Then spoke the horseman: 'He has said something about that, what he will grant him of England: a space seven foot long, or so much longer as he is taller than other men.'

Then says the jarl: 'Go now and tell King Haraldr that he should prepare for battle. Something other shall be the truth to be told among the Norwegians than this, that Jarl Tósti departed from King Haraldr Sigurðarson onto the side of his enemies when he was going to fight west in England. Rather than that, we shall all adopt the same course, die with honour or gain England by victory.'

Then the horsemen rode back. Then King Haraldr Sigurðarson spoke to the jarl:

'Who was this well-spoken man?'

Then says the jarl: 'It was King Haraldr Guðinason.'

Then spoke King Haraldr Sigurðarson: 'Too long has this been kept hidden from us. They were come in such a way in front of our troops that this Haraldr would not have been able to report the deaths of our men.'

[256] See note 242 above.

Then says the jarl: 'That is true, lord. He was behaving incautiously for such a ruler, and it could have been as you say. I could see that he wanted to offer me pardon and great power, but I would have been his slayer if I had told who he was. I would rather that he were my slayer than I his.'

Then said King Haraldr Sigurðarson to his men:

'This was a small man and he stood proudly in his stirrups.'

People say that King Haraldr spoke this verse:

155.	We go forward	*Mork* I 316
	in formation	*Fsk* 284
	without byrnies	*Skald* II 54
	under dark blades.	
	helmets shine.	
	I have not mine.	
[188]	Now lies our armour	
	at the ships below.	

His mailcoat was called Emma. It was long, so that it reached halfway down his leg, and so strong that never had a weapon pierced it.

Then King Haraldr Sigurðarson spoke: 'This was poorly expressed, and it will be necessary to make another verse that is better.'

Then he spoke this:

156.	We creep not because of weapons'	*Mork* I 316
	crash—so the discreet falcon-	*Fsk* 284
	field Hildr[257] ordered—in battle	*Hemings þáttr* 51
	into the shield's hollow.	*Skald* II 55
	To hold my helmet-stump[258]	
	high the necklace-prop[259] long ago	
	commanded me, in metal-din[260]	
	where met skulls and battle-ice.[261]	

Then Þjóðólfr also spoke:

157.	I shall not desert, though the sovereign	*Mork* I 314
	himself fall on the battlefield,	*Fsk* 284
	young heirs of the ruler;	*Hemings þáttr* 51
	it will go as God wills.	*Skald* II 174
[189]	The sun shines on no stronger	
	stuff of kingship than those two;	

[257] *valteigs Hildr*: 'Hildr (valkyrie) of the falcon's ground (arm)', woman.

[258] *hjalmstofn*: 'helmet-stump', head.

[259] *menskorð*: 'necklace-prop', woman.

[260] *gný malma*: 'din of steel (weapons)', battle.

[261] *hlakkar íss*: 'ice of battle', sword.

true hawks are the unhesitant
Haraldr's avengers.

CHAPTER NINETY-TWO

Now the battle begins, and the English men launch a charge at the Norwegians.
Their resistance was harsh. It became difficult for the English men to charge
the Norwegians because of their shooting at them, and they rode in a circle
round them. There was at first sporadic fighting as long as the Norwegians
kept their formation properly, but the English men charged them hard and
immediately withdrew, when they could not achieve anything. So when the
Norwegians saw this, and felt the charges had been made weakly, then they
attacked them and tried to pursue the rout, but when they had broken from
the shield wall, then the English men charged them from all sides and used
spears and missiles on them. So when King Haraldr Sigurðarson saw this,
he stepped forward in the battle to where the the fighting was densest. There
was then the most violent of battles, and many troops on both sides fell. Then
King Haraldr Sigurðarson got so furious that he leapt forward right out of the
formation and struck with both hands. There stood against him then neither
helmet not mailcoat. Then all those that were closest took to flight. The
English men were then right on the point of fleeing. So says Arnórr jarlaskáld:

158.	The mediocrity-shy leader	*Haraldsdrápa* 1
	little defence before him	*Mork* I 318
	had in helmet-din,[262] nor trembled	*Fsk* 286
	the heart, battle-swift, of the ruler,	*Skald* II 272
[190]	where, watching the lord of *hersar*,[263]	
	warriors the army saw	
	by the bloody sword bitten	
	of the bold prince-subduer.[264]	

King Haraldr Sigurðarson was struck in the throat by an arrow. That was his
death wound. Then he fell and all the company that had advanced with him,
except those that pulled back, and they held the standard. There was then
still the harshest of battles. Then Jarl Tósti went beneath the royal standard.
Then both sides began to form up a second time, and there was then a very
long pause in the battle. Then spoke Þjóðólfr:

159.	People have paid a heavy	*Mork* I 318
	penalty; now defeated	*Fsk* 288

---

[262] *hjalmþrima*: 'helmet-clash', battle.
[263] *hersa þengill*: 'lord of *hersar* (lords)', king.
[264] *dǫglinga hneitir*: 'suppressor of rulers', king.

I declare the host. Haraldr	*Hemings þáttr* 53
had men fare west needlessly.	*Skald* II 175
The bold leader's life ended	*Skáldsk* 104 (ll. 5–8)
leaving us all in an awkward	
place; the praised ruler	
experienced life-harm.	

[191] But before the battle was joined, then Haraldr Guðinason offered a truce to his brother Jarl Tósti and the other men who were then still alive of the Norwegian troops. But the Norwegians all shouted out together saying this, that every man should fall across the corpse of the next before they would accept a truce from English men, then shouted a war cry. Then the battle began a second time. So says Arnórr jarlaskáld:

160.	Not decorous was the death of	*Haraldsdrápa* 13
	the dread king; gold-reddened	*Mork* I 319
	spear-points did not spare	*Fsk* 288
	the slayer of wrongdoers.	*Skald* II 274
	All the glorious lord's liegemen	
	elected much rather	
	to fall round the king, fast	
	in fight, than accept quarter.	

CHAPTER NINETY-THREE

Eysteinn orri arrived at that moment from the ships with the troops that belonged to him. They had full mailcoats on. Eysteinn then took hold of King Haraldr's standard the Landeyða. [192] Now the battle began a third time, and it was of the bitterest. English men were now falling in large numbers, and they were on the point of fleeing. This battle was known as Orrahríð (Orri's storm). He and Eysteinn had gone in such a rush from the ships that they were already so tired as to be almost out of action before they got to the battle, but after that they were in such a fury that they did not protect themselves as long as they could stand up. In the end they threw off their mailcoats. It was then easy for the English men to find somewhere to land their blows, but some completely collapsed and died without being wounded. Nearly all the high-ranking men of the Norwegians fell. This was in the latter part of the day. It turned out, as might have been expected, that they still did not all act the same, many fled, and there were many too that were able to get away as the result of various pieces of good fortune. It had also got dark in the evening before all the killing was over.

CHAPTER NINETY-FOUR

King Haraldr Sigurðarson's marshal Styrkárr got away, a splendid person.
He got hold of a horse and thus rode away. In the evening some wind arose,
rather a cold one, but Styrkárr had no clothing other than a tunic and a
helmet on his head and some kind of sword in his hand. He got cold when
he recovered from his weariness. Then he was met by a wagoner and he was
in a fur-lined coat. Then spoke Styrkárr:

'Will you sell the coat, farmer?'

'Not to you,' he said. 'You must be a Norwegian, I recognise your speech.'

Then said Styrkárr: 'If I am a Norwegian, what do you want, then?'

The farmer answers: 'I would like to kill you, but unfortunately I have no
usable weapon.'

Then said Styrkárr: 'If you cannot kill me, farmer, then I shall try whether
I can kill you.'

He swings up his sword [193] and brings it down on his neck so that his
head flew off, after that took the fur-lined coat and leapt on his horse and
went down to the shore.

CHAPTER NINETY-FIVE

Viljálmr Bastard, jarl of Rúða, heard of the death of his kinsman King
Eatvarðr, and this too, that now Haraldr Guðinason was accepted as king
in England and had received consecration to the kingship. But Viljálmr
thought he had a better claim than Haraldr to power in England because
of his kinship with King Eatvarðr.[265] There was also the fact that he felt he
had to repay Haraldr for the disgrace in his breaking his engagement with
his daughter. And for all these reasons combined Viljálmr gathered an army
together in Normandy and had a very large host of men and a sufficient fleet
of ships. The day he rode out of the city to his ships and was mounted on his
horse, then his wife went up to him wanting to speak with him. So when he
saw this, then he struck at her with his heel and kicked his spur against her
breast so that it sank in deeply. She fell down and died straight away, and
the jarl rode to his ship.

[194] He travelled with his army out to England. There with him was his
brother Bishop Ótta. So when the jarl got to England, then he made raids
and subjected the land to himself wherever he went.

Viljálmr was bigger and stronger than anyone and a good horseman,
the greatest of fighters and very fierce, a most clever man and said to be
unreliable.

---

[265] William was great-grandson of Richard I of Normandy (the Fearless), Edward
the Confessor's mother Emma was Richard's daughter.

CHAPTER NINETY-SIX

King Haraldr Guðinason gave King Haraldr Sigurðarson's son Óláfr leave to depart, and also to the troops that were there with him and had not fallen in battle. Then Haraldr turned towards the south of England with his army, for he had now heard that Viljálmr Bastard was travelling from the south into England and was subjecting the land to himself. There were there now with King Haraldr his brothers, Sveinn, Gyrðr, Valþjófr. The encounter between King Haraldr and Jarl Viljálmr was in the south of England by Helsingjaport. A great battle took place there. King Haraldr and his brother Jarl Gyrðr fell there, and a large part of their troops. This was nineteen nights after the fall of King Haraldr Sigurðarson. Jarl Valþjófr got away by flight, and late in the evening [195] the jarl met a certain company of Viljálmr's men. And when they saw the jarl's troops, these men fled away to a certain oak wood. There were a hundred men. Jarl Valþjófr had the wood set on fire and completely burnt up with everything in it. So says Þorkell Skallason in *Valþjófsflokkr*: [266]

161. In hot fire a hundred   *V alþjófsflokkr* 1
      henchmen of the ruler   *Skald* II 382
      were burned by the Yggr of battle:[267]
      a broiling night for warriors.
      It is learned that men were laid under
      the ogress-steed's talon.[268]
      Flesh of Frakkar fed the dusky
      filly of the troll-woman.[269]

[196] CHAPTER NINETY-SEVEN

Viljálmr had himself taken as king in England. He sent word to Jarl Valþjófr that they should come to an agreement, and grants him a truce for the meeting. The jarl went with a few men, but when he got onto the heath to the north of Kastalabryggja, then there came against him two officers with a company of men and took him prisoner and put him in irons, and after that he was executed, and English people declare him to be a saint. So says Þorkell:

[266] Little is known of this poet other than the two stanzas preserved here. According to *Fagrskinna* he was the son of Þórðr skalli 'Bald-Head' and was a retainer of Jarl Valþjófr, and the poem was composed after the jarl's death. *Fagrskinna* uniquely gives a hagiographical account of the jarl's death and subsequent miracles; this material is said to be recorded in detail in Þorkell's poem, although only a half-stanza of it is cited in *Fagrskinna* (*Fsk* 295). Cf. *Hemings þáttr* 56, where he is described as dying a martyr's death.
[267] *sóknar Yggr*: 'Óðinn of battle', warrior.
[268] *flagðviggs kló*: 'claw of the ogress's horse (wolf)', wolf's claw.
[269] *óls blakkr*: 'horse of the troll-woman', wolf.

162. Verily brave Valþjófr
Viljálmr in truce cheated,
stainer of swords, who northwards
sliced the frosted ocean.
Truly, slow to cease will be—
no splendid prince more glorious
than my gallant master was will perish—
men's slaughter in England.

Valþjófsflokkr 2
Fsk 295 (ll. 1–4)
Skald II 383

[197] Viljálmr was afterwards king in England for one and twenty winters, and his descendants for ever after.

CHAPTER NINETY-EIGHT

King Haraldr's son Óláfr took his troops away from England and sailed out from Hrafnseyrr and came in the autumn to Orkney, and there the news was learnt that King Haraldr Sigurðarson's daughter Maria had died suddenly on the same day and at the same hour as her father King Haraldr had fallen. Óláfr stayed there during the winter. And the following summer Óláfr travelled east to Norway. He was then accepted as king with his brother Magnús. Queen Ellisif travelled from the west with her stepson Óláfr and her daughter Ingigerðr. Then there came also with Óláfr across the sea from the west Skúli, who was later known as konungsfóstri (King's Foster-Father), and his brother Ketill krókr (Hook). They were both great men and of high lineage in England, and both very intelligent. They were both very dear to King Óláfr. Ketill krókr went north to Hálogaland. King Óláfr arranged him a good marriage, and many high-ranking people are descended from him. Skúli konungsfóstri was an intelligent person and an outstanding man, the most handsome of men in looks. He became the steward in King Óláfr's court and spoke at assemblies and decided all the national policies with the king. King Óláfr offered to give Skúli an area of Norway, that which most appealed to him, with all the revenues and dues that belonged to the king. Skúli thanked him for his offer and said he wanted to request other things of him, because

'If there should be a change of king, it could be that the gifts would become void. I would like,' he says, 'to accept some properties that are situated close to the market towns in which you, king, are accustomed to stay and receive Yule feasts.'

[198] The king granted him this and transferred to him estates in the east near Konungahella and near Oslo, near Túnsberg, near Borg, near Bjǫrgvin and in the north near Niðaróss. They were practically the best properties in each place, and these properties have since remained with the family

that has descended from Skúli's line. King Óláfr gave him his kinswoman
Guðrún Nefsteinsdóttir in marriage. Her mother was King Sigurðr sýr and
Ásta's daughter Ingiríðr. She was King Óláfr the Saint and King Haraldr's
sister. Skúli and Guðrún's son was Ásólfr at Rein. He was married to Skopti
Ǫgmundarson's daughter Þóra. Ásólfr and his wife's son was Guthormr at
Rein, father of Bárðr, father of King Ingi and Duke Skúli.

CHAPTER NINETY-NINE

One winter after King Haraldr's fall his body was conveyed from the west
from England and north to Niðaróss and was buried in Máríukirkja, which he
had had built. It was everyone's opinion that King Haraldr has been superior
to other people in intelligence and good decision-making, whether he was
to act quickly or give long deliberation to what he was to do or others. He
was of all people the boldest in fighting. He was also blessed with victory,
as now has been shown in writing for a while. So says Þjóðólfr:

163.	The most splendid destroyer	*Sexstefja* 24
	of Selund-dwellers gained by daring.	*Skald* II 138
	Men's valour brings half the victory,	
	as verified by Haraldr.	

King Haraldr was a handsome man and noble-looking, fair-haired and with
a fair beard and long moustache, one eyebrow a little [199] higher than the
other,[270] large hands and feet and both well shaped. His height measured
five ells.[271] He was fierce to his enemies and harsh in punishments for any
opposition. So says Þjóðólfr:

164.	For proven pride Haraldr	*Sexstefja* 25
	punishes his followers, wise-counselling.	*Skald* II 138
	The king's fighters pay fittingly	
	for their deeds, I think.	
	Sword bearers have burdens	
	they bring upon themselves.	
	All gain—thus Haraldr hands out:	
	harshness—from justice to others.	

King Haraldr was most ambitious for power and for any advantageous
possessions. He was hugely liberal towards his friends, those that he was
well pleased with. So says Þjóðólfr:

---

[270] Cf. Faulkes 2011, I/170 and note.

[271] The length of an ell varied greatly in different places and at different times in
the Middle Ages, but it is probable that here it is the ell of 46 cm that is assumed,
which would make him 7ft 6½ in. tall. Cf. note 192 above.

165.   A mark for a work[272] the waker   *Sexstefja* 26
        of war of ships[273] had me granted.   *Skald* II 139
[200]   He makes merit of actions
        command his favour.

King Haraldr was fifty years of age when he fell. We have no noteworthy
accounts of his youth until he was fifteen winters old, when he was at
Stiklarstaðir in the battle along with his brother King Óláfr, and after that
he lived thirty-five winters. And all that time he never had any respite from
violence and warfare. King Haraldr never fled from a battle, but he often took
precautions in the face of overwhelming odds that he had to deal with. Everyone
said, who followed him in battle and warfare, that when he was in a situation
of great danger and it had suddenly come upon him, that he would adopt the
course that everyone realised afterwards had been the most likely to work.

CHAPTER ONE HUNDRED

Brynjólfr gamli úlfaldi's (Camel's) son Halldórr was an intelligent man and
a great leader. He said this, when he heard people's talk, and people were
assessing the characters of the brothers King Óláfr the Saint and Haraldr
quite differently, then Halldórr spoke as follows:
    'I was on very friendly terms with both the brothers, and I was [201]
acquainted with both their characters. I never came across two men more alike
in character. They were both most sensible and most bold as fighters, men
ambitious for wealth and power, imperious, not in sympathy with ordinary
people, natural rulers and stern in punishment. King Óláfr forced the people
of the country to Christianity and right conduct, and harshly punished those
that turned a deaf ear. The leaders of the land would not put up with his just
and fair judgments and rose against him here and killed him on his own
territory. As a result he became a saint. But Haraldr fought for fame and
power and forced all the people to submit to him, as far as he could. He also
fell on other kings' territory. Both the brothers were men that were virtuous
in general conduct and high-minded. They were widely travelled and men
of great energy and from this became widely renowned and famous.'

CHAPTER ONE HUNDRED AND ONE

King Magnús ruled over Norway, the son of Haraldr, the first winter after
the fall of King Haraldr, and after that he ruled two winters with his brother
Óláfr. There were then these two kings. Magnús held the more northerly
part of the country, and Óláfr the more easterly. King Magnús had a son

---

[272] *verki*: i.e. a poem.
[273] *snekkju hjaldrs vekjandi*: 'waker of the warship's battle', warrior, king.

that was called Hákon. He was fostered by Steigar-Þórir. He was a most promising man. After King Haraldr Sigurðarson's fall King Sveinn of the Danes reckoned that the peace between the Norwegians and the Danes was ended, reckoning that the peace had been agreed for no longer than they both lived, Haraldr and Sveinn. So a levy was called out in each of the two kingdoms. Haraldr's sons had a full levy from Norway in troops and ships, and King Sveinn travelled from the south with his army of Danes. Then messengers passed between them and brought offers of settlement terms. The Norwegians said that they would either keep to the same terms as had been agreed before or else fight. Therefore was this composed:

[202]   166.   Ǫleifr defended, with words   *Ágrip* 2008, 60
                of war and peace-talks,   *Mork* II 11
                his country, so to claim it   *Skald* II 824
                no king, mighty, ventured.

So says Steinn Herdísarson in *Óláfsdrápa*:

       167.   The war-strong one in Kaupangr   *Óláfsdrápa* 7
              where the holy king lies buried   *Mork* II 3
              will withhold from Sveinn his[274]   *Fsk* 297
              inheritance; he is a powerful ruler.   *Skald* II 373
              To his kin King Ǫleifr[275]
              conclusively will render
              all Norway; the heir of
              Úlfr[276] need make no claim there.

On this expedition to the arranged meeting, a settlement was made between the kings, and peace between the two countries. King Magnús caught an illness, ringworm disease,[277] and kept to his bed for some time. He died in Niðaróss and was buried there. He was a popular king with all the common people.

---

[274] i.e. Óláfr's.

[275] i.e. Saint Óláfr.

[276] *Úlfs arfi*: 'heir of Úlfr', i.e. Sveinn.

[277] Ringworm is not normally fatal. It has been supposed that Magnús died of ergotism, a kind of food poisoning derived from a fungal disease of rye and other cereals.

[203] Óláfs saga kyrra

CHAPTER ONE

King Óláfr was sole king over Norway after his brother Magnús's death. Óláfr was a big man in every part of his growth and well shaped. Everyone used to say that no one had seen a handsomer man or one nobler in appearance. He had yellow hair like silk and it became him extremely well, a shining body, the finest of eyes, well-shaped limbs, generally not given to saying much and silent in assemblies, merry with wine, a great drinker, talkative and cheerful in speech [then], peaceable as long as his rule lasted. Steinn Herdísarson mentions this:

168.	In all lands the lord of Þrœndr	*Óláfsdrápa* 12
	looks, blade-bold, to establish	*Mork* II 6
	peace—that well pleases	*Fsk* 299
	people—with ample skill.	*Skald* II 378
	Folk are glad that his followers	
	are forced into peace-talks	
	by the obstinate English-scarer.	
	. . . Óláfr born [under] the sun.[278]	

[204] CHAPTER TWO

It was an ancient custom in Norway for the king's high seat to be in the middle of the long bench. Ale was handed across the fire.[279] But King Óláfr was the first to have his high seat put on a dais across the room. He was also the first to have rooms built with fireplaces and the floor strewn with straw in winter as well as summer.[280] It was in the time of King Óláfr that market towns developed extensively in Norway, and some were founded from scratch. King Óláfr founded the market town in Bjǫrgyn. There soon came to be there a great settlement of wealthy men and shipping bringing in merchants from other countries. He had the great stone church Christchurch built up on foundations there, though little of it was completed, but he got the timber church finished. King Óláfr had the Miklagildi (Great Guild) set up in Niðaróss and many others in market towns where previously there had been just informal drinking clubs. Then [205] Bœjarbót, the great drinking-feast bell, was in Niðaróss. The club members had Margrétarkirkja, a stone church, built there. In the time of King Óláfr there were started public houses for drinking and wakes in the market

---

[278] For the completion of the *klofastef* 'split refrain', see st. 153.

[279] The long fire down the centre of the room between the two long benches.

[280] These fireplaces were built with a brick or stone surround at the side or in a corner of the room, instead of the open fires in the centre of the room. When the latter were lit (in winter), the floor could not be strewn because of the danger of fire.

towns. And then people took up new fashions in dress, wearing fancy hose gathered in to the legs, some clasped gold rings round their legs, and now people wore trailing gowns, ties to draw them in at the side, sleeves five ells long and so narrow that they had to be drawn up with arm bands and gathered right up to the shoulders, high shoes and all embroidered with silk, and in some cases covered in gold. There were many other new fashions introduced at that time.

CHAPTER THREE

King Óláfr used these customs in his court, that he had his cup-bearers stand before the table and serve him in goblets and likewise all the men of rank that sat at his table. He also had candle boys that [206] held candles before his table, as many as there were men of rank sitting there. Further out from the high table, there was also a marshals' seat, that the marshals would sit on, and other important men, and they would face in towards the high seat. King Haraldr and other kings before him were accustomed to drink from animal horns and carry ale from the high seat across the fire and drink a toast to anyone he wanted to. So says the poet Stúfr:

> 169.   I have known the strife-stirrer[281] —   *Stúfsdrápa* 1
>   very useful he was to know —   *Skald* II 351
>   with a good breeze of Gríðr[282]
>   greet me, victory-blessed,
>   when, fierce to rings,[283] eagerly
>   the feeder of the blood-starling[284]
>   held at Haugr the gilded
>   horn to toast me in person.

[207] CHAPTER FOUR

King Óláfr had a hundred members of his court and sixty guests and sixty housecarls[285] whose duty it was to convey to the palace whatever was needed, or to carry out other tasks that the king wanted done. And when the landowners asked the king about this, why he had more attendants than the law provided for or than previous kings had had when he travelled round to banquets where the landowners had put them on for him, the king replies as follows:

---

[281] *hildar hvessir*: 'stirrer of battle', warrior.

[282] *Gríðar byrr*: 'fair wind of Gríðr (giantess)', (kind) thought. For this kenning, see *Skáldsk* 108/28. Its origin is not known.

[283] 'fierce to rings', because he gives them away, i.e. generous with gold.

[284] *blóðstara brœðir*: 'feeder of the blood-starling (raven or eagle)', warrior.

[285] *Húskarlar* were members of the king's (or other nobleman's) personal following. On guests, see note 377 below.

'I would not be able to rule the kingdom any better, and I would not keep people more in awe of me than they were of my father, even if I had twice as many attendants as he had, but it is not just for the sake of imposing burdens on you or because I want to increase your expenses.'

CHAPTER FIVE

King Sveinn Úlfsson died of sickness ten winters after the fall of the two Haraldrs. The king there in Denmark next was his son Haraldr hein (Whetstone), four winters, then Sveinn's second son Knútr, seven winters and he is a true saint, then the third son of Sveinn, Óláfr, eight winters, then the fourth son [208] of King Sveinn, Eiríkr góði (the Good), again eight winters. King Óláfr of Norway married King Sveinn of the Danes' daughter Ingiríðr, and King Óláfr Sveinsson of the Danes married Ingigerðr, King Haraldr's daughter, King Óláfr of Norway's sister. Óláfr Haraldsson, whom some called Óláfr kyrri (the Quiet) and many Farmer Óláfr (Óláfr bóndi), he had a son with Þóra Jóansdóttir. He was called Magnús. This boy was most fair of face and very promising. He grew up in the king's court.

CHAPTER SIX

King Óláfr had a stone minster built in Niðaróss and sited it in the place that King Óláfr's body had at first been buried, and the altar was placed over where the king's grave had been. It was consecrated as Christchurch.[286] After that King Óláfr's shrine was also conveyed there and placed over the altar there. Then many miracles were performed there. And the next summer after, on the anniversary of the consecration of the church, then it was very well attended. It was on the eve of St Óláfr's day[287] that a blind man received his sight there. And on the feast-day itself, when the shrine and the holy relics were carried out—the shrine was set down in the churchyard, as it was the custom to do—then a man who for a long time previously had been dumb, received his speech, and he then sang praises to God and the blessed King Óláfr with fluent voice. The third person was a woman who had made her way there from the east in Svíþjóð and had on this journey suffered great difficulty because of blindness, and yet she trusted in God's mercy and arrived there on her journey at this festival. She was led sightless into the minster at Mass during the day, and before [209] the service was over she could see with both eyes and was now sharp-sighted and bright-eyed, but before that she had been blind for fourteen winters. She went from there with sublime joy.

---

[286] Actually it was dedicated to the Holy Trinity.
[287] i.e. 28th July. See note 191 above.

CHAPTER SEVEN

The event took place in Niðaróss that King Óláfr's shrine was being carried through the streets, and the shrine got heavy so that people could not carry it on from the spot. So after that the shrine was set down and the street was broken up and what was underneath was examined, and a child's body was found there that had been murdered and hidden there. This was then removed, and the street repaired as it had been before, and the shrine was carried on as usual.

CHAPTER EIGHT

King Óláfr stayed generally in country areas on great estates that he had. And when he was east in Ranríki at Haukbœr on an estate of his, then he caught a sickness that led to his death. He had then been king in Norway six and twenty years, and he was accepted as king one year after King Haraldr's fall. King Óláfr's body was conveyed north to Niðaróss and buried at Christchurch, which he had had built. He was a most popular king, and Norway had prospered and been improved greatly under his rule.

[210] **Magnúss saga berfœtts**

CHAPTER ONE

King Óláfr's son Magnús was immediately accepted as king over the whole of Norway in the Vík after King Óláfr's death. But when the Upplendingar heard of King Óláfr's death, then they took as king Magnús's cousin Hákon Þórisfóstri (foster-son of Steigar-Þórir). After that Hákon and Þórir travelled north to Þrándheimr, and when they got to Niðaróss, then they summoned Eyraþing, and at this assembly Hákon asked for the title of king for himself, and this was granted him, insofar as the farmers took him as king over half the country, which is what his father Magnús had had. Hákon abolished the land-dues payment for the Þrœndir and granted them many other changes in the law. He also abolished Yule gifts for them. Then all the Þrœndir switched to friendship with King Hákon. Then King Hákon set up a following for himself, going after that to Upplǫnd. He granted the Upplendingar the same changes in the law as he had granted the Þrœndir. They were also his absolute friends. At this time the following was composed in Þrándheimr:

> 170.   Young, Hǫkon came hither;   *Skald* II 828
> he, kindly with glory,
> born best of men on earth,
> brought with him Steigar-Þórir.
>
> [211]   He himself then kindly offered Ǫleifr's
> heir[288] rule in half of Norway,
> but well-spoken Magnús wanted
> to wield power over all.

CHAPTER TWO

In the autumn King Magnús travelled north to Kaupangr. And when he got there, then he went into the royal palace and stayed there in the quarters and remained there the first part of the winter. He kept seven longships in an opening where the ice had thawed in the Nið by the royal palace. So when King Hákon learnt that King Magnús was come to Þrándheimr, then he travelled west across Dofrafjall and so to Þrándheimr and to Kaupangr and took up his quarters in Skúlagarðr down from Clemenskirkja. This was the old royal palace. King Magnús was displeased at the great grants that King Hákon had given the farmers so as to gain their friendship. Magnús felt it was just as much his own property that had been given away, and he was very annoyed in his mind about this and felt himself wronged in this by his kinsman, that he should have so much less revenue than his father

---

[288] *Óláfs son*: 'son of Óláfr', Magnús.

had had or his forefathers, and he blamed what had been decided on Þórir. King Hákon and Þórir became aware of this, and were worried about what course Magnús might take. What seemed to them most suspicious was that Magnús had longships with awnings up, launched and ready. In the spring, close to Candlemas,[289] then King Magnús set out in the dead of night and sailed out the ships with awnings still up and lights underneath and made out for Hefring, spending the night there and making great fires up on the shore there. Then [212] King Hákon and the troops that were in the town assumed that this was done with an eye to treason. He had trumpets blown to call out his troops and all the Kaupangr people made their way up and were gathered together during the night. And in the morning when it began to get light and King Magnús saw the host of ordinary people on the Eyrar, then he sailed out from the fiord and so south to Gulaþingslǫg. King Hákon then prepared for a journey and was planning to go east into Vík, and first held a meeting in the town, then spoke and asked people for their friendship and promised his friendship to all. He said he was in the dark about the intentions of his kinsman King Magnús. King Hákon was sitting on a horse and was ready to travel. Everyone promised him friendship with goodwill and support, if it were necessary, and all the people escorted him out under Steinbjǫrg.

King Hákon travelled up to Dofrafjall. And as he was going over the mountain, he rode during the day after a ptarmigan that was flying away from him. Then he was taken ill and contracted a mortal sickness and died there on the mountain, and his body was conveyed north and arrived in Kaupangr a fortnight later than he had left it. Then all the townspeople went, and most of them weeping, to meet the king's body, for everyone loved him with deep affection. King Hákon's body was entombed in Christchurch.

King Hákon lived to be a good twenty-five years of age. He has been the one most popular of leaders in Norway among all the people. He had travelled north to Bjarmaland and fought a battle there and was victorious.

CHAPTER THREE

King Magnús sailed during the winter east into Vík, and when spring came he sailed south to Halland and raided in many places there. Then he burned Viskardalr there and other areas. He gained much wealth there and travelled back after that to his kingdom. So says Bjǫrn inn krepphendi (the Clenched-Handed) in *Magnússdrápa*: [290]

---

[289] The Feast of the Purification of the Virgin Mary, 2nd February.
[290] Nothing is known about this poet. Six full and four half-stanzas of his *Magnússdrápa* survive in *Heimskringla*, with a further half-stanza in *Morkinskinna*.

[213] 171.   The Vǫrsar's lord[291] had Halland—   *Magnússdrápa* 1
    the Hǫrðar's king burned buildings,   *Mork* II 38
    the flight was swiftly followed—   *Skald* II 396
    far and wide with sword, ravaged.
    The Þrœndr's ruler fired—flames were
    fanned by death of the woodpile[292]—
    the Viskardalr women lay wakeful—
    a wealth of districts later.

Here it mentions this, that King Magnús caused the greatest devastation in Halland.

CHAPTER FOUR

There is a man named Sveinn, son of Haraldr flettir (Plunderer), a Danish person by birth. He was a very great viking and a mighty fighter and a most valiant, a man of high lineage in his own country. He had been with King Hákon.

Now after the death of Hákon, then Steigar-Þórir was not confident that he would be able to achieve a settlement or friendly relations with King Magnús if his power was extended across the country, because of Þórir's offences and opposition that he had previously been involved in against King Magnús. After that Þórir and Sveinn adopted this plan, which was afterwards carried out, that they raised a troop with Þórir's resources and large numbers of adherents. But because Þórir was now an old man and infirm, Sveinn then took on the management of the troop and the title of leader. Other leaders joined in with this plan. [214] The most notable of these was Áslákr of Forland's son Egill. Egill was a landed man. He was married to Ǫgmundr Þorbergsson's daughter Ingibjǫrg, Skopti in Gizki's sister. There was a man called Skjálgr, powerful and wealthy, who also joined the troop. Þorkell Hamarskáld (Poet of Hamarr) mentions this in *Magnússdrápa*:[293]

172.   From far and wide his forces   *Magnússdrápa* 1
    he formed, high-minded Þorkell,   *Mork* II 19
    with Egill—not advantageous   *Fsk* 303
    those aims were for people.   *Skald* II 410

[291] *Vǫrsa dróttinn, Hǫrða ræsir, Þrœnda buðlungr*: 'lord of the Vǫrsar, ruler of the Hǫrðar, king of the Þrœndr', king of Norway.

[292] *kastar hel*: 'Hel (goddess of death, i.e. death) of the woodpile', fire.

[293] Þorkell Hamarskáld is listed in *Skáldatal* among poets of Óláfr kyrri and Magnús berfœttr (*Skáldatal* (269, 286). Two stanzas of *Magnússdrápa* are preserved in *Heimskringla* with a further two and a half in *Morkinskinna*. He also composed a poem about Eysteinn orri, mentioned but not cited in *Morkinskinna* (*Mork* I 321), and one *lausavísa* (st. 175 below).

I have heard that heavy
harm once befell Skjálgr's friends
when too large a stone[294] landed men
lobbed at the war-falcon's waterer.[295]

Þórir and his party raised their troops in Upplǫnd and came down into Raumsdalr and Sunn-Mœrr and got themselves ships there, after that sailing north to Þrándheimr.

CHAPTER FIVE

There was a man called Sigurðr ullstrengr (Wool-String), son of Loðinn Viggjarskalli (Bald-Headed Man from Vigg). He gathered troops by means of an arrow-summons[296] when he heard about Þórir and his party's company, and called out to Vigg all the troops he could get. So Sveinn and Þórir sailed their troops there and fought with Sigurðr and his men and were victorious and inflicted great loss of life, though Sigurðr fled [215] and went to see King Magnús. But Þórir and his party went to Kaupangr and stayed there in the fiord for a while, and many men came to them there. King Magnús heard about all these doings and immediately called troops together and after that sailed north to Þrándheimr. And when he got into the fiord and Þórir and his party heard about it—they were lying now by Hefring and were ready to sail out of the fiord—then they rowed to Vagnvíkastrǫnd and there disembarked from their ships and came north into Þexdalir in Seljuhverfi, and Þórir was carried on a stretcher over the mountain. After that they took to ships and travelled north to Hálogaland. So King Magnús followed them from Þrándheimr when he was ready. Þórir and his party travelled all the way north to Bjarkey, and Jón fled off, and his son Víðkunnr. Þórir and his men plundered all the movable property there and burned the farm and a good longship that Víðkunnr had. Then said Þórir as the warship burned and the ship tilted over:

'More to starboard, Víðkuðr!'

Then this was composed:

173.	There burns in mid Bjarkey	*Mork* II 26
	the best farm I know of.	*Fsk* 305
	The grief—no good from Þórir	*Skald* II 829
	is gained—of the stick[297] is roaring.	

---

[294] *urpu steinn of afl sér*: 'threw a stone beyond their strength', i.e. bit off more than they could chew.

[295] *morðhauks brynnir*: 'giver of drink to the battle-hawk (raven)', warrior.

[296] An arrow was sent round as a symbolic call to arms.

[297] *vandar bǫl*: 'bale, destruction of the stick', fire.

At evening Jóan need not complain at
an absence of fire and plundering.
Bright fire the broad farmstead
burns; to the clouds smoke rises.

[216] CHAPTER SIX

Jón and Víðkunnr travelled day and night until they met King Magnús.
Sveinn and Þórir also sailed from the north with their troops and plundered
widely round Hálogaland. And when they were lying in the fiord called
Harmr, then they saw King Magnús's fleet going by, and he and Þórir felt
they had not the forces to fight and rowed away and fled. Þórir and Egill
rowed to Hesjutún, but Sveinn rowed out to sea, and some of their troops
rowed into the fiord. King Magnús sailed after Þórir's party. And when the
ships rowed up to the landing place, then Þórir was in the middle part of his
ship. Then Sigurðr ullstrengr called to him:
'Are you sound in health, Þórir?'
Þórir replies: 'Sound in my hands, infirm in my feet.'
Then Þórir's party's troops all fled up on land, while Þórir was captured.
Egill was also captured, because he did not want to run leaving his wife.
King Magnús had them both taken to Vambarhólmr. And when Þórir was
led ashore, he staggered on his feet. Then spoke Víðkunnr:
'More to larboard, Þórir!'
After that Þórir was led to the gallows. Then he spoke:

| 174. | We were four fellows | *Ágrip* 2008, 66; *Mork* II 26 |
| | formerly, one the helmsman. | *Fsk* 305; *Skald* II 391 |

And when he stepped up to the gallows, he spoke:
'Evil are evil counsels.'
After that he was hanged, and when the gallows-beam was tilted up,[298]
Þórir was so heavy that his neck was severed, and his trunk fell to the ground.
Þórir was the biggest of all men, both tall and stout. Egill was also led to
the gallows, and when the king's slaves were about to hang him, then Egill
spoke:
'The reason for you hanging me is not that each of you would not be more
deserving of hanging.'
As it was said:[299]

---

[298] The gallows was evidently constructed as an upright with a pivoted cross piece
with arms of unequal length. The noose was suspended from the end of the short
arm, and the longer arm was hauled down sharply.

[299] In *Morkinskinna* this stanza is attributed to Þorkell Hamarskáld (see note 293
above).

[217] 175. I am told from tongue of Egill
            a true word was spoken
            to the king's slaves, restrained in loyalty,
            Sól of the wave's daylight.[300]
            he called them each far fitter
            for hanging, and higher,
            than himself; too great a sorrow
            the spoiler of battle-gleam[301] suffered.

Mork II 27
Fsk 306
Skald II 414

King Magnús was sitting by while they were hanged, and was so angry that none of his men was so bold as to dare to ask for quarter for them. Then the king spoke, when Egill kicked the gallows:

'Good kinsmen are of poor service to you when you need it.'

From this it could be seen that the king wished to have been asked that Egill's life might be saved. So says Bjǫrn inn krepphendi:

   176. Swords the bold lord of Sygnir[302]
        stained on raiding parties;
        the wolf began widely
        warm meat to tear on Harmr.
        You have heard how the ruler—
        hanged was Þórir, so it happened;
        well went the war-maker's venture—
        could wean men from treason.

Magnússdrápa 2
Mork II 39 (ll. 1–4)
Skald II 397

[218] CHAPTER SEVEN

After that King Magnús made his way south to Þrándheimr and sailed into Þrándheimr, dealing out heavy punishments there to the people that were guilty of treason against him. Some he killed, and burned the property of others. So says Bjǫrn inn krepphendi:

   177. Shield-shy, the raven-feeder[303]
        frightened the host of Þrœndr
        who seemed to see in settlements
        surging bane of forest.[304]

Magnússdrápa 3
Skald II 39

---

[300] *unnar dags Sól*: 'Sól (goddess) of the wave's daylight (gold)', woman.
[301] *hjaldrbliks eyðir*: 'destroyer of battle-gleam (sword)', warrior.
[302] *Sygna harri*: 'lord of Sygnir', i.e. king of Norway.
[303] *hrafngreddir*: 'raven-feeder', warrior; 'Shield-shy' means he scorned to carry a shield .
[304] *markar bǫl*: 'bale, destroyer of the forest', fire.

Of two *hersar* the host-Baldr[305]
halted the lives together,[306] I think.
The ogress's horse[307] was not empty.
The eagle flew to the hanged.

Sveinn Haraldsson first of all fled out to sea and on to Denmark, and stayed there until he had brought about a settlement for himself with Magnús's son King Eysteinn. He accepted a reconciliation with Sveinn and made him his cup-bearer and allowed him to be on very good terms with him and held him in honour. King Magnús now held the kingdom as sole ruler. He established peace for his country and destroyed all the vikings and pirates. He was a valiant man and warlike and diligent and in every way more like his grandfather Haraldr than his father in character.

[219] CHAPTER EIGHT

King Magnús set out on an expedition abroad, taking with him a large and splendid troop and a good naval force. He sailed this troop west across the sea and first of all to Orkney. He captured the jarls Páll and Erlendr and sent them both east to Norway, and appointed instead his son Sigurðr as ruler over the islands and provided him with counsellors.

King Magnús sailed his troop to the Suðreyjar, and when he got there, he began straight away to lay waste and burn the settlements, and slew the people and plundered everything wherever they went, and the inhabitants fled away in all directions, and some into the fiords of Scotland, and some south to Saltíri or out to Ireland. Some were given quarter and offered submission. So says Bjǫrn inn krepphendi:

178. All over Ljóðhús, limb-sorrow[308] leapt near the sky, fiercely. Far and wide folk were eager for flight; fire poured from buildings. The liberal lord—farmers lost life and wealth—ravaged Ívist with fire; the king coloured crimson the battle-beam.[309]	*Magnússdrápa* 5, 7 *Skald* II 399 (ll. 1–4) *Mork* II 42 (ll. 5–8) *Skald* II 401 (ll. 5–8).

---

[305] *her-Baldr*: 'army-Baldr (a god)', warrior.
[306] i.e. at the same time.
[307] *svǫru jór*: 'horse of the giantess', wolf.
[308] *limsorg*: 'branch-sorrow', fire.
[309] *róggeisli*: 'battle-beam (of light)', sword.

[220] 179.[310] The storm-gosling's hunger-slaker[311]   *Magnússdrápa* 6, 8
        Skíði caused to be harried.   *Mork* II 41 (ll. 1–2),
        In many wounds the wolf, merry,   *Skald* II 400, 401
        made its tooth red within Tyrvist.
        Grenland's lord[312] made maidens — *Mork* II 42 (ll. 5–8)
        men of Mull ran till weary;
        far inland went the Scots' scatterer —
        south in the islands[313] weep.

CHAPTER NINE

King Magnús brought his troop onto Eyin helga and there offered quarter and peace to everyone and everyone's goods. People say that he decided to open the small Kolumkillakirkja and the king did not go inside and immediately fastened the door shut with a lock, saying that no one was to be so bold as to enter this church after that, and this has been held to ever since.

Then King Magnús took his force south to Islay, laying waste and burning there. And when he had won that land, then he sets out south past Saltíri, then laid waste on both sides in Ireland and Scotland, [221] so harrying everywhere south to Man and laid waste there as in other places. So says Bjǫrn krepphendi:

180.   Far and wide on smooth Sandey   *Magnússdrápa* 8, 9
        the smart king bore shields.   *Mork* II 42 (ll. 1–4),
        All over Islay smoked when the   *Skald* II 401 (ll. 1–4)
        overlord's men stoked the burning.
        Sons of men stooped under   *Mork* 41 (ll. 7–8),
        sword-blades south of Sanntíri.   *Skald* II 402 (ll. 5–8)
        The bold builder of victory[314]
        brought about fall of Manxmen.

King Guðrøðr of the Suðreyjar's son was called Lǫgmaðr. Lǫgmaðr was appointed to the defence of the land in the Northern Isles.[315] But when King Magnús came to the Suðreyjar with his army, then Lǫgmaðr fled away from this army but stayed in the islands, though eventually King Magnús's men

---

[310] In *Morkinskinna*, ll. 1–2 of this stanza combine with ll. 7–8 of stanza 180 to make a half-stanza, and ll. 5–8 is the latter half of a stanza of which ll. 1–4 of stanza 180 is the first half.

[311] *hríðar gagls hungrþverrir*: 'hunger-diminisher (feeder) of the battle-gosling (raven)', warrior.

[312] *Grenlands dróttinn*: 'lord of Grenland', king of Norway.

[313] *suðr í eyjum* 'south in the islands' probably means *í Suðreyjum* (in the Hebrides).

[314] *sigrgœðir*: 'victory-increaser', warrior.

[315] i.e. of the Hebrides.

captured him with his ship's crew when he was about to flee to Ireland. The king had him set in irons and kept under guard. So says Bjǫrn krepphendi:

181. Every shelter owned by   *Magnússdrápa* 10
the heir of Guðrøðr was parlous.   *Mork* II 44
[222]   Lands were refused to Lǫgmaðr   *Skald* II 403
by the lord of Þrœndr there.[316]
The able king of Egðir,[317]
young, where tongues of battle-strips[318]
resounded, had the destroyer
of snake's bed[319] caught off the headlands.

CHAPTER TEN

After that King Magnús took his troop to Bretland. But when he got to Ǫngulseyjarsund, then there came against him an army from Bretland, and two jarls, Hugi prúði (the Courteous) and Hugi digri (the Stout) were in command of it, and they immediaely engaged in a fight. There was a tough battle there. King Magnús shot from a bow, but Hugi prúði was in a full coat of mail so that nothing of him was visible except his eyes. King Magnús shot an arrow at him, and so did a Hálogaland man that was standing next to the king. They both shot at the same time. One arrow hit the noseguard of his helmet, and it was deflected off it away in another direction, but the other missile hit the jarl in the eye and flew back through his head, and that one was attributed to the king. Jarl Hugi fell there, and after that the Bretar fled, having lost a large number of men. So says Bjǫrn krepphendi:

182. The tree of Laufi[320] contrived—   *Magnússdrápa* 11
tips of spears flew fast, where   *Mork* II 46
[223]   arms sped—in Ǫngulssund   *Skald* II 404
the end of Hugi inn prúði.

And this was also composed:[321]

183. Sword-point sounded on mailcoat.   Þorkell Hamarskáld,
Strongly shot the ruler.   *Magnússdrápa* 3
The Egðir's lord[322] bent the bow.   *Mork* II 46 *Fsk* 308
Blood spurted on helmets.   *Skald* II 411

---

[316] *lofðungr Þrœnda*: 'lord of Þrœndr', i.e. king of Norway..

[317] *Egða gramr*: 'king of the Egðir', i.e. of Norway.

[318] *véttrims tunga* 'tongue of the battle-strip (along the middle of the blade)', sword.

[319] *naðrbings tǫpuðr*: 'destroyer of the snake-bed (gold)', generous man.

[320] *Laufa lundr*: 'tree, grove of Laufi (sword)', warrior.

[321] In *Morkinskinna* and *Fagrskinna* this verse is ascribed to Þorkell Hamarskáld.

[322] *allvaldr Egða*: 'overlord of the Egðir', i.e. king of Norway.

The string's hail[323] flew—forces
fell, and in hard battle for land
the jarl's killing was caused by
the king of Hǫrðar[324]—into ring-mail.

King Magnús was victorious in that battle. Then he won Ǫngulsey, which was as far as the furthest south the previous kings that had been in Norway had gained power. Ǫngulsey is a third part of Bretland.

[224] After this battle King Magnús turns his troops back and made his way first to Scotland. Then men travelled between him and King Melkólmr of the Scots, and they made an agreement with each other. King Magnús was to have all the islands that lie to the west of Scotland, all those that a ship with a rudder attached could travel between and the mainland.[325] So when King Magnús came from the south to Saltíri, then he had a light warship dragged across Saltíriseið with the rudder fastened in position. The king himself sat on the raised deck holding the tiller and thus gained possession of the land, what lay on the port side. Saltíri is a large area and better than the best island in the Suðreyjar except Man. There is a narrow isthmus between it and the mainland of Scotland. Longships are often dragged across it.

CHAPTER ELEVEN

King Magnús stayed in the Suðreyjar during the winter. Then his men travelled all round the fiords of Scotland inside all the islands, both inhabited ones and uninhabited, and made all the islands possessions of the king of Norway. King Magnús obtained on behalf of his son Sigurðr the hand of Bjaðmynja, daughter of King Mýrjartak Þjálbason king of the Irish. He was ruling [225] over Kunnaktir. The following summer King Magnús went with his troops east to Norway. Jarl Erlendr had died of sickness in Niðaróss and is buried there, and Páll in Bjǫrgyn.

Skopti son of Ǫgmundr Þorbergsson was an excellent landed man. He lived at Gizki in Sunn-Mœrr. He was married to Þórðr Fólason's daughter Guðrún. Their children were Ǫgmundr, Finnr, Þórðr, Þóra, who was married to Ásólfr Skúlason. Skopti's sons were the most promising men in their youth.

CHAPTER TWELVE

King Steinkell of the Svíar died about the time of the fall of the two Haraldrs. The king that was next in Svíþjóð after King Steinkell was called Hákon. After that Steinkell's son Ingi was king, a good and powerful king, of all

---

[323] *strengs hagl*: 'hail of the (bow)string', arrows.

[324] *Hǫrða gramr*: 'king of the Hǫrðar', i.e. of Norway.

[325] i.e. that were separated from the mainland by a deep enough channel.

men the biggest and strongest. He was king in Svíþjóð at the same time as Magnús was in Norway. King Magnús claimed these had been the boundaries of the countries in ancient times, that the Gautelfr had been the frontier between the realms of the king of the Svíar and the king of Norway, and after that Lake Væni as far as Vermaland. King Magnús reckoned he had all the area that was west of Lake Væni, that is Sunndalr and Norðdalr, Véar and Varðynjar and all of Markir that belong to them. But these had now for a long time been subject to the power of the king of the Svíar and the taxes had belonged to Vestra-Gautland, but the [226] people of Markir wanted to carry on being subject to the king of the Svíar. King Magnús rode out of the Vík and up into Gautland and took a large and splendid troop with him, and when he got to the frontier area he laid waste and burnt, travelling thus through all the areas. People submitted to him and made over the lands to him by oath. But when he got up to Lake Væni, it was getting to the end of autumn. Then they went out onto Kvalðinsey and built a fortification there of turf and timber and dug a ditch round it. So when this stronghold was built, then food and other provisions that were necessary were conveyed into it. The king put into it three hundred men, and the commanders over them were Finnr Skoptason and Sigurðr ullstrengr, and they had the finest troops, and the king then went back out to the Vík.

CHAPTER THIRTEEN

So when the king of the Svíar heard about this, then he called troops together, and the word went round that he would be riding down, but this was delayed. Then Norwegians composed this:

> 184.   Overlong delays Ingi,   *Mork* II 59, *Fsk* 210
>   arse broad, his descending.   *Skald* II 831

But when Lake Væni was frozen over, then King Ingi rode down, taking nearly thirty hundred men. He sent word to the Norwegians that were occupying the stronghold, telling them to be off with the goods they had and go back to Norway. So when the messengers brought the king's words, then Sigurðr ullstrengr replied saying that King Ingi would achieve something other than driving them away like a herd to the pasture, and said he would need to come closer first. The messengers took back these words to the king. After that King Ingi went out to the island with his whole army. Then he a second time sent men to the Norwegians telling them to be off and take their weapons, clothing and horses, [227] but leave behind all their plunder. They refused this. So after this they launched an attack and shot at each other. Then the king had stones and timber brought up and the ditch filled. Then he had anchors and cables with long poles got and lifted up onto the timber wall.

Many men went up and dragged the wall apart. Then great fires were made and flaming brands were shot at them. Then the Norwegians asked for quarter, but the king told them to come out without weapons and without coats, and when they went out, then each of them was struck a blow with a rod. They went away thus and back home to Norway, and then the people of Markir all returned back to allegiance to King Ingi. Sigurðr and his companions went to see King Magnús and told him of their disaster.

CHAPTER FOURTEEN

Straight away in the spring when the ice melted, King Magnús went with a large troop east to the Elfr and made his way up along the eastern branch and laid waste all the realm of the king of the Svíar. And when he got up to Foxerni, then they went up ashore from the ships, and when they got across a certain river which flows there, then there came to meet them the army of Gautar, and a battle took place there, and the Norwegians were overpowered and resorted to flight, and a large number were killed near a waterfall. King Magnús fled and the Gautar followed them and slew as many as they could. King Magnús was easily recognised, the biggest of men, he had a red jacket over his mailcoat, his hair like pale silk and it fell down onto his shoulders. Qgmundr Skoptason was riding on one side of the king. He was also a very large and handsome man. He said:

'Give me your jacket, king!'

The king replied: 'What do you want the jacket for?'

'I want to have it,' he said. 'You have given me greater gifts.'

The lie of the land there was such that [228] there was open level ground all around, and one could see now everywhere Gautar and Norwegians, then there were more stony slopes and brushwood and then there was dead ground. Then the king gave Qgmundr his jacket and he put it on. After that they rode on over the open ground. Then Qgmundr turned abruptly aside with his men, and when the Gautr saw that, then they thought it was the king and all rode that way after him. Then the king rode on his way to his ship, and Qgmundr drew away with difficulty and yet reached the ship unharmed. After that King Magnús made his way down along the river and so north into the Vík.

CHAPTER FIFTEEN

The following summer a conference of kings was arranged by Konungahella on the Elfr, and King Magnús of Norway and King Ingi of the Svíar, King Eiríkr Sveinsson of the Danes attended it, and this conference was secured by a truce. So when the meeting was in session, then the kings went out in front of everyone else on the open ground and they spoke together for a short while, then went back to their followers, and thus the peace terms were concluded. Each of them was to have the area of rule that their fathers had had previously, and each of the kings was to compensate the people of their country for the plundering and loss of life, and each of them afterwards was to make it commensurate with what the other had given. King Magnús was to marry King Ingi's daughter Margrét. She was afterwards known as *friðkolla* 'Peace-Girl'. People said that [229] more princely-looking men than they all were had never been seen. King Ingi was biggest of all and most mightily framed, and he seemed most like a nobleman, but King Magnús seemed most imposing and most lively, while King Eiríkr was handsomest of all. But they were all fine, big men and noble-looking and eloquent. And thus they parted.

CHAPTER SIXTEEN

King Magnús married Queen Margrét. She was sent from the east from Svíþjóð to Norway, and she was provided with a splendid escort. But King Magnús had previously had some children that are named: a son of his was called Eysteinn, and his mother was of low rank. A second was called Sigurðr, and he was a winter younger. His mother was called Þóra. The third was called Óláfr, and he was by far the youngest. His mother was Sigríðr, daughter of Saxi in Vík, a noble person in Þrándheimr. She was the king's mistress.

People say that when King Magnús returned from raiding in the west, that he to a large extent adopted the customs and clothing fashions that were usual in the British Isles, as did many of his men. They went round the streets with bare legs and had short coats and then cloaks. So people called him Magnús berfœttr or berbeinn (Barelegged). Some called him Magnús hávi (the Tall), [230] and some Styrjaldar-Magnús (Warfare-). He was the tallest of men. There was a mark made for his height in Máríukirkja in Kaupangr, a church that King Haraldr had had built. There on the north doorway three crosses were chiselled in the stone wall, one Haraldr's height, one Óláfr's height, the third Magnús's height; and these indicated where each of them found it easiest to kiss, the highest Haraldr's cross, the lowest Magnús's cross and Óláfr's mark equidistant from the two.

CHAPTER SEVENTEEN

Skopti Ǫgmundarson had a quarrel with King Magnús, and they were disputing about a certain inheritance; Skopti was holding it, but the king was claiming it with such great vehemence that it almost amounted to a threat. Then many meetings were held, and Skopti advised that he and his sons should never all at once be at the king's mercy, saying that until then all would be fine. When Skopti was in the king's presence, he put forward the argument that there was close relationship between him and the king, and this too, that Skopti had always been a close friend of the king and their friendship had never failed, saying this, that people could be certain of this, that he was gifted with such intelligence 'that I,' he says, 'would not persist in a dispute with you, king, if I was in the wrong. And in this I take after my forebears, that I shall maintain my rights in the face of any person, and I will not make any distinction between one person and another in this.'

The king was the same, and his mood was not softened by such speeches. Skopti returned home.

CHAPTER EIGHTEEN

After that Finnr went to see the king and spoke with him and asked the king for this, that he should let him and his father get justice in this matter. The king replied angrily and [231] abruptly. Then Finnr spoke:

'I expected something else from you, king, than that you would deprive me of my legal rights after I went to stay on Kvaldinsey which few of your other friends were willing to do, saying, as was true, that those that occupied it were being handed over and doomed to death, if King Ingi had not shown us more generosity than you had treated us with, and even so it will have seemed to many that we left there with dishonour, if that means anything.'

The king's mood did not change with these words, and Finnr went home.

CHAPTER NINETEEN

Then Ǫgmundr Skoptason went to see the king, and when he came into the king's presence, he stated his purpose and asked the king to treat the family justly. The king maintained that what he had spoken was just, and they were remarkably impudent. Then spoke Ǫgmundr:

'You will be able to act in this way, treating us wrongfully, because of your power. In this it will be shown to be true, as they say, that most whose life have been saved give little or no reward. I will add this to what I have said, that never again shall I enter your service, nor any of our family, if I have my way.'

After that Ǫgmundr went home, and he and King Magnús never saw each other afterwards.

CHAPTER TWENTY

In the following spring Skopti Ǫgmundarson sets out away out of the country. He had five longships and all of them well fitted out. His sons

Qgmundr and Finnr and Þórðr joined him on this journey. They were rather late getting ready, sailed in the autumn to Flæmingjaland and stayed there for the winter. Early in the spring they sailed west to Valland [232] and in the summer they sailed out through Nǫrvasund and in the autumn to the City of Rome. There Skopti died. The whole family died on this journey. Þórðr lived longest of them. He died in Sicily. People say that Skopti was the first of the Norwegians to sail through Nǫrvasund and that journey became most famous.

CHAPTER TWENTY-ONE

An event took place in Kaupangr, where King Óláfr lies, that a house in the town caught fire and the fire spread. Then King Óláfr's shrine was carried out of the church and placed facing the fire. After that a reckless and foolish man leapt up and banged on the shrine and spoke threateningly at the blessed man, saying this, that everything was now going to burn up unless he saved them by his prayers, both the church and other buildings. Now almighty God caused the burning of the church to be prevented, but to the foolish man he sent a pain in the eyes immediately the following night, and he lay there right on until the blessed King Óláfr prayed to almighty God for mercy for him, and he was cured in the selfsame church.

CHAPTER TWENTY-TWO

Another event took place in Kaupangr, that a woman was conveyed to the foundation there in which King Óláfr lies. She was so misshapen that she was all curled up so that both feet lay bent up by her thighs, and since she was all the time in prayer and had prayed to him with tears, then he cured her from that great affliction, so that feet and legs and other limbs were straightened from their curving, and [233] afterwards every joint and limb served its correct purpose. Previously she was not able to crawl there, but afterwards she walked sound and joyful to her home.

CHAPTER TWENTY-THREE

King Magnús set out on a journey abroad and took a great army. He had now been king over Norway for nine winters. Now he went west across the sea and had the finest troops that were available in Norway. All the men of the ruling class that were in the country went with him, Sigurðr Hranason, Víðkunnr Jóansson, Dagr Eilífsson, Serkr from Sogn, the king's marshal Eyvindr ǫlbogi (Elbow), Sigurðr's brother Úlfr Hranason and many others of the ruling class. The king went with all this troop west to Orkney, and took with him from there Jarl Erlendr's sons Magnús and Erlingr. Then he sailed to the Suðreyjar, and while he was lying off Scotland, then Magnús Erlendsson leapt from the king's ship during the night and swam ashore, went after that up into the forest and turned up at the court of the king of the Scots. King Magnús took his troop to Ireland and made raids there. Then King Mýrjartak came to join him, and they defeated much of the country, Dublin and the county of Dublin, and King Magnús stayed during the winter up in Kunnaktir with King Mýrjartak, but set his men to guard the land where he had conquered it. And when spring came, the kings went with their army west into Ulster and fought many battles there and defeated the land and had defeated the greater part of Ulster. Then Mýrjartak went back to Kunnaktir.

[234] CHAPTER TWENTY-FOUR

King Magnús then prepared his ships and was planning to sail east to Norway. He set his men in Dublin to guard it. He was lying off Ulster with all his troops and they were ready to sail. They felt they needed animals at the coast for slaughter, and King Magnús sent some of his men to King Mýrjartak [asking him] to send him animals for slaughter, and named a day for them to come, the next before Bartholomeusmass[326] if the messengers were unharmed. But on the eve of the feast day they were not come. So on the feast day, when the sun rose, King Magnús went ashore with the greater part of his troop and went inland from the ships, wanting to search for his men and cattle. The weather was still and sunny. The way led over bogs and fens and there were logs cut across there, [235] but scrub on both sides. When they pressed on, they were faced by a very high rise in the ground. From it they could see a long way all round. They saw a great cloud of dust from horses up inland, then discussed among themselves whether it would be an army of Irish, but some said that it must be their men with the cattle for slaughter. They called a halt there. Then said Eyvindr ǫlbogi:

'King,' he says, 'what is your opinion about that group travelling there? People think you are going on incautiously. You know that the Irish are treacherous. Work out some plan now for your troop.'

Then the king spoke: 'Let us now draw up our troops and be prepared in case this is a trap.'

Then they were drawn up. The king and Eyvindr stepped out in front of the battle line. King Magnús had a helmet on his head and a red shield with a lion depicted on it in gold, was girded with a sword that was called Leggbítr (Leg-Biter), with the fittings on the hilt of walrus ivory and the haft wrapped in gold, a very fine weapon. He had a halberd in his hand. He was wearing

---

[326] St Bartholomew's day is 24th August.

a red silk jacket over his tunic with lions cut out in yellow silk on the front and back. And people said that there had not been seen a more imposing or gallant-looking person. Eyvindr also had a red silk jacket of the same style as the king's. He was also a big man and handsome and most warrior-like.

CHAPTER TWENTY-FIVE

But when the cloud of dust came closer, then they recognised their men, and they were travelling with a large herd of cattle for slaughter that the king of the Irish had sent them, and he had kept all his promises to King Magnús. After that they turned back out to the ships, and it was then about the period of midday. But when they got out onto the bogs the going was slow for them over the fens. Then an army of Irish rushed forward from every forest edge and immediately engaged in battle, but the Norwegians were in scattered order and many soon fell. Then spoke Eyvindr:

'King,' he says, 'Our troops are faring unfortunately. [236] Let us now quickly adopt a good plan.'

The king spoke: 'Blow a war trumpet to call all the troops under the standards, but the troop that is here, let it set up a shield wall, and after that let us go away in retreat out across the bogs. After that it will not matter, when we get to the level ground.'

The Irish were shooting boldly, and yet they were falling in very large numbers, but always another man took over every man's place. And when the king got to the lowest ditch—it was there very hard going and in few places possible to get across—the Norwegians were falling in large numbers. Then the king called to his landed man Þorgrímr skinnhúfa (Fur Cap)—he was an Upplander—and told him to go across the ditch with his company.

'And we shall hold the defence meanwhile,' he says, 'so that you will not be hurt. Go afterwards to that knoll that is over here, and shoot at them while we get over the ditch. You are good bowmen.'

But when Þorgrímr and his men got over the ditch they threw their shields over their backs and ran down to the ships. So when the king saw that, he spoke:

'You are deserting your king in an unmanly way. It was unwise of me to make you a landed man, and to make Sigurðr hundr an outlaw. He would never have behaved so.'

King Magnús got a wound, a halberd was stabbed through both thighs above the knee. He grasped the shaft between his legs and broke off the shank and spoke:

'Thus we break every foreleg, boys.'[327]

---

[327] It is said to have been considered a feat of strength to break a sheep's (or other animal's) foreleg between one's hands.

King Magnús was struck in the neck by a battleaxe,[328] and that was his death-wound. Then those that remained fled. Víðkunnr Jóansson took the sword Leggbítr and the king's standard to the ships. Those that ran last were he, secondly Sigurðr Hranason, thirdly Dagr Eilífsson. Eyvindr ǫlbogi, Úlfr Hranason and many other men of rank fell there with King Magnús. Many of the Norwegians fell, but yet very many more of the Irish. And those Norwegians that [237] got away went off immediately in the autumn. Jarl Erlendr's son Erlingr fell in Ireland with King Magnús. And when the troops that had fled from Ireland got to Orkney and Sigurðr heard of his father King Magnús's fall, then he immediately joined them on their journey, and they travelled in the autumn east to Norway.

CHAPTER TWENTY-SIX

King Magnús was over Norway ten winters, and in his time there was satisfactory peace within the country, but people had a hard and costly time with the expeditions. King Magnús was most popular with his men, but to the farmers he seemed harsh. People report words of his, when his friends would say that he often went on incautiously when he was raiding abroad, he would say this:

'A king should be had for fame and not for long life.'

King Magnús was nearly thirty years of age when he fell. In the battle Víðkunnr slew the man that had caused the death of King Magnús. Then Víðkunnr fled, and had received three wounds. And for these reasons King Magnús's sons admitted him to the closest friendship.

---

[328] *Sparða* was a type of Irish axe.

[238] **Magnússona saga**

CHAPTER ONE

After the fall of King Magnús berfœttr his sons took over the kingdom in Norway: Eysteinn, Sigurðr, Óláfr. Eysteinn had the more northerly part of the country, and Sigurðr the more southerly. King Óláfr was now four winters old or five. So the third of the country that was his, they both had in their keeping. Sigurðr was accepted as king when he was thirteen winters old or fourteen, but Eysteinn was a winter older. King Sigurðr left the King of the Irish's daughter behind across the sea to the west.

When Magnús's sons were accepted as kings, there came back from Jórsalaheimr and in some cases from Mikligarðr the men that had travelled out with Skopti Ǫgmundarson, and they were most famous and were able to tell about all kinds of events, and because of this news a large number of people in Norway became keen to undertake that journey. It was said that in Mikligarðr, Norwegians who were willing to become mercenaries received great wealth. They asked the kings that one or other of them, Eysteinn or Sigurðr, should go and be the leader of this party that was undertaking the journey. So the kings agreed to this and made preparations for the journey at the expense of both of them. Many of the ruling class, both landed men and powerful landowners, resolved upon this journey. So when preparations had been made for the journey, then it was decided that Sigurðr should go, and Eysteinn should have the rule over the land on behalf of both of them.

[239] CHAPTER TWO

One winter or two after the fall of Magnús berfœttr there came from the west from Orkney Jarl Páll's son Hákon, and the kings gave him a jarldom and government in Orkney, the same as jarls had had before him, his father Páll and his uncle Erlendr. Hákon travelled west to Orkney.

CHAPTER THREE

Four winters after King Magnús's fall, King Sigurðr left Norway with his party. He now had sixty ships. So says Þórarinn stuttfeldr (Short Cloak):[329]

| 185. | So large and fine | *Stuttfeldardrápa* 2 |
| | a force assembled | *Mork* II 73 |

[329] Þórarinn stuttfeldr is unknown other than from *Morkinskinna*, which identifies him as an Icelander and recounts a brief episode accounting for his nickname; it also refers to a poem called *Stuttfeldardrápa*, to which the stanza cited here (along with five others and a further couplet) is considered to belong, although *Morkinskinna* itself attributes this stanza to Þorvaldr blǫnduskáld (*Morkinskinna* II 134–37).

of the most wise leader   *Skald* II 474
beloved of the king,
that sixty ships
slid hence over sea,
fine-planked, governed
by pure God's decrees.

In the autumn King Sigurðr sailed to England. Now Viljálmr Bastard's son
Heinrekr was king there. King Sigurðr stayed there for the winter. So says
Einarr Skúlason:[330]

[240] 186. The leader went, unwearied,   *Sigurðardrápa* 1
              west with the largest of forces.   *Skald* II 538
              To English soil under the ruler
              the ocean's steed waded.
              The prince let, pleased with battle,
              the prows rest, and stayed there
              winter-long. No better leader
              alights from a Valr of Vimur.[331]

CHAPTER FOUR

The following spring King Sigurðr went west to Valland with his party and
turned up in the autumn out in Galizuland and stayed there the second winter.
So says Einarr Skúlason:

        187. And he who highest power   *Sigurðardrápa* 2
              had got under the sun's mansion,[332] *Skald* II 539
              the nation's king, his soul nourished
              the next winter in Jacob's land.[333]
              There, I heard, the prince of the people
              paid the fine jarl for cheating
              speech; the black swan of battle[334]
              the bold-spirited king gladdened.

[330] Einarr Skúlason was an Icelander, mentioned in a catalogue of priests living in
western Iceland in 1143. He recited his poem *Geisli* 'Beam of Light' in honour of
St Ólafr in Trondheim in 1153. He composed encomia for Sigurðr Jórsalafari and
his brother Eysteinn, Haraldr gilli, Magnús blindi, Haraldr gilli's sons Ingi, Sigurðr
and Eysteinn, and about Norwegian and Swedish nobles.
[331] *Vimrar Valr:* 'Valr (name of a horse) of Vimur (name of a mythical river)', ship.
[332] *sóls rann*: 'the sun's house', the sky, heaven.
[333] The land of St James (the Great, apostle) of Compostella, i.e. Galicia.
[334] *hjaldrs svartr svanr*: 'black swan of battle', raven.

[241] Now these were the circumstances with this event, that the jarl that was ruling over that country there made an agreement with King Sigurðr, and the jarl was to have a market set up for Sigurðr for the purchase of food the whole winter. But it lasted no longer than until Yule, and then it became difficult to get hold of food, for the country is barren and a poor country for food. Then King Sigurðr took a large troop to the castle that the jarl owned and the jarl fled away, as he had few troops. From there King Sigurðr took much food and a great deal of other plunder and had it conveyed to his ships, after that setting off and travelling west past Spain. As King Sigurðr was sailing past Spain, it happened that some pirates that were going about after booty came towards him with a host of galleys, so King Sigurðr joined battle with them and so they began their first battle with heathens, winning from them eight galleys. So says Halldórr skvaldri (the Clamorous):[335]

188.	And pirates went, worthless—	*Útfarardrápa* 1
	war-gods of the roof of Fjǫlnir[336]	*Mork* II 77 (ll. 5–8)
	the prince piled up—to encounter	*Skald* II 484
	the powerful ruler.	
	Eight galleys the army	
	emptied. True to the people,	
	the warriors' friend, where fell no	
	few troops, gained booty.	

[242] After that King Sigurðr made for the castle that is called Sintré, and fought a second battle there. This is in Spain. It was occupied by heathen people making raids on Christians. He won the castle and killed all the people there, as they were unwilling to have themselves be made Christian, and took much wealth there. So says Halldórr skvaldri:

189.	Mighty deeds of the monarch	*Útfarardrápa* 2
	I must tell, that happened	*Mork* II 78
	in Spain; Ván's daylight's slinger[337]	*Skald* II 485
	assaulted Sintré proudly.	

[335] Halldórr skvaldri is otherwise unknown. He is said in *Skáldatal* to have composed for Jarl Sóni Ívarsson of Gautland, and for Magnús berfœttr, Sigurðr Jórsalafari, Haraldr gilli and Ingvi Haraldsson, all kings of Norway, King Eiríkr eymuni of Denmark, and Jarl Karl Sónason, Jarl Jón Sørkvisson and King Sørkvir Kolsson of Sweden; but of all his poetry only seven full and eleven half-stanzas survive.

[336] *Fjǫlnis hróts vígæsir*: 'war-gods of Fjǫlnir's (Óðinn's) roof (shields)', warriors. Óðinn's hall was said to be roofed with shields.

[337] *Vánar dags sløngvir*: 'slinger (dispenser) of the daylight of Ván (a mythical river) (gold)', generous man.

> Opposing the stern prince
> proved, for warriors, rather
> fearsome, but they flatly
> refused God's law, offered to them.

CHAPTER FIVE

After that King Sigurðr took his party to Lisbon. This is a great city in Spain, and half Christian and half heathen. There is the dividing line between Christian Spain and heathen Spain. All the areas that lie to the west of there are heathen. There King Sigurðr fought his third battle with heathens and was victorious, winning much wealth there. So says Halldórr skvaldri:

[243] 190.	South near the city, daring	*Útfarardrápa* 3
	descendant of a ruler,	*Mork* II 79
	they call Lisbon, when you landed,	*Skald* II 486
	you won the third victory.	

Then King Sigurðr took his party west past heathen Spain and sailed to the city that is called Alkasse, and there fought his fourth battle with heathens and won the city, killing many people there so that he caused the city to be deserted. There they won an enormous amount of wealth. So says Halldórr skvaldri:

191.	I heard you were eager	*Útfarardrápa* 4
	out at so-called Alkasse	*Mork* II 80
	for the fourth time fiercely	*Skald* II 487
	to fight, war-advancer.[338]	

And also this:

192.	I heard it was enacted	*Útfarardrápa* 5
	in one sacked town, to a heathen—	*Mork* II 80
	folk found it best to hasten	*Skald* II 487
	into flight—woman's sorrow.	

[244] CHAPTER SIX

Then King Sigurðr continued his journey and made for Norvasund, but in the straits he was faced by a large army of pirates, and the king joined battle with them and fought there his fifth battle and was victorious. So says Halldórr skvaldri:

193.	Edge of swords you ventured	*Útfarardrápa* 6
	east of Norvasund to redden.	*Mork* II 81

---

[338] *folkþeysandi*: 'one who makes battle rush on', warrior.

To fresh wounds—God favoured you—   *Skald* II 488
flew the gull of carrion.[339]

After that King Sigurðr sailed his army on along the southerly coast by
Serkland and came to the island that is called Formentera. At that time there
had established themselves there a great army of heathen blacks in a certain
cave, and they had set up a stone wall in front of the cave entrance. They made
raids widely over the country and conveyed all the booty to the cave. King
Sigurðr made a foray up onto the island and went to the cave, and it was in
a certain cliff, and it was a long way to go up into the cave to the stone wall,
and the cliff jutted out forwards above the stone wall. The heathens defended
the stone wall and were not afraid of the Norwegians' weapons, but they were
able to get stones and missiles down below their feet onto the Norwegians
from above. The Norwegians also did not attempt the ascent as things were.
Then the pirates took fine silk clothes and other costly items and carried them
out onto the wall and shook them at the Norwegians and shouted at them and
egged them on and taunted them for lack of courage. Then King Sigurðr made
himself a plan. He had two ships' boats taken, those that are called *barkar*, and
hauled up onto the cliff above [245] the entrance to the cave and poles with
thick cables all the way beneath the ribs and round the stems. After that as
many men as there was space for got in, then they let the boats down in front
of the cave by ropes. Those that were in the boats shot and threw stones so that
the heathens retreated from the stone wall. Then King Sigurðr went up into
the cliff with his army under the stone wall and broke down the wall and so
got up into the cave, so the heathens fled in past the stone wall that was built
across the cave. Then the king had large timbers brought into the cave and
a great bonfire heaped up in the entrance to the cave and set alight. And the
heathens, when the fire and smoke overcame them, then some lost their lives,
some went onto the Norwegians' weapons, but all the people were killed or
burnt. There the Norwegians got the greatest amount of booty that they had
taken on this expedition. So says Halldórr skvaldri:

194.   Formentera   *Útfararkviða* 1
        before the war-keen   *Skald* II 483
        peace-disturber's[340]
        prow appeared.
        There blades and fire
        the black men's troop
        must endure, till
        death they received.

[339] *náskári*: 'corpse-gull', raven or eagle.
[340] *friðraskaðr*: 'disturber of peace', warrior.

And also this:

> 195.   From above, battle-strengthener,[341]   *Útfarardrápa* 7
>   boats you had lowered—the prince's   *Mork* II 83
>   feats on Serkir become famous—   *Fsk* 317
>   before the ogress's short cut.[342]   *Skald* II 488
> [246] And up the cliff to the crowded
>   cavern you pressed forward
>   with your company, keen on battle,
>   clash-Þróttr of Gǫndul's meeting.[343]

Again Þórarinn stuttfeldr says:

> 196.   The king, battle-skilled,   *Stuttfeldardrápa* 4
>   bade men drag onto   *Mork* II 84
>   the cliff breeze-wolves,[344]   *Skald* II 476
>   dark black, two,
>   when strong beasts of ship-rails[345]
>   sank down on cables,
>   bringing the company, before
>   the cave's opening.

CHAPTER SEVEN

Then King Sigurðr went forward on his way and came to the island that is called Íviza, and there fought a battle and was victorious. This was his seventh. So says Halldórr skvaldri:

> 197.   The death-wheel marker[346] moved,   *Útfarardrápa* 9
>   much glorified, his ship-fleet—   *Mork* II 85
> [247] keen for fame was peace-fracturing's   *Skald* II 490
>   forwarder—to Íviza.[347]

After that King Sigurðr came to the island that is called Manork, and there fought his eighth battle with heathens and was victorious. So says Halldórr skvaldri:

---

[341] *bǫðstyrkir*: 'battle-strengthener', warrior.

[342] *gýgjar gagnstígr*: 'giantess's short cut', cliff.

[343] *Gǫnduls þings gný-Þróttr*: 'Óðinn of the clash of Gǫndul's (valkyrie's) assembly (battle)', warrior.

[344] *byrvargr*: 'wolf of favourable wind', ship.

[345] *þrama ramdýr*: 'strong animal of ship's rails', ship.

[346] *morðhjóls merkir*: 'the marker (with blood) of the death-wheel (shield)', warrior.

[347] *ræsir friðslits*: 'advancer of peace-breaking', warrior.

198. And once more the eighth   *Útfarardrápa* 10
     arrow-storm[348] was wakened   *Mork* II 85
     on green Manork; the monarch's   *Skald* II 491
     men reddened the Lapp's payment.[349]

CHAPTER EIGHT

In the spring King Sigurðr came to Sicily and stayed there a long time. Duke Roðgeirr was there at this time. He welcomed the king and invited him to a banquet. King Sigurðr came to it and a large troop with him. There was splendid entertainment there, and every day at the banquet Duke Roðgeirr stood and served at King Sigurðr's table. And the seventh day of the banquet, when people had taken a wash, then King Sigurðr took the duke by the hand and led him up into a high seat and gave him the title of king and the right of being king over the realm of Sicily, for previously jarls had been there over that realm.

[248] CHAPTER NINE

King Roðgeirr of Sicily was a most powerful king. He defeated the whole of Púll and made it subject to himself, and many great islands in Griklandshaf. He was known as Roðeirr ríki (the Great). His son was King Viljálmr in Sicily, who for a long time conducted a great war with the emperor of Mikligarðr. King Viljálmr had three daughters, but no son. He gave one of his daughters in marriage to Emperor Frírekr's son Emperor Heinrekr, and their son was Frírekr who was now emperor in the City of Rome. King Viljálmr's second daughter was married to the Duke of Kapr, the third was married to Margrít yfirkussari (Corsair Chief). Emperor Heinrekr slew both these men. King Rodgeirr of Sicily's daughter was married to Emperor Mánúli in Mikligarðr. Their son was Emperor Kirjalax.

[249] CHAPTER TEN

In the summer King Sigurðr sailed out across Griklandshaf to Jórsalaland, after that went up to Jórsalaborg and there met King Baldvini of Jórsalir. King Baldvini welcomed King Sigurðr exceedingly warmly and rode with him out to the River Jórðán and back to Jórsalaborg. So says Einarr Skúlason:

199. The lord set the hull sailing,   *Sigurðardrápa* 3
     sea-cold—the poet's praise of   *Skald* II 540
     the mighty king's munificence
     is many-sided—in Gríksalt,

[348] *oddhríð*: 'point-storm', storm of arrows.
[349] *Finns gjǫld*: arrows; see st. 134 above; reddened, i.e. with blood.

until by extra broad Akrsborg
the injurer of wealth[350] his vessel
moored; all men awaited
a morn of joy with the leader.

200. I tell how the king travelled   *Sigurðardrápa* 4
to the town of Jórsalir, strife-glad;   *Skald* II 540
men know no lord nobler
beneath the wind's wide dwelling.[351]
And the foe of hawks' land flame—[352]
famous was that action—
[250]   was able to wash in the pure
water of Jórðán, valiant.

King Sigurðr stayed a very long time in Jórsalaland in the autumn and the
first part of winter.

CHAPTER ELEVEN

King Baldvini gave a fine banquet to King Sigurðr and a great troop of his
men with him. Then King Baldvini gave King Sigurðr many holy relics, and
now a piece of the Holy Cross was taken with the consent of King Baldvini
and the Patriarch, and they both swore on a holy relic that this piece of wood
was from the Holy Cross that God himself was tormented on. After that this
holy relic was given to King Sigurðr, on condition that he and twelve other
men with him first swore that he would promote Christianity with all his
might and establish in his country an archbishop's see, if he could, and that
the cross should be kept there where the blessed King Óláfr lay, and that he
should introduce tithes and pay them himself.

King Sigurðr went after this to his ships in Akrsborg. Now King Baldvini
also got his army ready to go to Sýrland to the city that is called Sæt. This
city was heathen. King Sigurðr joined him on this expedition. And when
the kings had been surrounding this city for a short while, the heathens gave
themselves up, and the kings won the city for themelves, and the troops [had]
the rest of the plunder. King Sigurðr [251] let King Baldvini have the whole
city. So says Halldórr skvaldri:

201. You seized the heathen city,   *Útfarardrápa* 11
sater of the wound-bitch,[353]   *Fsk* 319

---

[350] *auðlestir*: 'harmer of wealth', generous man.
[351] *glyggs salr*: 'hall of the wind', the sky.
[352] *hauka fróns leyghati*: 'hater of the flame (gold) of hawks' land (arm)', generous man.
[353] *benja tíkr bræðir*: 'feeder of the bitch of wounds (she-wolf)', warrior.

with force—each fight nobly   *Skald* II 491
fought—but yielded it kindly.

Here Einarr Skúlason also tells of this:

202.   Dœlir's king[354] captured—the warrior[355]   *Sigurðardrápa* 5
       recalls it—Sætt, I heard;   *Skald* II 541
       death-slings[356] started wildly
       swinging in Hrist's tempest.[357]
       The strife-hawk's mouth-stainer,[358]
       strong, breached the harmful
       fort; fair swords were reddened;
       and the fast king could hail victory.

[252] After this King Sigurðr went to his ships and prepared to leave Jórsalaland. They sailed north to the island that is called Kípr, and King Sigurðr stayed there a certain time, going after that to Grikland, and sailed his whole troop out off Engilsnes and lay there a fortnight, and every day there was a fresh fair wind north across the sea, but he wanted to wait for a wind that would be a cross wind and the sails could be set longways down the ship, for all his sails had fine silk cloths stitched on them, both the side that faced forwards and that which faced back, since both those in the bows and those that were aft did not want to have to look at the less beautiful side of the sails.

CHAPTER TWELVE

When King Sigurðr sailed in to Mikligarðr, he sailed close to the shore. There are everywhere there up on the shore cities and castles and villages in an unbroken line. Then could be seen from the shore into the inner sides of all the sails, and there was no space between them just as if it was a fence. All the people were standing outside that could see King Sigurðr sailing by. Emperor Kirjalax had also heard about King Sigurðr's journey, and he had the city gate in Mikligarðr that is called Gullvarta opened. The emperor must ride in through that gate when he has been a long time previously away from Mikligarðr and has had successful victories. Then the emperor had silk cloths spread over all the streets of the city from Gullvarta and up to [253] Laktjarnir. There the most splendid imperial palaces are. King Sigurðr spoke with his men, saying that they were to ride proudly into the city and not to seem impressed

[354] Dœlir's king: i.e. the king of Norway.
[355] i.e. the poet.
[356] *valslǫngur*: ballistas, catapults.
[357] *Hristar hríð*: 'storm of Hrist (a valkyrie)', battle.
[358] *gunnar vals munnlituðr*: 'colourer (with blood) of the mouth of the falcon of battle (eagle or raven)', warrior.

by all the new sights they saw, and they did this. King Sigurðr and all his men rode into Mikligarðr with this kind of pomp and on to the most splendid palace, and there everything was prepared for them. King Sigurðr stayed here for some time. Then King Kirjalax sent men to him to see whether he wished to accept six pounds of ship's cargo of gold, or would rather that the king made arrangements for the games that the emperor was accustomed to have performed in the Hippodrome. King Sigurðr chose the games, and the messengers said that the games cost the emperor no less than that amount of gold. Then the king made arrangements for the games, and the games were performed in the usual way, and all the games went better for the king that time. Half the games are the queen's, and their men compete in all the games. And the Greeks say that when the king wins more games than the queen in the Hippodrome, then the king will be victorious if he goes on a warlike expedition.

CHAPTER THIRTEEN

After that King Sigurðr prepared for his journey home. He gave the emperor all his ships, and gold-ornamented figureheads were on the ship that the king had commanded. They were placed in Pétrskirkja. Emperor Kirjalax gave King Sigurðr many [254] horses and provided him with a guide all the way across his realm. Then King Sigurðr left Mikligarðr, but a large number of men stayed behind and became mercenaries. King Sigurðr returned from abroad going first to Bolgaraland and then through Ungaraland and through Pannonia and through Sváfa and Býjaraland. There he met Emperor Lozarius[359] of the City of Rome, and he welcomed him exceedingly warmly, providing him with a guide all the way across his realm and had a market held for them for all the purchases that they needed. And when King Sigurðr got to Slésvík in Denmark, then Jarl Eilífr gave him a splendid banquet. It was about the time of midsummer. In Heiðabýr he met King Níkolás of the Danes, and he welcomed him extremely warmly and himself accompanied him north to Jótland and gave him a ship with all its fittings that he had in Norway. Then King Sigurðr went home to his kingdom, and he was warmly welcomed, and people said that no more honourable journey has been made out of Norway than this one was, and he was now twenty years of age. He had been three years on this journey. His brother Óláfr was now twelve winters old.

CHAPTER FOURTEEN

King Eysteinn had done a great deal in the country that was beneficial while King Sigurðr was on his journey. He started the Monastery in Bjǫrgyn on

[359] At this time Henry V was Roman Emperor (1111–25), and Lothair III (Lozarius), at this time Duke in Saxony, did not become emperor until 1133. Henry had returned to Germany in the spring of 1111; Sigurðr may well have met him there.

Norðnes and spent a lot of money on it. He had Mikjálskirkja built there, a [255] most magnificent stone minster. He also had built in the royal palace grounds Postolakirkja, a timber church. He also had built there the great palace, which is the most magnificent timber building that has been built in Norway. He also had a church built on Agðanes and a fortress and harbour where before there was no place to land. He also had Níkoláskirkja built in Niðaróss in the royal palace grounds, and that building was very elaborately finished with carvings and all kinds of craftsmanship. He also had a church built at Vágar in Hálogaland and provided it with an income for its maintenance.

CHAPTER FIFTEEN

King Eysteinn sent word to Jamtaland to the wisest and greatest people, inviting them to visit him, and he welcomed all who came with much warmth and sent them on their way with friendly gifts, thus drawing them into friendship with him. And since many of them became accustomed to going to him and accepted his gifts, while some sent him gifts who did not visit him, so he got himself on completely friendly terms with all the people that were in authority in the land. After that he spoke before them, saying the Jamtr had behaved badly when they had turned away from the kings of Norway in their fealty and paying of taxes, going over the story of how the Jamtr had gone under the sway of King Hákon Aðalsteinsfóstri (foster-son of Aðalsteinn) and after that been for a long time under the kings of Norway, going also into how many benefits they could receive from Norway and how much trouble it must be for them to have to go to the king of the Svíar for anything they wanted. And he so managed his speech that the Jamtr themselves suggested to him and asked him if they might switch to fealty to King Eysteinn, and claimed that this was what they both needed and must have. Their friendship became so close that the Jamtr handed over all their land to the rule [256] of King Eysteinn. In order to achieve this, the men of the ruling class there took oaths of loyalty from all the people, after that going to King Eysteinn and swearing the land to him, and this has remained valid ever since. King Eysteinn won Jamtaland by the use of reason, and not by making attacks like some of his predecessors.

CHAPTER SIXTEEN

King Eysteinn was a man most handsome in looks, blue-eyed and rather wide-eyed, fair-haired and curly-haired, a man not taller than average, of great good sense, well-informed about everything, law and history and genealogy, wise in advice and sensible in speech and very well-spoken, the most cheerful of men and most humble, attractive to and popular with all the common people. He

was married to Guthormr Steigar-Þórir's daughter Ingibjǫrg. Their daughter
was called Maria, who was later married to Guðbrandr Skafhǫggsson.

CHAPTER SEVENTEEN

King Sigurðr was a man of large build and brown-haired, imposing in
appearance, not handsome, with a well-formed body, brisk in movements,
reticent and not generally sociable, kind to his friends and steadfast in mind,
not a great talker, of virtuous life and noble-minded. King Sigurðr was a
firm ruler and stern in punishment, kept the laws well, generous with wealth,
powerful and splendid.

King Óláfr was a tall and slender person, handsome in looks, cheerful and
humble, popular. When the brothers were kings in Norway, they abolished
many taxes that the Danes had imposed on the people while Sveinn Álfífuson
was ruling the land, and as a result they became extremely popular with the
common people and the men of rank.

[257] CHAPTER EIGHTEEN

King Óláfr caught a sickness that led to his death, and he is buried at
Christchurch in Niðaróss, and he was greatly mourned. After that the two
kings Eysteinn and Sigurðr ruled the land, but previously the three brothers
had been kings for twelve winters, five since Sigurðr came back to the country
and seven before. King Óláfr was seventeen winters old when he died, and
that was the eleventh of the calends of January.[360] When King Eysteinn had
been one winter in the east of the country, and Sigurðr was in the north, then
King Eysteinn remained for a large part of the winter in Sarpsborg.

CHAPTER NINETEEN

There was a powerful landowner called Óláfr in the Dale, a wealthy man. He
lived at Aumorð in Dalr mikli. He had two children. His son was called Hákon
faukr (Drifter?), and his daughter Borghildr. She was the fairest of women and
a sensible person and very knowledgeable. Óláfr and his children were for
a large part of the winter in Borg, and Borghildr was always in talk with the
king, and there were different opinions among people about their friendship.

Now the following summer King Eysteinn travelled to the north of the
country, while Sigurðr travelled to the east, and the next winter after that
King Sigurðr remained in the east of the country. He stayed for a long time
in Konungahella and extended that market town greatly. He built a great
fortification there and had a great ditch dug round it. It was built of turf and
stone. He had buildings erected inside the fortress. He had a church built

---

[360] 22nd December.

there. He let the Holy Cross stay in Konungahella and in doing so did not keep to his oaths that he had sworn in Jórsalaland, but he promoted tithes and almost everything else that he had sworn. But in placing the Cross east by [258] the frontier, he imagined that it would be a safeguard to the whole land, but it turned out to be most ill-advised to place that holy relic so much under the power of heathens, as it proved later.

Borghildr Óláfsdóttir heard the rumour wherein people slandered her and King Eysteinn about their talk and friendship. So she went to Borg and undertook a fast before an ordeal of carrying hot iron and carried the iron to clear her from this slander and was proved innocent. And when King Sigurðr heard about this, then he rode in one day a distance equivalent to two long days' travel, and turned up in Dalr at Óláfr's, and stayed there the night. Then he took Borghildr as his mistress and carried her away with him. Their son was Magnús. He was soon sent away for fostering north to Bjarkey in Hálogaland to Víðkunnr Jóansson, and he was brought up there. Magnús was the handsomest of all men and matured early in stature and strength.

CHAPTER TWENTY

King Sigurðr married Málmfríðr, daughter of King Haraldr Valdamarsson from the east from Hólmgarðr.[361] King Haraldr's mother was King Haraldr Guðinason of the English's daughter Queen Gyða gamla (the Old). Málmfríðr's mother was King Ingi Steinkelsson of the Svíar's daughter Kristín. Málmfríðr's sister was Ingilborg, who was married to Knútr lávarðr (Lord), son of King Eiríkr góði (the Good) of the Danes, son of Sveinn Úlfsson. Knútr and Ingilborg's children were Valdamarr, who took over the kingdom in Denmark after Sveinn Eiríksson, Margrét, Kristín and Katrín. Margrét was married to Stígr hvítaleðr (White Leather). Their daughter was Kristín, who was married to King Karl Sørkvisson of the Svíar. Their son was King Sørkvir.

[259] CHAPTER TWENTY-ONE

King Eysteinn and King Sigurðr were one winter both being entertained at a banquet in Upplǫnd, and each of them was staying at a different place. And since there was only a short distance between the residences where the kings were to receive their banquets, then people adopted this plan, that they should be both together at the banquets, alternately at the residences of each. First of all they were both together at the residence that belonged to Eysteinn. And in the evening when people began to drink, then the beer was not good, and people were silent. Then King Eysteinn spoke:

[361] This Haraldr is also known as Matislav, and was actually son of Valdamarr, son of Vissivaldr, son of Jarizleifr).

'But people are silent. That is a better custom with ale, that people should provide themselves with some amusement. Let us get ourselves some ale-cheer. Then people's fun will start up again. Brother Sigurðr, that will by everyone be thought most suitable that we engage in some entertaining conversation.'

King Sigurðr replies rather curtly:

'You be as expansive as you want, but let me be allowed to be silent before you.'

Then spoke King Eysteinn: 'This ale custom has often been indulged in, for people to choose their equals to compare themselves with. I wish that to be done here.'

Then King Sigurðr said nothing.

'I see,' says King Eysteinn, 'that I am going to have to start this entertainment. I will choose you, brother, to compare myself to. I adduce this, that we have equal titles and equal possessions. I can see no difference in our descent or upbringing.'

Then King Sigurðr replies: 'Do you not remember how I was able to force you over backwards, if I wished, and you were a winter older?'

Then King Eysteinn replies: 'I remember it no less clearly, how you were unable to take part in any sport that required agility.'

Then King Sigurðr spoke: 'Do you remember how it went with our swimming? I was able to duck you if I wished.'

King Eysteinn says: 'I could swim no less far than you, and I was no worse at swimming under water. And I was able to go on ice-skates so well that I knew no one that could compete with me at it, but [260] you could not do it any better than an ox.'

King Sigurðr says: 'I think it a nobler and more useful accomplishment to be well skilled with a bow. I believe you will not be able to get any use from my bow even if you use your feet to bend it.'

King Eysteinn replies: 'I am not as strong with a bow as you, but there is less difference between us in marksmanship, and I am much more skilled on skis than you, and that has always before been said to be a fine accomplishment.'

King Sigurðr says: 'In this there seems to be a great difference, that it is more princely that one that is going to be a superior over others should stand out in a crowd, be strong and a better fighter than others, and conspicuous and easily recognised when there are most people around.'

King Eysteinn says: 'It is a no less distinguishing feature for a man to be handsome, and he will also be easily recognised in a crowd. That also seems to me princely, for the finest outfit suits handsomeness. I am also much better acquainted with the law than you, and also, whatever we have to talk about, I am a much more fluent speaker.'

King Sigurðr replies: 'It may be that you have learned more legal tricks, for at that time I had other things to occupy me. And while no one questions your fluency, yet many also say that you are not too reliable in what you say, and little notice can be taken of what promises you make, you speak to please those that are present at the time, and that is not kinglike.'

King Eysteinn replies: 'The reason for this is that when people bring their suits before me, then I am concerned first to conclude everyone's business in a way that will please them best. Then there often comes another that has a suit against him, and then it is often necessary to make adjustments to reach a compromise so that both will be pleased. It also often happens that I promise something that someone asks, because I would like everyone to go from his audience with me happy. The alternative I can see, if I wished to follow it, is what you do, to promise [261] everyone something unpleasant, and I never hear anyone complaining of your failure to fulfil those promises.'

King Sigurðr says: 'People have said that the journey that I took abroad was pretty princely, but you sat at home in the mean time like your father's daughter.'

King Eysteinn replies: 'Now you have touched on a sore spot. I would not have started this conversation if I had had no answer to give to this. I think it more to the point that I fitted you out as I would my sister before you were ready to set out on your journey.'

King Sigurðr says: 'You must have heard that I fought very many battles in Serkland that you must have heard tell about, and that I won the victory in all of them and many kinds of treasure such that none like them have ever come into this country. I was considered the more highly where I met the noblest people, but I think you have not yet ceased to be a stay-at-home.'

King Eysteinn replies: 'I have heard that you fought some battles abroad, but of more benefit to our country was what I did meanwhile. I built five churches from their foundations, and I built a harbour by Agðanes where before there was no place to land, it being on the route for everyone travelling north or south along the coast. I also built the tower in Sinhólmssund and the hall in Bjǫrgyn, while you were chopping up blacks for the devil in Serkland. I guess that was of little benefit to our kingdom.'

King Sigurðr says: 'The furthest away I travelled on that journey was to the Jórðán, and I swam across the river. And out on the bank there is a sort of thicket. And in the foliage there I tied a knot, and I laid this spell on it, that you were to untie it, brother, or else be the subject of the curse that is attached to it.'[362]

---

[362] Cf. *Orkneyinga saga* (ÍF XXXIV) pp. 231–32.

King Eysteinn says: 'I shall not be untying the knot you have tied for me, but I could have tied a knot for you that you would have been much less able to untie, when [262] you sailed with a single ship into my fleet when you came ashore.'

After that they were both silent, and each of the two was angry. There were other things in the dealings between the brothers in which one could see that each wanted to make much of himself and his importance, and each wanted to be superior to the other, and yet the peace was kept between them as long as they lived.

CHAPTER TWENTY-TWO

King Sigurðr was in Upplǫnd at a certain banquet, and hot baths were prepared there. And while the king was in the hot bath and the tub had an awning over it, then he thought there was a fish gliding round in the bath beside him. Then he had such a great fit of laughter that he seemed out of his mind, and after that this afflicted him very frequently.

Her brothers gave King Magnús berfœttr's daughter Ragnhildr in marriage to Haraldr kesja (Halberd). He was King Eiríkr góði of the Danes' son. Their sons were Magnús, Óláfr, Knútr, Haraldr.

CHAPTER TWENTY-THREE

King Eysteinn had a great ship built in Niðaróss. It was built in shape and after the fashion in accordance with how Ormr inn langi had been, which Óláfr Tryggvason had had made. It also had a dragon-head on the front and a curved tail at the back and both were gilded. The ship floated high in the water, but the stems seemed somewhat smaller than would have been most suitable. He also had built there in Niðaróss boat sheds that were both so big that they were outstanding, and also built with the best materials and with very splendid craftsmanship.

King Eysteinn was at a banquet in Hústaðir at Stimr. There he caught a sudden illness that led to his death. He died on the fourth of the calends of September,[363] and his body [263] was conveyed north to Kaupangr and he is buried there in Christchurch. And people say that over no one's body have so many people in Norway stood as sad as over King Eysteinn's since the blessed King Óláfr's son Magnús was dead. Eysteinn was king in Norway twenty winters. And after King Eysteinn's death Sigurðr was sole king in the country as long as he lived.

[363] 29th August.

CHAPTER TWENTY-FOUR

King Níkolás Sveinsson of the Danes after that married Ingi's daughter Margrét, who had previously been married to King Magnús berfœttr, and the son of her and Níkolás was called Magnús inn sterki (the Strong). King Níkolás sent word to King Sigurðr Jórsalafari (Jerusalem-Farer) and asked him to give him troops and every kind of support from his kingdom and go with King Níkolás east past Svíaveldi to Smálǫnd to Christianise people there, as those that lived there did not observe Christianity, though some had accepted Christianity. At this time widely in Svíaveldi many people were heathen and many poorly Christian, since now there were some of the kings that had abandoned Christianity and maintained heathen worship, as did Blót-Sveinn (Heathen-Worship-) and later Eiríkr inn ársæli (of the Prosperous Seasons). King Sigurðr promised to go, and the kings arranged an appointment for meeting up in Eyrarsund. After that King Sigurðr called out a full levy from the whole of Norway, both in troops and ships. And when this army assembled, then he had a good three hundred ships. King Níkolás arrived much earlier at the arranged place and waited there a long time. Then the Danes complained bitterly, saying that the Norwegians would not be coming. After that they broke up the expedition force. The king went away and the whole army. After that [264] King Sigurðr arrived there, and he was displeased, sailing then east to Svimraróss and holding a meeting of his troops there, and King Sigurðr spoke about King Níkolás's breaking his word and it was agreed that they should carry out some depredation on his land because of this. They plundered a village that is called Tumaþorp and lies a short way from Lund and made their way after that east to the market town that is called Kalmarnar, and raided there and also on Smálǫnd, and exacted a payment in food from Smálǫnd, fifteen hundred cattle, and the Smálendingar accepted Christianity. After that King Sigurðr turned his army back and came into his kingdom with many very costly things and items of value that he had gained on this journey, and this expedition was known as the Kalmarnar expedition. This was the summer before the great darkness.[364] This was the only warlike expedition by sea that King Sigurðr undertook while he was king.

CHAPTER TWENTY-FIVE

King Sigurðr was on one occasion at his residence, and in the morning when the king was dressed, he was quiet and gloomy, and his friends were afraid that now one of his fits would be coming over him again. But the steward was a sensible and bold person and begged the king to speak, asking if he had

---

[364] The solar eclipse on the 11th August 1124.

had some news that was so significant that it prevented him being cheerful, or whether it was that he was not well pleased with the banquet, or whether there were any matters that people could do something about. King Sigurðr says that none of the things he had mentioned were the reason for it.

'But the reason for it is,' he says, 'that I am pondering on the dream that came to me in the night.'

'Lord,' he says, 'it ought to be a good dream, and we would very much like to hear it.'

The king [265] spoke: 'I dreamt I was outside here at Jaðarr, and I looked out to sea and saw there a great darkness and it was moving and was getting near here. It seemed to me as if it was a certain large tree, and the branches could be seen up above the water, but the roots went into the sea. And when the tree reached land, then it broke up, and the pieces of the tree were carried widely over the country, both over the mainland and the outlying islands, skerries and shores, and then I had a vision, so that I thought I was looking over all the coastal parts of Norway by the sea, and I saw into every inlet, that pieces of this tree had drifted in, and most of them were small but some larger.'

Then the steward replies: 'It is most likely with this dream that you yourself will be the best person to explain it, and we would very much like to hear you interpret it.'

Then spoke the king: 'It seems to me most likely that it will be a portent of the arrival of some person into this country, and he will establish himself here and his offspring will spread widely over this land and be of varying importance.'[365]

CHAPTER TWENTY-SIX

Jóan smjǫrbalti's (Butter Mound's) son Hallkell húkr (Bent) was a landed man in Mœrr. He travelled west across the sea and all the way to the Suðreyjar. There a man that was called Gillikristr came to see him from out in Ireland, saying he was King Magnús berfœttr's son. His mother was with him and said that his other name was Haraldr. Hallkell welcomed these people and took them with him to Norway and [he went] straight to see King Sigurðr with Haraldr and his mother. They announced their business to the king.[266] King Sigurðr discussed this matter before the leading men, so that each could put forward his thoughts as he felt inclined, but they all bade him decide for himself. Then King Sigurðr had Haraldr summoned to him and says this to him, that he will not refuse Haraldr the opportunity to carry out an ordeal to prove his paternity on condition that he will give a guarantee that even if his paternity is proved to be what he says it is, Haraldr shall not claim the

---

[365] Possibly the future King Sverrir, or perhaps Sigurðr slembidjákn.

kingdom while King Sigurðr or the king's son Magnús is alive, and these guarantees were given with oaths. King Sigurðr said that Haraldr was to tread over hot bars to prove his paternity, though this ordeal seemed rather demanding since he was now to perform the ordeal for his paternity, and not for the kingdom. He had already sworn oaths about that. But Haraldr agreed to this. He fasted in preparation for the ordeal by hot iron, and this ordeal was performed, which was the heaviest that has been performed in Norway, in which nine glowing ploughshares were put down, and Haraldr walked over them with bare feet with two bishops leading him. And three days later the results of the ordeal were examined. His feet were then unburned. After this King Sigurðr welcomed his kinship with Haraldr, but his son Magnús grew to hate Haraldr heartily, and many leading men sided with him. King Sigurðr was so confident of his popularity with all the people in the country that he asked that everyone should swear oaths that King Sigurðr's son Magnús should be king after him, and he received oaths from all the people in the country.

[267] CHAPTER TWENTY-SEVEN

Haraldr gilli (Servant [of Christ]) was a tall man and slenderly built, long in the neck, rather long in the face, black-eyed, dark haired, lively and quick, very Irish in his dress, short clothing and lightly clad. He was not fluent in the Norwegian language, found it very difficult to find words, and many people used to make a great deal of fun of this. Haraldr was sitting drinking on one occasion and was talking with another man and speaking about the west of Ireland. Part of what he said was that there were men in Ireland that were such fast runners that no horse could catch up with them in a race. The king's son Magnús heard this and said:

'Now he is lying again, as usual.'

Haraldr replies: 'It is true,' he says, 'that men can be found in Ireland that no horse in Norway will be able to overtake.'

They spoke a few words about this. They were both drunk. Then Magnús spoke:

'You shall wager your head on it, if you cannot run as hard as I ride my horse, and I will stake against you my gold ring.'

Haraldr replies: 'I do not say that I can run so hard. I can find the men in Ireland, that will run so, and I can bet about that.'

The king's son Magnús replies: 'I am not going to go to Ireland. We shall wager here, but not there.'

Haraldr then went to bed and would have nothing more to do with him. This was in Oslo. And the next morning, when early Mass was over, [268] Magnús was riding up through the streets. He sent word to Haraldr that he was to come there. And when he came, he was dressed like this: he had on

a coat and breeches with straps under the feet, a short cloak, an Irish hat on
his head, the shaft of a spear in his hand. Magnús marked out the course.
Haraldr spoke:

'You are intending too long a course.'

Magnús immediately decided on a much longer one, saying that it was
still too short. A large number of people were present. Then they had a race
along the course, and Haraldr kept up with the horse's shoulder. So when
they got to the end of the course, Magnús spoke:

'You are holding on to the saddle-girth, and the horse was pulling you.'

Magnús had a very swift Gautish horse. They now had another race back.
Then Haraldr ran the whole race ahead of the horse. So when they got to the
end of the course, then Haraldr asked:

'Was I holding on to the saddle-girth this time?'

Magnús says: 'This time you set off first.'

Then Magnús let his horse have a breather for a while and when it was
ready, then he drives his spurs into his horse and it was soon at a gallop.
Haraldr then stood without moving. Then Magnús looked back and shouted:

'Now run,' he says.

Then Haraldr ran and was soon ahead of the horse and a long way ahead,
and on to the end of the course. He arrived a long way in front, so he lay
down and sprang up and greeted Magnús when he arrived. After that they
went back to the town. But King Sigurðr had meanwhile been at Mass, and
it wasn't until after his meal during the day that he knew about all this. Then
he spoke angrily to Magnús:

'You say Haraldr is silly, but I think you are a fool. You have no knowledge
about people's way of life abroad. Didn't you know before that people abroad
train themselves to other sports than swilling drink and making themselves
crazy and incapable and losing their senses? Give Haraldr his ring and never
again try to make a fool of Haraldr as long as my head is above the ground.'

[269] CHAPTER TWENTY-EIGHT

Once when King Sigurðr was out with his ships, they sailed into harbour and
a certain merchant ship beside them, a trader with Iceland. Haraldr gilli's
place was in the middle part of the king's ship, and next to him to the fore
would lie Sveinn Hrímhildarson. He was son of Knútr Sveinsson of Jaðarr.
Sigurðr Sigurðarson was a splendid landed man. He was captain of a ship
there. It happened one day of fine weather—there was hot sunshine—many
men were going swimming both from the longships and from the merchant
ship. A certain Icelandic man who was swimming was having fun from
ducking those men that were not such good swimmers. People were laughing
at this. King Sigurðr saw and heard all this. After that he threw off his clothes

and leapt into the water and swam to the Icelander, takes hold of him and pushed him under the water and held him down, and straightway a second time, when the Icelander came up, the king forced him down and time and time again. Then spoke Sigurðr Sigurðarson:

'Are we to let the king kill the man?'

Someone said that no one was very keen to go up to him. Sigurðr spoke: 'There would be someone to do it if Dagr Eilífsson were here.'

After that Sigurðr leapt overboard and swam to the king, took hold of him and said:

'Don't kill the man. Everyone can now see that you are much the better swimmer.'

The king said: 'Let me go, Sigurðr. I am going to kill him! He wants to duck our men.'

Sigurðr replies: 'We must play together first, but you, Icelander, make for the shore.'

He did so, and the king let Sigurðr go and swam to his ship. Sigurðr did the same. And the king spoke, telling [270] Sigurðr not to be so bold as to come into his sight. Sigurðr was told, and he went up ashore.

CHAPTER TWENTY-NINE

In the evening, when people were going to bed, some men were playing games up on land. Haraldr was in the games, and told his boy to go out to the ship and prepare his bed and wait for him there. The boy did so. The king was gone to bed. So when the boy felt it was getting late, then he lay down upon Haraldr's bed. Sveinn Hrímhildarson spoke:

'It is quite disgraceful for valiant men to go out from home from their dwellings in order to drag up servant boys here to the same level as themselves.'

The boy replies, saying that Haraldr had directed him to come there. Sveinn Hrímhildarson said:

'We don't think it any great advantage having Haraldr lying here, without him dragging in here slaves or beggars.'

And he snatches up a net pole and struck the boy on the head so that blood flowed all over him. The boy immediately ran up ashore and tells Haraldr what had happened. Haraldr went straight out onto the ship and aft to the middle. He struck at Sveinn with a hand-axe and gave him a great wound on the arm. Haraldr went straight up ashore. Sveinn leapt up ashore after him. Then Sveinn's kinsmen rushed up and took Haraldr prisoner and were going to hang him. But while they were making preparations for this, then Sigurðr Sigurðarson went out onto King Sigurðr's ship and woke him. So when the king opened his eyes and recognised Sigurðr, he said:

'For this very thing, that you have come into my sight, you shall die, for I forbade you to do that.'

And the king leapt up. Sigurðr said:

'You will have a chance to do that, king, whenever you like, but other business is now more urgent first. Go as quickly as you can up [271] ashore and help your brother Haraldr. The Rygir are just going to hang him.'

Then the king spoke: 'God forbid! Sigurðr, call the trumpeter, have the troops summoned up by trumpet to follow me.'

The king leapt up ashore, and everyone that recognised him followed him and went to where the gallows was set up. He immediately took Haraldr into his charge, and all the people that the trumpet had summoned immediately rushed up to the king fully armed. Then the king said that Sveinn and all his companions were to go into exile, but at everyone's entreaty it was conceded by the king that they should be allowed to stay in the country and keep their possessions, but the wound would not be compensated for. Then Sigurðr Sigurðarson asked if the king wished him to go away now.

'That I do not wish,' says the king. 'I can never do without you.'

CHAPTER THIRTY

There was a man called Kolbeinn, young and poor, and King Sigurðr Jórsalafari's mother Þóra had his tongue cut out of his head, and there was no greater reason for this than that this young man Kolbeinn had eaten half a piece of meat from the king's mother's plate, saying that the cook had given it him, but did not dare to confess this before her. After that this man went without being able to speak for a long time. Einarr Skúlason mentions this in *Óláfsdrápa*:[366]

203.	A drinking-horn Hǫrn,[367] high-ranking,	*Geisli* 37
	had the tongue, for a young man's	*Skald* VII 37
	small fault, from the head severed	
	of the seeker of wealth, wretched.[368]	
[272]	We saw, certainly deprived of	
	speech, that hoard-breaker[369]	
	when we, some weeks later,	
	were at the place called Hlíð.	

---

[366] An alternative name for Einarr's poem *Geisli*, composed in honour of St Óláfr.

[367] *hvítings Hǫrn*: 'Freyja (goddess) of the drinking-horn', woman.

[368] *auðar beiðir*: 'seeker of wealth', man.

[369] *hodda brjótr*: 'breaker, destroyer of hoards of treasure', generous man.

He made his way after that to Þrándheimr and to Niðaróss and watched at Christchurch. But about the time of mattins on the later St Óláfr's day[370] then he fell asleep and dreamt he saw King Óláfr the Saint come to him and take hold of the stump of his tongue and pull it. And he awoke healed and thanked Our Lord joyfully and the blessed King Óláfr for having received health and grace from them, having gone there without speech and visited his holy shrine, and gone from there healed and clear-spoken.

CHAPTER THIRTY-ONE

Heathens captured a certain young man of Danish origin and took him to Vinðland and kept him there in bonds with other men captured in warfare. He was now in irons unguarded during the daytime on his own, but at night a farmer's son was then in the fetter with him so that he could not escape from him. But this poor man could never get any sleep or peace because of his grief and sorrow, thinking out many ways in which help might be available, very anxious about his difficult situation and afraid of both hunger and torments and expecting no ransoming from his kinsfolk, since they had twice previously freed [273] him from heathen lands with treasure, and so he felt sure that they would now find it both very difficult and costly to undertake it a third time. It is well for the man who does not have to endure such evil in this world as he felt he had endured. Now he could see nothing else for it but for him to run off and get away if it turned out to be possible. Next he sets about trying at night-time and kills the farmer's son, cuts off his leg and so makes away for the forest with the fetter. But the next morning when it got light, then they realise and go after him with two dogs that were accustomed to track down those that ran away, find him in the forest where he was lying and hiding from them. Now they capture him and beat him and baste him and ill-treat him in all sorts of ways. After that they drag him back, nevertheless grant him his life and no other kind of mercy, drag him to torture and put him straight into a dungeon where there were already present inside sixteen others, all Christians, fastened him there both in irons and other bonds as securely as they could. He felt the misery and torments he had had before were as it were a kind of shadow of all the evil that he had had previously.[371] He saw no one with his eyes in this prison that would beg for mercy for him. No one felt pity for this wretch except the Christians that there lay bound with him. They lamented and wept for his hurts and his distress and misfortune. So one day they put to him a plan, bidding him make a vow to the blessed King Óláfr and offer

---

[370] *Óláfsvǫkudagr inn síðari*: 'the night before the later feast of St Óláfr' (anniversary of his translation in 1031), 3rd August. Mattins was held in the early morning.

[371] Clearly an error for something like 'that he was having to suffer now'. Cf. *A History of Norway and The Passion and Miracles of the Blessed Óláfr* 2001, 43/9–11.

himself as servant in his glorious house if he by God's grace and his [274] intercession got out of this prison. Now he happily agreed to this and dedicated hinself immediately to that foundation as they bade him. The following night he thought he saw in a dream a man, not very tall, standing there next to him and speaking to him in this manner:

'Listen, you unhappy man,' he says, 'why do you not get up?'

He says: 'My Lord, what person are you?'

'I am King Óláfr, whom you invoked.'

'Oh ho, my good lord,' he says, 'I would gladly get up if I could, but I lie fastened in irons and moreover in a fetter with other men that here sit bound.'

After that he exhorts him and addresses him with these words:

'Stand up straight away and do not lose heart, indeed you are now free.'

Next he awoke and then told his companions what vision he had had. After that they told him to stand up and see if it was true. Up he stands and found that he was free. Now his other companions spoke, saying it would do him no good, since the door was locked outside and inside. Then an old man that was sitting there painfully bound put in a word and told him not to doubt the grace of that person that he had received release from.

'And he for this reason must have performed a miracle upon you, so that you should benefit from his grace and get free from here, not so that you should have more misery and torment. Now be quick about it,' he says, 'and find the doorway, and if you can get out, then you are saved.'

This is what he did, finds the doors already open, leaps out straight away and immediately off into the forest. They discovered this. Then they set on their dogs and went after him as swiftly as they could, but he is lying and hiding and sees clearly, poor fellow, where they are going after him. Now the dogs immediately lose the track when they passed up to him, and their eyes were all deceived so that no one could find him, and he was lying there in front of [275] their feet. They now turned back home from there and bewailed and lamented that they could not catch him. King Óláfr did not let him perish now he was come to the forest, gave him his hearing and complete health when they had previously battered and lambasted him all over his head so that he had gone deaf. Next he got on a ship together with two Christians who had long been tormented there, and they all together took advantage of this vessel with as much haste as they could and were conveyed on their way then from that escape route. After that he made his way to that holy man's house, having now become healed and capable of war service. Then he repented of his vows, went back on his word to the gracious king and ran away during the day and came in the evening to a certain farmer's who gave him lodging for God's sake. After that, in the night while he was asleep, he saw three maidens go up to him, fair and beautifully clothed, and they immediately addressed him and loaded him with great reproaches for having been so bold as to run away from the good king that had granted him such great grace, since he had freed him from fetters and the whole prison, and desert the dear lord whose service he had entered. Next he awoke full of fear and got up straight away early in the morning and told the master of the house, and the good farmer declared that he could do nothing other than return back home to the holy place. This miracle was written down in the first place by a person that had himself seen the man and the marks of the irons on him.

CHAPTER THIRTY-TWO

King Sigurðr had the market town at Konungahella developed so much that now there was no wealthier one in Norway, and he stayed there for long periods to guard the land. He had buildings erected in the royal palace grounds within the fortifications. He imposed on all the areas that were in [276] the vicinity of the market town, and also on the citizens, that every twelve months each man nine winters old or older was to carry to the fortification five stone war-missiles or another five stakes, and these must be sharpened at one end and five ells high.[372] Inside the fortification there King Sigurðr had Krosskirkja built. It was a timber church and very carefully constructed in materials and workmanship. When Sigurðr had been king four and twenty winters, Krosskirkja was consecrated. Then the king deposited there the Holy Cross and many other holy relics. It was known as Kastalakirkja (Fortification Church). He placed a table before the altar there that he had had made in Grikland. It was made of copper and silver and beautifully gilded, ornamented with enamelling and jewels. On it was a shrine that King Eiríkr eimuni (Ever Remembered) of the Danes had sent King Sigurðr, and a plenarius[373] written in gold lettering that the Patriarch had given King Sigurðr.

CHAPTER THIRTY-THREE

Three winters after Krosskirkja was consecrated, King Sigurðr caught a sickness. He was at the time staying in Oslo. He died there one night after Máríumass in Lent.[374] He was buried at Hallvarðskirkja, laid in the stone wall outside the choir on the southerly side. [277] King Sigurðr's son Magnús was there in the town at the time. As soon as King Sigurðr died, he took charge of all the king's treasuries. Sigurðr was king over Norway seven and twenty winters. He was forty years of age. And his time was good for the people of the country: there was then both prosperity and peace.

[372] About 230 cm or 7 ft 6 in.
[373] A Missal, or a book that included the Gospels and Epistles for use with High Mass.
[374] The Feast of the Annunciation, 25th March.

[278] **Magnúss saga blinda ok Haralds gilla**

CHAPTER ONE

King Sigurðr's son Magnús was accepted as king over the whole country in Oslo, as the common people had sworn to King Sigurðr. Then many men, including landed men, immediately entered his service. Magnús was more handsome than any man that was then in Norway. He was a proud-minded and stern person, a man of great ability, and his father's popularity was what most ensured him the friendship of the common people. He was a great drinker, avaricious, unfriendly and difficult to deal with.

Haraldr gilli was affable, cheerful, playful, humble, generous, so that he spared nothing for his friends, open to advice, so that he let others make decisions with him on anything they wanted. All this brought him friendship and praise. Many men of the ruling class then came to be on good terms with him no less than with Magnús.

Haraldr was then in Túnsberg when he learnt of the death of his brother King Sigurðr. He then immediately held meetings with his friends, and they decided to hold a Haugaþing there in the town. At that assembly Haraldr was accepted as king over half the country. It was declared to be oaths taken under duress when he had abjured his patrimony. Haraldr then got himself a following and appointed landed men. Troops soon gathered to him no whit less than to King Magnús. Then men passed between them and so matters stood for seven nights. But because Magnús got many fewer forces, then he saw no other [279] choice than to divide the kingdom between himself and Haraldr. Then it was so divided that each of them was to share half the kingdom that King Sigurðr had had with the other, while King Magnús had the ships and table service and things of value and all the money that King Sigurðr had had, and yet he was the less pleased with his share, and yet they ruled the land for some time in peace, though their thoughts ran on very different lines.

King Haraldr had a son that was called Sigurðr with Guthormr grábarði's (the Grey-Bearded's) daughter Þóra. King Haraldr married Rǫgnvaldr's daughter Ingiríðr. He was King Ingi Steinkelsson's son. King Magnús was married to Knútr lávarðr's daughter Kristín, sister of King Valdamarr of the Danes. Magnús got to be not fond of her and sent her back south to Denmark, and after that everything went worse for him. He came to be greatly disliked by her relatives.

CHAPTER TWO

When the two of them, Magnús and Haraldr, had been kings for three winters, they both stayed the fourth winter north in Kaupangr, and each invited the other to a banquet. And yet battle was always on the point of breaking out among their followers. So in the spring Magnús makes his way south along the coast with a naval force and gathered troops to himself, all that he could get, then seeking from his friends whether they were willing to give him support in order to deprive Haraldr of the kingdom and share with him such of his rule as he [280] thought fit, pointing out to them that Haraldr had abjured the kingdom. King Magnús got the agreement to this from many men of the ruling class. Haraldr travelled to Upplǫnd and took the inland route east to Vík. He also gathered troops to himself when he heard about King Magnús. And wherever they went each side slaughtered the other's cattle, and also slew their men for them. King Magnús had many more men, since he had had all the greater part of the land to collect troops from. Haraldr was in Vík on the eastern side of the fiord and gathered troops to himself, and then each was taking both men and animals that were the other's. His half-brother on the mother's side, Kristrøðr was now there with Haraldr, and many landed men were with him, and yet many more were with King Magnús.

King Haraldr was with his troops in a place called Fors in Ranríki, and travelled from there out to the sea. On the eve of the Feast of Láfranz[375] they took their evening meal in a place called Fyrirleif. Now the watchmen were on horses and were keeping mounted guard on all sides of the residence, and now the watchmen became aware of King Magnús's men, that they were now approaching the residence, King Magnús having nearly sixty hundred men, and Harald having fifteen hundred men. Then the watchmen came and brought King Haraldr intelligence, saying that King Magnús's troops were now come to the residence. Haraldr replies:

'What can my kinsman King Magnús want? It cannot be that he is wanting to fight with us.'

Then says Þjóstólfr Álason: 'Lord, you must make plans for yourself and our troops on the assumption that King Magnús will have been assembling an army all this summer for this purpose, that he is intending to fight as soon as he finds you.'

Then the king stood up and spoke with his men, bidding them take up their weapons:

'If Magnús wishes to fight, then we shall also fight.'

Next a trumpet was blown, and King Haraldr's troops went [281] right out of the residence into a certain enclosed arable field and there set up his standards. King Haraldr had two mailcoats, but his brother Kristrøðr, who was said to be a most valiant man, had no mailcoat. When King Magnús and his men saw King Haraldr's troops, then they drew up their forces and made

375 The Feast of St Laurentius (St Lawrence of Rome) is on 10th August.

such a long battle line that they would be able to encircle King Haraldr's troops entirely. So says Halldórr skvaldri:

> 204.   There Magnús got much longer—   *Haraldsdrápa* 1
>   he made use of a large following;   *Skald* II 493
>   warm carrion came to
>   cover the field—battle-lines.

CHAPTER THREE

King Magnús had the Holy Cross carried before him in battle. There was a great and tough battle fought there. The king's brother Kristrøðr had gone with his company to the middle of King Magnús's battle line and was striking out on both sides, and men were fleeing before him in two directions. So one powerful landowner that had been in King Haraldr's troop was stationed behind Kristrøðr. He swung up his halberd with both hands and thrust it through his shoulders and it came out through his breast, and Kristrøðr fell there. Then many that were standing nearby spoke, asking why he had done this so evil deed. He replied:

'Now he knows that, for they slaughtered my animals in the summer and took everything that was in the house, and forced me to go with them into their army. I had been planning this for him earlier if I had an opportunity.'

After that King Haraldr's troops began to take to flight, and he fled himself and all his troops. Now many of King Haraldr's troops had fallen. Ingimarr [282] Sveinsson of Askr, a landed man from King Haraldr's troops, received a mortal wound there and nearly sixty of his followers. King Haraldr then fled east into Vík to his ships and went after that to Denmark to see King Eiríkr eimuni and went to ask him for support. They met south in Sjáland. King Eiríkr welcomed him, most of all because they had sworn oaths of brotherhood. He granted Haraldr Halland for revenue and government and gave him eight unrigged longships. After that King Haraldr travelled north round Halland, and now troops joined him.

King Magnús subjected the whole country to himself after this battle. He gave quarter to everyone that was wounded and had them healed like his own men and then claimed the whole country as his. He had now all the best choice of troops that were in the country. But when they held discussions about their policies, then Sigurðr Sigurðarson and Þórir Ingiríðarson and all the most sensible people wanted them to take their host into the Vík and wait there to see if Haraldr was going to try to come from the south. King Magnús adopted a contrary course on his own initiative, going north to Bjǫrgyn and settling down there for the winter, and let his troops go away and his landed men to their estates.

[283] CHAPTER FOUR

King Haraldr came to Konungahella with the troop that had accompanied him from Denmark. Now they had gathered together to oppose him, the landed men and the citizens, and drew up a line of battle above the town. But King Haraldr disembarked from his ships and sent men to the troop of landowners and asked them not to shut him out of the country by warfare, saying he would make no other demands than he had a right to, and men passed between them. In the end the landowners abandoned their muster and submitted to King Haraldr. Then in order to get support for himself, Haraldr gave fiefs and revenues to landed men and improved rights to landowners that joined his party. After that large numbers of people gathered to King Haraldr. He travelled from the east round the Vík and gave satisfactory peace to all men except King Magnús's men. These he had plundered or killed wherever he found himself. And when he got from the east to Sarpsborg, he took there two of King Magnús's landed men, Ásbjǫrn and his brother Nereiðr, and offered them the choice that one of them should be hanged and the other thrown into the Sarp waterfall, and told them to choose for themselves. Ásbjǫrn chose to go into Sarp, since he was the elder and this death seemed the more terrible, and this was done. Halldórr skvaldri mentions this:

205.   Ásbjǫrn was, who kept his words   *Haraldsdrápa* 3
     to the lord badly—widely   *Skald* II 494
     the king fed the corpse-falcon[376]—
     forced to leap into Sarpr.
[284] Nereiðr the king had hanged on
     the harm-tree, cruel, of Sigarr's[377]
     foe; for speeches at followers'
     assemblies the spoiler of wave-fire[378] suffered.

After that King Haraldr travelled north to Túnsberg, and there he was welcomed warmly. There too a great army gathered round him.

CHAPTER FIVE

King Magnús was still in Bjǫrgyn and learnt of these events. Then he had called to a discussion with him the leading men that were in the town, and asked for advice about what was to be done. Then Sigurðr Sigurðarson replied:

[376] *vígs valr*: 'falcon of slaughter', carrion bird.
[377] *fjanda Sigars grandmeiðr*: 'harm-tree of Sigarr's enemy (Hagbarðr)', gallows. According to Saxo Grammaticus, Hagbarðr was hanged by Sigarr, whose daughter's lover he was. Cf. *Skáldsk* 103.
[378] *hrannbáls glǫtuðr*: 'destroyer of fire of wave (gold)', generous man.

'I can suggest a good plan for this situation. Have a small warship manned with good fellows and put on it as captain myself or another landed man to go to see your kinsman King Haraldr and offer him terms in accordance with the arbitration that just men who are in the country decide on between you, including this stipulation, that he is to have a half share of the kingdom with you. And it seems to me likely with the support of the persuasion of good men that King Haraldr will accept this offer and then there will be a settlement between you.'

Then King Magnús replied: 'And I do not want this course, for what would then have been the good of our getting the whole kingdom into our power last autumn, if we are now to share half the kingdom? So give some other advice.'

Then Sigurðr Sigurðarson replied: 'It seems to me as if your landed men are now staying at home and do not want to come to you, those that in the autumn asked you for leave to go home. You acted then much against my advice when you then dispersed so much the large numbers that we had, for I felt sure [285] that Haraldr and his companions would make back for the Vík as soon as they heard that there was no ruler there. Now there is another course available, and it is a bad one, and yet it may be that it will work. Send out guests[379] and other men with them, let them go and visit the landed men, and kill those that are now unwilling to respond to your distress, and give their posessions to some that you can rely on, though in the past they have been of little account. Let them then whip up the people, and having no fewer evil men than good, travel after that east against Haraldr with the troops that you can get, and fight.'

The king replied: 'It will be very unpopular to have many great men killed, and to raise up insignificant men. They have often failed us no less, and been less efficient in managing the country. I wish to hear yet more suggestions from you.'

Sigurðr replied: 'I am now finding it difficult to work out any plans, since you will not make terms and will not fight. Let us then go north to Þrándheimr where the main power of the country is well-disposed to us, taking whatever troops we can get the whole of the way there. Then it may be that the Elfargrímar will get tired of wandering about after us.'

The king replied: 'I don't want to flee from those we were chasing last summer. So give me better advice.'

Then Sigurðr stood up and was about to go off, and said:

'I shall give you the advice that I see you want to have and that will be carried out. Stay here in Bjǫrgyn until Haraldr comes with a crowd of warriors, and then you will have to endure one of two things, death or disgrace.'

And Sigurðr stayed no longer at this discussion.

[379] *Gestir* were officials of low rank at the king's court who could be sent to do particular tasks. (Cf. Vol. II, notes 119, 356.)

CHAPTER SIX

King Haraldr travelled from the east along the coast, taking a very large army. This winter was known as the Winter of Crowds. Haraldr came to Bjǫrgyn on Yule Eve and sailed his troops into Flóruvágar and did not want to fight over Yule because of the sanctity of the time. But King Magnús had his preparations made in the town. He had [286] a ballista set up out on Hólmr, and he had iron chains and some timber booms made and placed across the bay over below the royal palace. He had caltrops forged and thrown across onto Jóansvellir, and no more than three days over Yule were kept sacred so that no work was done. But on the last day of Yule,[380] then King Haraldr had the trumpet blown for the troop's departure. Nine hunded men had joined King Haraldr over Yule.

CHAPTER SEVEN

King Haraldr vowed to the blessed King Óláfr in return for victory for himself to have Óláfskirkja built there in the town at his own expense. King Magnús drew up his line of battle out in Christchurch churchyard, but Haraldr rowed first to Norðnes. So when King Magnús and his party saw that, they turned into the town and in to the head of the bay. But as they went in along the streets, then many townspeople leapt in to their courtyards and to their homes, while those that were going across to the open ground ran onto the caltrops. Then Magnús and his party saw that Haraldr had rowed all his troops across into Hegravík and were walking up there onto the ridge above the town. Then King Magnús turned out along the streets. Then his troops fled from him, some up onto the mountain, some up through Nunnusetr, some into churches or hid in other places. King Magnús went out onto his ship, but they had no chance to get away, since the iron chains blocked the exit. Moreover few men were accompanying the king, so that they were unable to do anything. So says Einarr Skúlason in *Haraldsdrápa*:

206.	They closed Bjǫrgyn's	*Haraldsdrápa* II 2
	bay week-long;	*Skald* II 545
[287]	no chance had thole-bulls[381]	
	to hurry off.	

A little later King Haraldr's men came out onto the ships. Then King Magnús was captured, but he was sitting back amidships on the high seat chest, and with him his uncle Hákon faukr, a most handsome-looking man and said to be not clever, and Ívarr Qzurarson and many others of his friends were now captured, and some already killed.

[380] *Affaradagr* 'Departure Day' (after the long Christmas holiday), 7th January.
[381] *há-Skrautar*: 'rowlock-Skrauti (bull)', See *Skald* for alternative interpretations.

CHAPTER EIGHT

King Haraldr now held meetings with his advisers and asked them to make plans with him, and at the conclusion of this meeting they reached the decision to deprive Magnús of his kingship in such a way that he could not call himself a king from then on. He was then handed over to the king's slaves, and they mutilated him, putting out his eyes and cutting off one leg and finally castrating him. Ívarr Qzurarson was blinded, Hákon faukr was killed. After this the whole country submitted to the rule of King Haraldr. Then it was diligently enquired who had been the greatest friends of King Magnús and who would know most about his stores of treasures and precious things. Magnús had had the Holy Cross with him since the Battle of Fyrileif had taken place, and he would not tell where it had got to now. Bishop Reinaldr in Stafangr was English and said to be very avaricious. He was [288] a close friend of King Magnús and it was thought most likely that he would have been got to look after great wealth and valuable things. He was sent for, and he came to Bjǫrgyn. Then this charge was brought against him and he denied it and offered to undergo an ordeal about it. Haraldr did not want that. He imposed a fine on the bishop of paying him fifteen marks of gold. The bishop said that he did not wish thus to impoverish his establishment, he would rather risk his life. After that they hanged Bishop Reinaldr out on Hólmr on the ballista. And as he walked to the gallows he shook his boot off his foot and spoke, swearing:

'I know of no more of King Magnús's wealth than what is there in the boot.'

In it there was a gold ring. Bishop Reinaldr was buried on Norðnes at Mikjálskirkja, and this deed was spoken very ill of.

After this Haraldr was sole king over Norway as long as he lived.

CHAPTER NINE

Five winters after the death of King Sigurðr great events took place in Konungahella. The prefects there then were Haraldr flettir's son Guthormr and Sæmundr húsfreyja (Housewife). He was married to the priest Andreas Brúnsson's daughter Ingibjǫrg; their sons Páll flípr (Flap Lip) and Gunni físs (Fart). Ásmundr was Sæmundr's illegitimate son. Andreas Brúnsson was a very distinguished person. He officiated at Krosskirkja. His wife was called Solveig. At this time there was with him being fostered and brought up Jóan Loptsson and he was eleven winters old. Jóan's father the priest Loptr Sæmundarson was also there at this time. [289] The priest Andreas and Solveig's daughter was called Helga, who was married to Einarr. It happened in Konungahella the next Saturday night after Easter week that there was a great noise out in the streets all over the town, as when the king passed through with all his followers, and dogs made such a racket that they could not be restrained and they broke out, and all those that got out went mad and bit whatever they came across, people and animals, and all that were bitten and bled then went mad, and all that were with young lost their foetuses and went mad. This portent happened nearly every night from Easter to the Ascension. The people were very frightened at this prodigy, and many decided to leave and sold their premises, going into the country or to other market towns, and it seemed most significant to all those that were most intelligent, and they feared that it must be a portent for great events that had then not yet come about, as it was. But the priest Andreas then spoke long and eloquently on Whit Sunday and finally turned his speech to this, that he spoke about the duties of the citizens, and told people to take heart and not to desert that so glorious place, rather to keep watch over themselves and take thought about what they should do and guard themselves against everything that might happen, against fire or hostility, and pray to God for grace for themselves.

CHAPTER TEN

Thirteen trading ships set out from the town and were making for Bjǫrgyn, and eleven were lost with men and goods and everything that was on them, but the twelfth was wrecked and the men were saved but the goods were lost. Then the priest Loptr travelled to Bjǫrgyn, and he was kept safe. It was on the Feast of Láfranz[382] that the trading ships were lost. King Eiríkr of the Danes and Archbishop Qzurr both sent word to Konungahella bidding them to be on their guard about their town, and saying that Vinðr had a great army out [290] and were raiding widely on Christians and were always being victorious. The citizens paid too little attention to their situation, neglecting and being oblivious of it the more time that passed from the terror that had been afflicting them.

On the Feast of Láfranz, while the address was being made before High Mass, King Réttiburr of the Vinðr came to Konungahella bringing five hundred and fifty Wendish warships, and on every warship there were forty-four men and two horses. Dúnímiz was the name of the king's nephew and Úniburr was the name of one leader that was in charge of a huge troop. These two leaders rowed up with part of their army along the eastern branch of the river round Hísing and thus came down to the town, and with part of their troop they sailed up the western branch to the town. They came ashore out by the stakes[383] and took the mounted force up there and rode there round Bratsáss

---

[382] Láfranzvǫkudagr: see note 375 above; the vigil (vaka) was the night before the Feast (not the day before). Cf. note 370 above..

[383] Poles driven into the river by the banks to moor ships to. Cf note 484 below.

and so up through the town. Andreas's son-in-law Einarr carried news of this up to Kastalakirkja, since the townspeople were there, having come for High Mass, and Einarr arrived while the priest Andreas was speaking. Einarr told people that an army was coming to the town with a large number of ships, though some of the troops were riding down round Bratsáss. Then many said that it must be King Eiríkr of the Danes there, and people expected to get quarter from him. Then all the people ran down into the town to their goods and armed themselves and went down to the jetties and then immediately saw that there was hostility and an overwhelming army. Nine ships trading with the eastern Baltic that were owned by merchants were afloat in the river at the jetties. The Vinðr attacked there first and fought with the merchants. The merchants armed themselves and defended themselves well and valiantly for a long time. A tough battle was fought there before the merchants were defeated. In this attack the Vinðr lost a hundred and fifty ships with all their crews. When the battle was at its fiercest, the townspeople were standing on the jetties and shooting at the heathens, but when the attack subsided the townspeople fled up into the town and after that all the people fled to the fortification, and people took [291] with them their valuable items and all the money that they could escape with. Solveig and her daughters and two other women went up inland. When the Vinðr had defeated the trading ships, they went ashore and mustered their troops and then their losses became apparent. Some of them ran into the town, some onto the trading ships, and they took all the goods that they wanted to take away with them. Next they set fire to the town and burnt it all and also the ships. After that they made for the fortification with all their troops and lined themselves up for their attack.

CHAPTER ELEVEN

King Réttiburr had an offer made to those that were in the fortification that they might go out and have quarter for their lives with weapons and clothing and gold. All without exception shouted in opposition and went out into the town, some shooting, some casting stones, some throwing stakes, and there was now a great battle. Now there were casualties on both sides, and many more among the Vinðr. Solveig came up to Sólbjargir and tells there what has happened. Then a war arrow was raised and sent to Skúrbágar. There a kind of drinking party was being held and many people were there. A farmer was there that was called Ǫlvir miklimunnr (Big Mouth). Now he leapt up immediately and took shield and helmet and a great axe in his hand and spoke:

'Stand up, good fellows, and take your weapons and let us go to help the townspeople, for it will be considered a disgrace by everyone that hears of it if we sit here and swill ale while good fellows are putting their lives in danger in the town for our sakes.'

Many replied speaking against it, saying that they would destroy themselves and be no help to the townspeople. Then Ǫlvir leapt up and spoke:

'Even if everyone stays behind, yet I shall go on my own, and the heathens shall lose one or two in exchange for me before I fall.'

He runs down [292] to the town. So people go after him, wanting to see how he was getting on, and also whether he could be given any help. But when he got so near the fortification that the heathens could see him, then eight men ran towards him fully armed. And when they met, the heathens leapt all round him. Ǫlvir swung up his axe and with the foremost point of the axe-blade struck the one that was behind him under the throat so that it cut his jaw and windpipe in two, and he fell over backwards onto his back. Then he swung the axe forwards in front of himself and strikes a second on the head and split him down to the shoulders. After that they attacked him and he now killed two more and was himself badly wounded, but the four that remained now fled. Ǫlvir ran after them, but a kind of dyke was before them, and two of the heathens leapt into it, and Ǫlvir slew them both. Now he stood and was stuck fast in the dyke. So two heathens of the eight got away. The men that had followed Ǫlvir took him and carried him with them to Skúrbágar, and he was fully healed. And people say that no one has carried out a nobler exploit. Two landed men, Philippus's brother Sigurðr Gyrðarson and Sigarðr, came to Skúrbágar with six hundred men, and Sigurðr turned back with four hundred men and was considered of little worth after that and lived a short time. Sigarðr went to the town wih two hundred men and fought there with heathens and fell there with his whole troop. The Vinðr attacked the fortification, but the king and the ships' captains stayed away from the battle. In one place where Vinðr were standing there was one man and he was shooting from a bow and was shooting a man to death with each arrow. Two men stood in front of him with shields. Then Sæmundr spoke with his son Ásmundr, saying that they should both shoot at the marksman at once.

'And I shall shoot at that one [293] that is holding the shield.'

He did so, and the man slid the shield in front of himself. Then Ásmundr shot between the shields and the arrow hit the marksman in the forehead so that it came out at the back of his head and he fell over backwards, dead. So when the Vinðr saw that, then they all howled like dogs or wolves. Then King Réttburr had someone call to them and offer them quarter, but they refused this. After that the heathens launched a fierce assault. Then there was one of the heathens that went so close that he went right up to the entrance to the fortification and thrust with his sword at the man that was standing inside the entrance, and men hurled missiles and stones at him, and he was without a shield but was so skilled in magic that no weapon could penetrate him. So the priest Andreas took consecrated fire and made the sign of the cross over it and cut tinder and set it on fire and fastened it on an arrow point and gave it to Ásmundr, and he shot this arrow at the man skilled in magic, and this shot pierced him so that he was completely done for, and he fell dead to the ground. Then the heathens made horrible sounds again as before, howling and snarling. Then all the people went up to the king. The Christians thought that now they were discussing whether they should withdraw. Now an interpreter that could understand Wendish understood what the leader that is named Úniburr was saying. He spoke as follows:

'This people is savage and terrible to deal with, and even if we took all the wealth that is in this place, then we might well give as much wealth again not to have come here, so many troops have we lost, and so many leaders. And to begin with today when we began to fight against the fortification, then they had for their defence missiles and spears, next they battered us with stones, and now they are hitting us with sticks like dogs. I can see therefore that their supplies for defence are on the wane, and we shall again make a fierce attack on them and try them.'

And it was as he said, that they were now shooting [294] with stakes, but in the first attack they had been using missiles and stones imprudently. So when the Christians realised that the stock of stakes was geting low, they cut each stake in two. But the heathens attacked them and made a fierce assault and rested in between. They got both weary and wounded. And in each of the pauses then the king again had them offered quarter, that they might keep their weapons and clothing and what they could themselves carry out across the fortification. Now Sæmundr húsfreyja was fallen, and what the men that were left decided to do was to give up the fortification and submit themselves to the power of the heathens, and this was a most unwise thing to do, for the heathens did not fulfil their promise, they took all the people, men and women and children, slew many, all those that were wounded or young and they felt would be a nuisance to take with them. They took all the wealth that was there in the fortification. They went in to Krosskirkja and plundered it of all its finery. The priest Andreas gave King Réttiburr a silver-mounted mace and his nephew Dúnímiz a gold finger-ring. As a result they felt sure that he must have some kind of authority in the place, and they honoured him more than other men. They took the Holy Cross and carried it away.[384] Then they took the table that stood before the altar, which King Sigurðr had had made in Grikland and brought to the country. They laid it down on the step in front of the altar. Then they went out of the church. Then the king said:

---

[384] There is no indication of how the Cross was recovered after King Magnús's refusal to reveal its whereabouts in ch. VIII above.

'This building has been ornamented out of great love for the God whose building this is, and it seems to me that little care must have been taken of the place or the building, since I can see that God is angry with those that are in charge of it.'

King Réttiburr gave the priest Andreas the church and the shrine, the Holy Cross, the plenarius book and four clerics. But the heathens burnt [295] the church and all the buildings that were within the fortification. But the fire that they had kindled in the church went out twice. Then they knocked down the church. Then it all began to blaze inside and burnt like the other buildings.

Then the heathens went to their ships with their plunder and mustered their troops, and when they realised their losses, then they took all the people as prisoners of war and divided them between their ships. Then the priest Andreas and his companions went to the king's ship and took with them the Holy Cross. Then the heathens were struck with fear because of the portent whereby such a great heat came over the king's ship that they all felt they were almost burning. The king told the interpreter to ask a priest why this was. He said that almighty God, in whom Christians believed, was sending them a sign of his anger, in that they, who refused to believe in their creator, dared to take in their hands the sign of his Passion.

'And there is so much power in the Cross, that such miracles have often taken place upon heathens, in some cases much plainer ones, when they have taken it in their hands.'

The king had the clerics shoved into the ship's boat, and Andreas carried the Cross in his bosom. They drew the boat forward the whole length of the ship and on past the beak and back along the other side to the raised deck, pushed it after that with poles and thrust the boat in to the jetties. After that during the night the priest Andreas went taking the Cross to Sólbjargir, and there was both storm of wind and torrential rain. Andreas conveyed the Cross to a good place of safety.

[296] CHAPTER TWELVE

King Réttiburr and his troops, what remained of them, went away and back to Vinðland, and many of the people that had been captured in Konungahella were for long after in Vinðland in bondage, while those that were ransomed and returned to Norway to their native places prospered very little. The market town at Konungahella has never recovered the success it had before.

Magnús, who had been blinded, went after that to Niðaróss and entered a monastery and took on a monk's habit. Then Hernes mikla in Frosta was conveyed to that foundation for his maintenance.

So Haraldr now ruled the land alone the following winter and granted all men reconciliation that wished to have it, then took many men into his service that had previously been with Magnús. Einarr Skúlason says this, that King Haraldr had two battles in Denmark, one off Hveðn, the other off Hlésey:

207. On untrusty warriors   *Haraldsdrápa* I 1
       you had, under high Hveðn,   *Mork* II 164
       thin blades with blood reddened,   *Fsk* 329
       brave raven's mouth-stainer.[385]   *Skald* II 542

And also this:

208. You fought a fight by Hlésey's   *Haraldsdrápa* I 2
       flat shore, Hǫarr's shirt-reddener,[386] *Mork* II 164
       strong, where storms buffeted   *Fsk* 329
       standards over warriors.   *Skald* II 542

[297] CHAPTER THIRTEEN

There is a man named Sigurðr that was brought up in Norway. He was said to be the priest Aðalbrikt's son. Sigurðr's mother was Saxi in Vík's daughter Þóra, sister of Sigríðr mother of King Óláfr Magnússon and of the king's brother Kári, who was married to Dagr Eilífsson's daughter Borghildr. Their sons were Sigurðr in Austrátt and Dagr. Sigurðr's sons were Jóan in Austrátt and Þorsteinn, Andreas daufi (the Deaf). Jóan was married to Sigríðr, sister of King Ingi and Duke Skúli.

Sigurðr was set to book-learning in his childhood and he became a cleric and was ordained deacon. But when he became full-grown in age and strength, then he was the most valiant of men and strong, a big man, and in all accomplishments he was superior to all those of his own age and almost everyone else in Norway. Sigurðr was at an early age a very overbearing man and an unruly man. He was known as slembidjákn (Careless Deacon). He was the most handsome of men, with rather thin and yet fine hair. Then it got about concerning Sigurðr that his mother says that his father was Magnús berfœttr. So as soon as he became independent in his way of life, then he neglected the clerical life, then left the country. He stayed a long time on his travels. Then he set out on a journey to Jórsalir and reached the Jórdán and visited the holy relics, as is customary with pilgrims. And when he got back, then he spent time on [298] trading voyages. One winter he was present for some time in Orkney. He was with Jarl Haraldr at the fall of Þorkell fóstri (foster-father) Sumarliðason. Sigurðr was also up in Scotland with King David of the Scots. He was regarded very highly there. After that

---

[385] *hrafns munnlituðr*: 'colourer of the raven's mouth (with blood)', warrior.
[386] *Hǫars serkrjóðr*: 'reddener (with blood) of Óðinn's shirt (coat of mail)', warrior.

Sigurðr travelled to Denmark and according to his own and his followers' account, he had there performed an ordeal about his paternity and it was proved that he was King Magnús's son, and there were five bishops present. So says Ívarr Ingimundarson in Sigurðarbǫlkr:[387]

209.	Five bishops,	Sigurðarbálkr 10
	felt to be foremost,	Mork 172
	ran the ordeal	Fsk 326
	for the ruler's kin.	Skald II 507
	Proofs appeared	
	that of this powerful king,	
	this munificent one,	
	Magnús was father.	

Haraldr's friends said that this had been a deceit and lie of the Danes.

CHAPTER FOURTEEN

When Haraldr had been king over Norway for six winters, Sigurðr came to Norway and went to see his brother King Haraldr, meeting him in Bjǫrgyn, went straight to see him, revealed his paternity to the king and asked the king to accept his kinship with him. The king gave [299] no immediate decision on that matter and put it before his friends, having discussions and meetings with them. And the outcome of their discussions was that the king brought charges against Sigurðr about his having been present at the killing of Þorkell fóstri west of the sea. Þorkell had accompanied King Haraldr to Norway in the beginning when he had come to the country. Þorkell had been a very close friend of King Haraldr. This case was pressed so hard that Sigurðr was adjudged because of it to be guilty of a capital crime, and on the authority of landed men it now came about that late one evening some guests[388] went to where Sigurðr was and called him to go with them and took a kind of small boat and rowed away from the town and south to Norðnes with Sigurðr. Sigurðr sat aft on a chest and considered his situation and suspected that this might be a plot. He was dressed like this, he had on dark breeches and coat and a cloak with ties as overcoat. He was looking down in front of himself and had his hands on the cloak-ties, sometimes taking them off his head, sometimes putting them on his head. And when they had got round a certain headland—they were merry and drunk and were

[387] A þáttr in Morkinskinna relates that Ívarr Ingimundarson was an Icelander of good family (Morkinskinna II 102–05). According to Skáldatal he composed about Magnús berfœttr, Eysteinn Magnússon and Sigurðr Jórsalafari as well as Sigurðr slembidjákn. Morkinskinna preserves 45 stanzas of his Sigurðarbǫlkr.

[388] See note 379 above.

rowing furiously and little suspected anything—then Sigurðr stood up and went to the side, and the two men that had been set to guard him stood up and went to the side, both grasping the cloak and holding it away from him, just as it is common to do with high-ranking men. And as he suspected that they might be holding other clothing of his, then he grabbed both of them, one with each hand and threw himself overboard with the whole lot, and the boat glided on forward a long way, and they took a long time to turn it and there was a long delay before they were able to rescue their men. And Sigurðr swam away so far under water that he was up ashore before they had turned their ship to follow him. Sigurðr was the fastest [300] of runners and he makes his way up inland, and the king's men went and searched for him all night and could not find him. He was lying in a kind of cleft in the rock. He got very cold. He took off his breeches and cut a hole in the seat and pulled them on [over his head] and put his arms out [through the legs] and so saved his life for the time being. The king's men went back and were unable to conceal their failure.

CHAPTER FIFTEEN

Sigurðr realised that it would not help him to go to see King Haraldr and was now in hiding all the autumn and the first part of the winter. He stayed in the town in Bjǫrgyn with a certain priest and was plotting how he might bring about King Haraldr's death, and there were very many men in this conspiracy with him including some of those that were now followers of King Haraldr and members of his household, they having earlier been followers of King Magnús. They were now on very good terms with King Haraldr, so that there was always one of them that was sitting at the king's table. In the evening on Lucia's day[389] there were two men sitting there who were talking together. One of them spoke to the king:

'Lord, we have now referred the judgment in our dispute to you for the final decision, and we have each of us wagered a bowl of honey. I say that tonight you will lie with your wife Queen Ingiríðr, but he says that you will lie with Þóra Guthormsdóttir.'

Then the king replied with a laugh, and completely unaware that this question was posed with so much cunning, saying:

'You will not win your bet.'

From this they felt certain where he would [301] be to be found that night, though the bodyguard was still kept over the chamber that most people thought the king would be in and that the queen slept in.

[389] St Lucia's day is 13th December.

CHAPTER SIXTEEN

Sigurðr slembidjákn and some men with him came to that chamber where the king was asleep, and broke down the door and went in there with weapons drawn. Ívarr Kolbeinsson was the first to wound King Haraldr, but the king had lain down drunk and was fast asleep and awoke to men attacking him and spoke while still unconscious:

'You are treating me roughly, Þóra!'

She leapt up at this and spoke:

'Those that wish you worse than I are treating you roughly.'

King Haraldr lost his life there, but Sigurðr went off with his men. Then he had the men called to him that had promised to be his supporters if he got King Haraldr's life put an end to. Then Sigurðr and his men went to a certain warship and set men to the oars and rowed out into the bay below the royal palace. Then day began to dawn. Then Sigurðr stood up and spoke with those that were standing on the royal jetty, and announced the killing of King Haraldr at their hands and requested acceptance by them and that they should take him as king, as his birth entitled him to be. Then crowds of men from the royal palace rushed there onto the jetties, and all swore as if they spoke with one mouth, saying that it should never be that they granted allegiance and service to a man that had murdered his brother.

'But if he was not your brother, than your descent does not entitle you to be king.'

They clashed their weapons together, condemning [302] them all as outlaws and proscribed. Then the royal trumpet was blown and all the landed men and members of the king's following were summoned together, and Sigurðr and his men saw their most attractive course was to be off. He sailed to Norðr-Hǫrðaland and there held an assembly with landowners. They submitted to him and gave him the title of king. Then he travelled in to Sogn and held an assembly there with landowners. He was also accepted there as king. Then he travelled north into Firðir. He was welcomed there. So says Ívarr Ingimundarson:

210.	The Hǫrðar and Sygnir,	*Sigurðarbálkr* 13
	Haraldr having fallen,	*Mork* 179
	accepted the generous	*Fsk* 330
	son of Magnús.	*Skald* II 509
	There swore many	
	men at assembly	
	to be like brothers	
	to the lord's son.	

King Haraldr was buried in the old Christchurch.

[303] **Haraldssona saga**

CHAPTER ONE

Queen Ingiríðr together with landed men and the following that King Haraldr had had, decided this, that a fast ship should be dispatched and sent north to Þrándheimr to tell of King Haraldr's fall, and this too, that the Prœndir were to take as king King Haraldr's son Sigurðr, who was now there in the north and being fostered by Sáða-Gyrðr (Seed-) Bárðarson, but Queen Ingiríðr immediately travelled east into Vík. Ingi was the name of her and King Haraldr's son, who was being fostered there in the Vík with Gyrðr Lǫg-Bersason's (Law-) son Ámundi. So when they got to the Vík, Borgarþing was summoned. Ingi was taken as king there. He was now in his second winter. Ámundi and Þjóstólfr Álason and many other great leaders supported this resolution. And when the news reached Þrándheimr in the north that King Haraldr was deprived of life, then King Haraldr's son Sigurðr was taken as king there, and this resolution was supported by Óttarr birtingr (Trout) and Pétr Sauða-Úlfsson and the brothers Guthormr Ásólfsson of Rein and Óttarr balli (the Dangerous) and a large number of other leaders. And nearly all the people now switched their allegiance to the brothers, most of all because their father was said to be saintly, and the land was sworn to them with the stipulation that it should submit to no other person as long as any of the sons of King Haraldr was alive.

[304] CHAPTER TWO

Sigurðr slembidjákn made his way north past Staðr, and when he got to Norð-Mœrr, there were already letters and tokens for him from the influential men that had switched their allegiance to King Haraldr's sons, and he met with no acceptance or success. So since he himself had only a small following, they now decided to make their way in to Þrándheimr, as he had previously sent word on his own behalf in there to his friends and to the friends of King Magnús, who had been blinded. So when he got to Kaupangr, he rowed up into the river Nið and got his cables ashore in the royal palace grounds and had to retreat from there because the people all opposed him. They sailed after that to Hólmr and took away out of the monastery there Magnús Sigurðarson against the wishes of the monks. He had before this taken vows as a monk. A number of people say that Magnús left of his own free will, since it was done in order to better his situation and he was hoping thereby to get troops to support him, and so it happened and turned out. And this was directly after Yule. Sigurðr and his party went out along the fiord. After that they were pursued by Bjǫrn Egilsson, Gunnarr of Gimsar, Halldórr Sigurðarson,

Áslákr Hákonarson and the brothers Benedikt and Eiríkr and the following that had previously been with King Magnús, and a number of other men. They went with their band south past Mœrr and right on past the entrance to Raumsdalr. There they divided their troop, and Sigurðr slembidjákn travelled west across the sea straight away during the winter, but Magnús travelled to Upplǫnd, hoping for many troops there, which he got. He stayed there for the winter and all through the summer there in Upplǫnd and now had a large troop. So King Ingi went with [305] his troop, and they met in the place that is called in Mynni. A great battle took place there, and King Magnús had a larger force. It is said that Þjóstólfr Álason had King Ingi in his lap while the battle was raging, and went beneath the standard, and Þjóstólfr got into great distress because of his tiredness and the attack, and people say that it was then that Ingi caught the sickness that he suffered from all the rest of his life, and his back became crooked and one leg was shorter than the other, and he was so lacking in strength that he had difficulty in walking as long as he lived. Then the casualties started to go against King Magnús's men, and these men fell that were in the van of the battle line, Halldórr Sigurðarson and Bjǫrn Egilsson, Gunnarr of Gimsar and a large part of Magnús's force, before he was willing to flee or ride away. So says Kolli: [390]

211.	You waged east by Mynni	*Ingadrápa* 1
	arrow-storm,[391] and soon after,	*Mork* II 181
	ruler, the host with swords rendered	*Skald* II 528
	raven's food, wearing helmets.	

And also this:

212.	Felled lay all his forces	*Ingadrápa* 2
	before the ring-generous	*Mork* II 182
	lord to leave was willing.	*Skald* II 529
	The war-skilled king heaven . . .[392]	

Magnús fled from there east to Gautland and from there to [306] Denmark. At that time Jarl Karl Sónason was in Gautland. He was mighty and ambitious. Magnús blindi (the Blind) and his men used to say, wherever they came into the presence of leaders, that Norway would lie open to grabs if any great leaders wanted to go for it, as there was no king over the country and the government of the realm was in the hands of landed men, while

---

[390] Kolli inn prúði (the Magnificent), as he is called in *Morkinskinna*, is unknown apart from the three stanzas attributed to him there, and two further stanzas of 'a *drápa* about King Ingi' that may belong to the same poem.

[391] *oddhríð*: 'point-storm', battle.

[392] This is probably part of a *klofastef* 'split refrain', but the rest does not survive.

those landed men that were first appointed as rulers had all fallen out with each other because of their jealousy. So because Jarl Karl was greedy for power and open to persuasion, he now gathers troops and rides from the east into the Vík, and many people submitted to him out of fear. So when Þjóstólfr Álason and Ámundi heard about this, then they went against him with whatever troops they could get, and with them took King Ingi. They met Jarl Karl and an army of Gautar east in Krókaskógr and there fought another battle, and King Ingi was victorious. There Jarl Karl's uncle Munán Ǫgmundarson fell. Munán's father Ǫgmundr was son of Jarl Ormr Eilífsson and Jarl Finnr Árnason's daughter Sigríðr. Ǫgmundr's daughter Ástríðr was Jarl Karl's mother. Many fell at Krókaskógr, but the jarl fled east out of the forest. King Ingi drove them all the way eastwards out of his kingdom, and their expedition came to be regarded as most contemptible. So says Kolli:

	213.	I'll show how the ruler reddened—	*Ingadrápa* 3
		raven over wounds of Gautar	*Mork* II 183
		stooped; eagle was not seldom	*Skald* II 530
		sated—bright wound-icicles.[393]	
[307]		Repaid were—your power	
		is proven—strengtheners	
		of sword-noise,[394] who started	
		strife, at Krókaskógr.	

CHAPTER THREE

Magnús blindi made his way to Denmark to see Eiríkr eimuni, and he had a warm reception there. He invited Eiríkr to accompany him into Norway, if Eiríkr would like to subject the land to himself and take an army of Danes into Norway, saying that if he comes with the backing of an army, that no one in Norway will dare to let fly a spear against him. So the king responded by calling out a levy. He went with six hundred ships north into Norway, and Magnús blindi and his men joined in this expedition with the king of the Danes. But when they got to the Vík, then they proceeded with some restraint, [acting] sensibly and peaceably on the eastern side of the fiord, and when they got to Túnsberg with their troops, they found there before them a great gathering of King Ingi's landed men. Gregorius's brother Vatn-Ormr (Lake-) Dagsson had most authority over them. The Danes were unable to get ashore there or to get themselves water. Many of them were killed there. Then they sailed in along the fiord to Oslo, and there they came up against Þjóstólfr Álason. It is said that they wanted to have the blessed Hallvarðr's

---

[393] *sáríss*: 'ice of wounds', weapons.
[394] *sverða glaumherðǫndum*: 'strengthener of sword-noise (battle)', warrior.

shrine carried out of the town in the evening and as many as could manage it got under the shrine and they were unable to carry it further than just out onto the floor of the church. But in the morning when they saw that the army was travelling in to Hǫfuðey, then four men carried the shrine up out of the town, and Þjóstólfr and all the townspeople were accompanying the shrine.

[308] CHAPTER FOUR

King Eiríkr and his men made their way up into the town, and some ran after Þjóstólfr and his men. Þjóstólfr shot a spiked shaft at a man that is called Áskell—he was King Eiríkr's forecastle man—and struck him under the chin so that the point appeared out at the back of his head, and Þjóstólfr thought he had never achieved a better shot, for there was no bare skin visible on him except just that spot. The blessed Hallvarðr's shrine was conveyed up into Raumaríki and was there for three months. Þjóstólfr travelled round Raumaríki and he gathered troops during the night and came down to the town in the morning. King Eiríkr had Hallvarðskirkja set on fire and various other places through the town and burnt absolutely everything up. Next Þjóstólfr came down with a large troop, and King Eiríkr set off with his naval force and they could nowhere get ashore on the northern side of the fiord because of the gathering of landed men, and wherever they sought to go ashore, then they left five or six or more lying behind. King Ingi lay in Hornborusund with a large force. So when King Eiríkr heard that, then he turns back south to Denmark. King Ingi went after them and picked up from them all that they could. And people say that no worse expedition has been undertaken with a large force into another king's realm, and King Eiríkr was displeased with Magnús and his men and thought they had made a great fool of him when he had entered on this expedition, saying that never again would he be their friend as he had been before.

[309] CHAPTER FIVE

Sigurðr slembidjákn came that summer from west across the sea to Norway. And when he heard of his kinsman Magnús's misfortune, he realised that now he would get little support in Norway. He now sailed all along the outer route south along the coast and ended up in Denmark. He sailed into Eyrarsund. But south off Erri he came across some warships of Vinðr and joined battle with them and was victorious, cleared there eight warships and killed there a large number of men, and hanged some. He also fought a battle by Mǫn with Vinðr and was victorious. Then he laid his course from the south and sailed up into the Elfr by the eastern branch and defeated there three ships from the force of Þórir hvinantorði (Dung Beetle or Whistling

Auk?) and his nephew, Haraldr kesja's son Óláfr. Óláfr's mother was King
Magnús berfœttr's daughter Ragnhildr. He chased Óláfr ashore. Þórir was
in Konungahella and had a host waiting there. Sigurðr sailed there and they
shot at each other and men fell from both sides and many were wounded.
Sigurðr's party were unable to get ashore. Úlfheðinn Sǫxólfsson, a man
from the north of Iceland, Sigurðr's forecastle man, fell there. Sigurðr sailed
away and laid his course north into the Vík and plundered widely. He lay in
Portyrja on Lungarðssíða and laid an ambush for ships that were going into
or out of the Vík, and plundered them. The people of Túnsberg sent a force
against him and took him unawares, so that Sigurðr and his men were ashore
and sharing out their booty. Some troops came down upon them, and they
positioned their ships across the harbour outside of them. Sigurðr leapt on
his ship and rowed out at them, but Vatn-Ormr's ship was the closest there,
and he drew back. But Sigurðr rowed out past them and got away on a single
ship, but many of his troops fell. So this was composed:

[310] 214.   Poorly in the fight Vatn-Ormr   *Mork* II 190
               at Portyrja did perform.   *Skald* II 836

CHAPTER SIX

After that Sigurðr slembidjákn sailed south to Denmark, and a man was lost
from his ship who was called Kolbeinn Þorljótsson from Bataldr. He was
in a boat in tow that was tied to the ship, and they were sailing fast. Sigurðr
wrecked the ship when they got south, and he stayed in Álaborg during the
winter. And the following summer, then he and Magnús travelled from the
south with seven ships and reached Listi unexpectedly during the night and
sailed their ships to land. Waiting there was Benteinn Kolbeinsson, a follower
of King Ingi and a most valiant man. Sigurðr and his party went ashore there
at daybreak and arrived unexpectedly and captured them in the building and
were going to set fire to the residence, but Benteinn got out into a kind of
storehouse in armour and well equipped with weapons and stood inside the
entrance with drawn sword and had a shield before him and a helmet on his
head, being now ready for defence. The entrances were rather low. Sigurðr
asked why they did not go in. They replied that no one was keen to do that. So
while they were discussing this most eagerly, Sigurðr leapt into the building
past him. Benteinn struck after him and missed. After that Sigurðr turned
round to him and they exchanged few blows before Sigurðr killed him and
carried his head out in his hand. They took all the valuables that were in the
residence, after that went to their ships. And when King Ingi and his friends
and Kolbeinn's sons, Benteinn's brothers Sigurðr and Gyrðr, learnt of the death
of Benteinn, then the king sent out a troop against Sigurðr and his party, and

went along himself, taking a ship from Hákon pungelta (Curry Bag), [311] son of Páll, grandson of Áslákr Erlingsson of Sóli and cousin of Hákon magi (Belly). Ingi chased Hákon up ashore and took every last thing from them. These fled away in to Firðir, Eindriði in Gautdalr's son Sigurðr storkr (Stork) and his brother Eiríkr hæll (Peg), and Grímr from Vist's son Andreas kelduskítr (Bog Dirt), but Sigurðr and Magnús and Þorleifr skjappa (Half-Bushel) sailed north on three ships by the outer route to Hálogaland. Magnús was during the winter in Bjarkey with Víðkunnr Jónsson. But Sigurðr cut the stems off his ship and knocked holes in it and sank it down in the inner part of Ægisfjǫrðr, and Sigurðr stayed during the winter in Tjaldasund on Hinn in a place called Gljúfrafjǫrðr. In the inner part of this fiord there is a cave in the cliff. There Sigurðr and his party, more than twenty men, stayed during the winter, and closed off the entrance to the cave so that the entrance could not be seen from the beach. Sigurðr was provided with food during the winter by Þorleifr skjappa and Einarr, son of Ǫgmundr of Sandr and Guðrún, daughter of Ari of Reykjahólar's son Einarr. That winter, it is said, Sigurðr had Lapps build him two light ships deep in the fiord and they were fastened together with sinews and there were no nails in them, and they had withies instead of knees [under the beams], and they had twelve rowers on each side. Sigurðr stayed with the Lapps while they were building the ships, and the Lapps had beer there and put on a banquet there for him. Afterwards Sigurðr composed this:

[312] 215. It was good in the *gammi*[395]   *Mork* II 193
       when we gladly drank,   *Skald* II 499
       and the glad king's son
       would go between benches.
       Cheer was not lacking
       at the cheerful drinking.
       Thane gladdened thane
       there as everywhere.

These light ships were so fast that no ship could overtake them in the water, as this composition says:

     216. Only few can keep up with   *Mork* II 194
       the fir-ship from Hálogaland: *Skald* II 837
       under sail speeds
       the sinew-bound vessel.

So in the spring Sigurðr and Magnús travelled from the north with the two light ships that the Lapps had built. And when they got to Vágar, they killed the priest Sveinn and his two sons there.

[395] a Lappish hut.

CHAPTER SEVEN

Sigurðr then travelled south into Víkar and there captured Viljálmr skinnari (Skinner)—he was one of King Sigurðr's landed men—and secondly Þóraldi keptr (Chops), and killed them both. Then Sigurðr travelled south along the coast and met Styrkárr glæsirófa (Splendid Tail) south there by Byrða when he was travelling from the south from Kaupangr, and they killed him. And when Sigurðr got south to Valsnes, then he met Svína-Grímr (Swine-) and had his right hand cut off. Then he went south to Mœrr beyond Þrándheimsmynni and there captured Heðinn harðmagi (Tough Belly) and Kálfr [313] kringluauga (Circle Eye), and let Heðinn go away, but they killed Kálfr. King Sigurðr and his foster-father Sáða-Gyrðr heard about Sigurðr's movements and what he was up to. Then they sent men to find him. They then put in charge Kálfr inn rangi's (the Crooked's) son Jón kaða (Hen), brother of Bishop Ívarr, and secondly the priest Jón smyrill (Merlin). They manned Hreinninn, which had two and twenty rowing benches and was the swiftest of all ships. They went to look for Sigurðr and could not find him and returned with little glory, for people say that they saw them and dared not attack them. Sigurðr travelled south to Horðaland and got to Herðla. There Laxa-Páll's (Salmon-) son Einarr had an estate, and he was gone in to Hamarsfjorðr to the Rogation Days assembly.[396] They took all the valuables that were in the house and a twenty-five-benched longship that was owned by Einarr and his four-winter-old son who was staying with his workman. There were some that wanted to kill the boy, but some to carry him off with them. The workman said to them:

'It will be no stroke of luck for you to be able to kill this boy, and no benefit to you to carry him off. That is my son, and not Einarr's.'

And because of what he said they left the boy behind, and they went off. So when Einarr came back, then he gave the workman money to the value of two ounces of gold and thanked him for what he had done and said he would be his friend for ever after. This is what Eiríkr Oddsson says, who first wrote down this account, that he heard Einarr Pálsson tell of these events in Bjorgyn.

Sigurðr then travelled south along the coast and right on east to Vík and met Finnr Sauða-Úlfsson east at Kvildir where he was going round collecting King Ingi's land dues, and had him hanged. They then travelled south to Denmark.

[314] CHAPTER EIGHT

The Víkverjar and Bjorgynjarmenn said it was a disgrace that King Sigurðr and his friends sat doing nothing north in Kaupangr, though the slayers of

---

[396] Rogation Days are days of prayer and fasting on the three days before Ascension day.

his father were sailing the high seas outside Þrándheimsmynni, and King
Ingi and his troops were staying east in Vík in danger and defending the land
and had fought many battles. So King Ingi sent a letter north to Kaupangr.
In it stood these words:

'King Haraldr's son King Ingi sends God's and his own greetings to his
brother King Sigurðr and to Sáða-Gyrðr, Ǫgmundr sviptir (Loss), Óttarr
birtingr and all landed men, followers and housecarls and all the common
people, rich and poor, young and old. All are acquainted with the problems
that we have and also with our youth, that you are reckoned to be five
winters old, and I three winters. We can undertake nothing except what we
do with the help of our friends and kind people. It seems to me that now I
and my friends are more afflicted with the trouble and distress that we both
suffer than you or your friends. Now be so kind as to go to see me as soon
as possible and with as many men as possible, and let us be both together
whatever happens. Now he is our greatest friend who continues to ensure
that we may be always on the best of terms and treated in as equal a manner
as possible in everything. But if you neglect to come and are unwilling to
respond to my urgent message again, as you have done before, you must
be prepared for me to come against you with a force. Let God then judge
between us, for we cannot go on any longer with things as they are, staying
with such great expense and large numbers as are necessary here because of
the hostility, while you are taking half of all the [315] land dues and other
revenues in Norway. Live in the peace of God!'

Then Óttarr birtingr replies and stood up at the assembly and spoke.

CHAPTER NINE

'These are King Sigurðr's words in reply to his brother King Ingi, that may
God thank him for his kind greeting and also the labour and difficulty that
you and your friends have had in this kingdom in our common time of need.
And though some things seem rather harsh in the words of King Ingi to his
brother Sigurðr, yet there is a great deal in what he says in many respects.
Now I will make known to you my mind and find out whether the wishes of
King Sigurðr and other men of the ruling class are in accordance with it, that
you, King Sigurðr, should also make ready such force as is willing to follow
you to defend your land and go with as large numbers as are available to
meet your brother King Ingi as soon as you can, and that each of you should
support the other in all useful matters, and may almighty God [support] both
of you. Now we wish to hear what you have to say, king.'

Sauða-Úlfr's son Pétr, who was afterwards known as Pétr byrðarsveinn
(Load-carrying Lad), had carried King Sigurðr to the assembly. Then the
king spoke:

'Let all men know that if I have my way I shall go to see my brother King Ingi as soon as I can.'

Now one after another there spoke and each began in his own way but ended his speech at the same spot as Óttarr birtingr had replied, and now it was decided to summon a troop together and travel to the east of the country. After that King Sigurðr travelled east into Vík and there met his brother King Ingi.

CHAPTER TEN

The same autumn there came Sigurðr slembidjákn and Magnús blindi from the south from Denmark with thirty ships, both Danish troops and Norwegian. It was close to the winter nights.[397] [316] So when the kings and their troops learn of this, they travel east against them. They met at Hvalir by Hólmr inn grái. This was the next day after Marteinsmass.[398] It was a Sunday. Kings Ingi and Sigurðr had twenty ships and all large ones. A great battle took place there, but after the first onslaught the Danes fled back south with eighteen ships. Then Sigurðr's and Magnús's ships were cleared. And when Magnús's ship was pretty well cleared, but he was resting in his bed, Hreiðarr Grjótgarðsson, who had been with him a long time and had been one of his personal followers, he took King Magnús in his arms and was going to jump onto another ship. Then Hreiðarr was hit by a spear between the shoulders and in through them, and people say that there King Magnús met his death from the same spear, and Hreiðarr fell over on his back onto the deck with Magnús on top of him. But everyone tells that he was felt to have served his liege lord well and gallantly. It is well for each one that gets such report. There fell Loðinn saupruðr (Soup Swallower) of Línustaðir on King Magnús's ship, and Sigurðr slembidjákn's forecastle man Brúsi Þormóðarson and Ívarr Kolbeinsson and Sigurðr slembidjákn's midshipman, Hallvarðr fægir (Polisher). This Ívarr had gone in against King Haraldr and been the first to injure him. Now a large part of Magnús's party's troops fell, for Ingi's men let none escape that they could lay hands on, though I name but few men to whom this happened. They killed on one islet more than sixty men. Two Icelandic men were killed there, Bergþórr Másson's son the priest Sigurðr and secondly Ari Einarsson's son Klémet. Kálfr inn rangi's son Ívarr skrauthanki (Ornamented Hasp), who was later bishop north in Þrándheimr—he was Archbishop Eiríkr's father; Ívarr had steadfastly followed Magnús—he [317] managed to get onto his brother Jón kaða's ship, and Jón was married to Gyrðr Bárðarson's daughter Cecilia, and was there among the troops. And there were these three that managed

[397] The last three nights before the beginning of winter (late October).
[398] The Feast of St Martin of Tours (Marteinsmessa) is 11th November.

to get onto Jón's ship, the second being Arnbjǫrn Ambi who later married Þorsteinn in Auðsholt's daughter, the third Ívarr dynta (Dandy) Starason. He was Helgi Starason's brother and Þrándish on his mother's side, a most promising man. But when the troops realised that they were there, then they grabbed their weapons and went for Jón and his friends, and they got on the defensive and the whole host was on the point of fighting among themselves. And this settlement was reached among them, that Jón redeemed his brother Ívarr and Arnbjǫrn and he pledged ransom for them and he was paid back this money afterwards. But Ívarr dynta was taken up ashore and executed, for Kolbeinn's sons Sigurðr and Gyrðr would not take payment for him, as they recognised him as having been at the killing of their brother Benteinn. Bishop Ívarr said it had affected him in this way, that he felt the worst thing was when Ívarr was taken up ashore to face the axe and first he turned to them and said he hoped they would meet again in happiness. This is what Archbishop Jón's sister Guðríðr Birgisdóttir told Eiríkr Oddsson, and she said she had heard Bishop Ívarr say that.

CHAPTER ELEVEN

There was a man called Þrándr gjaldkeri (Steward) that captained a ship in Ingi's fleet. And now it had reached the stage where Ingi's men were rowing in small boats to the men that were in the water and killing each one that they got hold of. Sigurðr slembidjákn dived into the water from his ship when it had been cleared, and threw off his mailcoat [318] while under the water, after that swimming and holding his shield above him. And some men from Þrándr's ship captured one man in the water and were going to kill him, but he begged to be released, saying he would tell them where Sigurðr slembir was, and they agreed to that. But shields and spears and dead men and clothing were floating all over round the ships.

'You will see,' he says, 'where a red shield is floating. He is underneath that.'

After that they rowed over there and captured him and took him to Þrándr's ship, and Þrándr sent word to Þjóstólfr and Óttarr and Ámundi. Sigurðr slembir had had a tinderbox on him, and the touchwood was inside a walnut shell and wax poured over it. This is mentioned because it seemed a clever way to keep it from ever getting wet. He held his shield above himself while he swam so that no one would know whether it was that shield or some other when there were many of them floating on the sea. They said that they would never have come across him if they had not been told where he was. When Þrándr got ashore with him, then the troops were told that he had been captured. Then a shout of joy arose from the army. And when Sigurðr heard that, he said:

'Many a wicked man will be joyful over my head today.'

Then Þjóstólfr Álason went up to where he was sitting and brushed off his head a silken cap adorned with lace. Then Þjóstólfr said:

'Why were you so bold, you son of a slave, as to dare to call yourself King Magnús's son?'

He replied: 'You have no reason to regard my father as like a slave, for your father was worth little in comparison with my father.'

Þorgeirr Steinsson the physician's son Hallr was one of King Ingi's followers and was present while this was going on. He dictated the story to Eiríkr Oddsson, and he wrote down this account. Eiríkr wrote the book that is known as *Hryggjarstykki*. In that book it tells about Haraldr gilli and his two sons[399] and [319] about Magnús blindi and about Sigurðr slembir, right up until their deaths. Eiríkr was an intelligent man and was at this time for a long period in Norway. He wrote some of his account according to what Haraldr's sons' landed man Hákon magi dictated. Hákon and his sons were in all these conflicts and strategies. Eiríkr further mentions others that told him about these events, intelligent and reliable people, and were nearby, so that they heard or saw what happened, and some things he wrote according to what he himself had heard or seen.

CHAPTER TWELVE

Hallr says this, that the leading men wanted to have him [Sigurðr slembir] killed straight away, but the men that were fiercest and felt the need to avenge their griefs on him decided his torments, and there were named for this the brothers of Benteinn, Kolbeinn's sons Sigurðr and Gyrðr, and Pétr byrðarsveinn wanted to avange his brother Finnr, but the leading men and most of the ordinary people went off. They broke his legs in two with the backs of axes and his arms. Then they stripped him of his clothes and were going to flay him alive and cut the scalp off his head. They got no further with this because of the blood flowing. Then they took whips of hide and beat him for a long time so that all his skin was completely off as if it had been flayed. And after that they took a log of wood and banged it on his spine so that it broke in two. Then they dragged him to a tree and hanged him and after that cut off his head and dragged his body away and buried it in a sort of heap of stones.

[320] Everyone said, his friends and enemies, that no man in Norway had been more accomplished in everything than Sigurðr within the memory of the people that were then around, though he was an unlucky man in some things. Hallr said that he spoke little and often did not reply very much even if people addressed words to him, and Hallr says this, that he never reacted any more

[399] i.e. Ingi and Sigurðr.

than if they were striking a stock or a stone. But he added this, that it could be true of a good fellow that was well endowed with endurance that he might be able to bear torture to the extent that he might keep his mouth shut or react very little, but he said that he [Sigurðr] never altered his voice and he spoke as lightheartedly as when he was indoors on the ale bench, he spoke neither louder nor more softly nor with more of a tremor than his custom was. He went on speaking right on until he died, and sang a third of the psalter, and he [Hallr] declared that this seemed to him beyond the endurance and strength of other men. And the priest that had a church there a short way away had Sigurðr's body conveyed there to the church. This priest was a friend of Haraldr's sons. And when this got about, then they directed their anger towards him and had the body taken back to where it had been before, and yet the priest had to pay money for it. But Sigurðr's friends afterwards went from south in Denmark by ship to fetch the body and conveyed it to Álaborg and buried it at Máríukirkja there in the town. The provost Ketill, who was in charge of Máríukirkja, told Eiríkr that Sigurðr was buried there. Þjóstólfr Álason had King Magnús's body conveyed to Oslo and buried at Hallvarðskirkja by his father King Sigurðr. They conveyed Loðinn sauprúðr to Túnsberg, but all the other troops they buried where they were.

[321] CHAPTER THIRTEEN

Sigurðr and Ingi had been ruling Norway six winters. That spring Eysteinn came from the west from Scotland. He was Haraldr gilli's son. Árni sturla (Trouble) and Þorleifr Brynjólfsson and Kolbeinn hrúga (Heap), they had travelled west across the sea after Eysteinn and accompanied him to land and immediately sailed north to Þrándheimr, and the Þrœndir welcomed him and he was accepted as king at Eyraþing around Rogation Days,[400] so that he was to share a third of Norway with his brothers. Sigurðr and Ingi were now in the east of the country. Then people passed between the kings and made a settlement between them whereby Eysteinn was to have a third of the kingdom . . .[401] except that what King Haraldr had said about it was believed. King Eysteinn's mother was called Bjaðǫk, and she came to Norway with him.

CHAPTER FOURTEEN

The fourth son of King Haraldr was called Magnús. He was fostered by Kyrpinga-Ormr (Feeble Steps-). He was also accepted as king and had his share of the land. Magnús was diseased in the feet and lived a short time and died of sickness. Einarr Skúlason speaks of him:

[400] See note 396 above.

[401] Some words are accidentally missing here, perhaps something like what is in *Fagrskinna*: 'No trials of Eysteinn's paternity were made'.

217.   Eysteinn bestows wealth on people.   *Haraldssonakvæði* (?) 1
        Sigurðr adds to shield-clamour.[402]   *Skald* II 549
[322]   Ingi makes metal[403] sing.
        Magnús makes peace among men.
        The kin of the king much valued[404]
        colour with blood the war-tent.[405]
        Never came beneath the sun,
        four nobler brothers.

After the fall of King Haraldr gilli Queen Ingiríðr was married to Óttarr birtingr. He was a landed man and a great leader, Þrándish by descent. He was a great helper of King Ingi while he was in his childhood. King Sigurðr was not a great friend of his and felt he was rather too biassed in favour of his kinsman-in-law King Ingi. Óttarr birtingr was killed north in Kaupangr by a single attacker one evening when he was supposed to be going to evensong. And when he heard the whistling of the blow, then he moved up his arm and cloak against it, thinking that a snowball was being thrown at him, as often happens with young boys. He fell at the blow. But his son Álfr hroði (Trash) now came walking into the churchyard. He saw his father's fall and also that the man who had attacked him was running eastwards round the church. Álfr ran after him and killed him by the corner of the choir, and people said his vengeance had turned out well for him, and he was thought a much greater man than before.

CHAPTER FIFTEEN

King Eysteinn Haraldsson was now inside Þrándheimr when he heard of Óttarr's fall, and he summoned a troop of farmers to him. He went out to the town and came to have a very large following. [323] But Óttarr's kinsmen and other friends blamed the plot mainly on King Sigurðr, and he was now in Kaupangr, and the farmers were greatly incensed against him. But he offered to undergo an ordeal and pledged a trial by hot iron that would prove his innocence, and they settled for that. After that King Sigurðr travelled to the south of the country, and this ordeal was never performed.

CHAPTER SIXTEEN

Queen Ingiríðr had a son by Ívarr sneis (Pin). He was called Ormr, and later known as King's Brother. He was most handsome in looks and became a great

---

[402] *skaldar hjaldr*: 'din of the shield', battle.
[403] *slǫg*: blows (from weapons); also used to mean the weapons themselves.
[404] Haraldr gilli.
[405] *folktjald*: 'battle-tent', shield.

leader, as will be described further later. Queen Ingiríðr was married to Árni in Stoðreimr. He was later known as King's Brother-in-Law. Their children were Ingi, Níkolás, Philippus in Herðla and Margrét, who was married to Bjǫrn bukkr (Buck) and afterwards to Símun Kárason.

CHAPTER SEVENTEEN

Erlingr was the name of the son of Kyrpinga-Ormr and Sveinki Steinarsson's daughter Ragnhildr. Kyrpinga-Ormr was son of Sveinn Sveinsson, son of Erlendr from Gerði. Ormr's mother was Ragna, daughter of Jarl Ormr Eilífsson and Jarl Finnr Árnason's daughter Ingibjǫrg. Jarl Ormr's mother was Jarl Hákon inn ríki's daughter Ragnhildr. Erlingr was an intelligent man and was a great friend of King Ingi's, and with his consent Erlingr married Kristín, daughter of King Sigurðr and Queen Málmfríðr. Erlingr had an estate in Stuðla [324] in Sunn-Hǫrðaland. Erlingr travelled abroad and with him Eindriði ungi (the Young) and still other landed men, and they had a fine force. They set out on a journey to Jórsalir and travelled west across the sea to Orkney. From there Jarl Rǫgnvaldr, who was known as Kali, travelled [with them], and Bishop Viljálmr. They took altogether from Orkney fifteen longships and sailed to the Suðreyjar and from there west to Valland and after that the route that King Sigurðr Jórsalafari had travelled, out to Nǫrvasund, raiding widely out round heathen Spain. A little after they had sailed through the straits, Eindriði ungi and those that were accompanying him separated off with six ships, and each party then went their own way. But Jarl Rǫgnvaldr and Erlingr skakki (the Crooked) encountered a *drómundr*[406] on the sea and attacked it with nine ships and fought with them. And in the end they brought smaller warships underneath the *drómundr*. Then the heathens brought down on them both weapons and stones and pots of boiling pitch and olive oil. Erlingr was positioned with his ship closest to them and the heathens' shower of weapons came down outside this ship. Then Erlingr and his men knocked holes in the *drómundr*, some down under the water, some up in the sides, so that they could get in there. So says Þorbjǫrn Skakkaskáld (Skakki's Poet) in *Erlingsdrápa*: [407]

218. With the axe's blades underwater —   *Erlingsdrápa* 1
      eagerly it was done — Northmen,   *Skald* II 631
      bold, in the new boarding
      broke openings, fearlessly.

[406] A very large warship used on the Mediterranean (Greek δρόμων).

[407] Þorbjǫrn is unknown from elsewhere. Only the three stanzas from his poem for Erlingr skakki cited here survive, though *Skáldatal* claims that he composed also for Erlingr's son Magnús and for Sverrir Sigurðarson.

[325]   Enders of eagle's hunger[408]
               in the dark wave-animal's[409]
               iron-cladding saw your cunning.
               You opened war-slits[410] from above.

Auðunn inn rauði (the Red) was the name of the man, Erlingr's forecastle man, that first went up into the *drómundr*. They defeated the *drómundr* and slew there a huge number of men, taking there a large amount of wealth and winning a fine victory there. On this journey Jarl Rǫgnvaldr and Erlingr skakki got to Jórsalaland and out to the River Jórðán, then turned back, first to Mikligarðr, leaving their ships behind there, travelling home by land, and kept all safe until they got to Norway, and their journey was very highly praised. Erlingr was seen now as a much greater man than before, both from his journey and his marriage. He was also a very intelligent person, wealthy and of good family, well spoken and was most attached in full friendship to Ingi of the brothers.

CHAPTER EIGHTEEN

King Sigurðr was riding round attending banquets east in Vík with his following and rode past a farm owned by a powerful man that was called Símun. And as the king was riding through the farm, then could be heard from inside one of the buildings such beautiful singing that he was quite enchanted with it, and rode up to the building and saw inside that there was a woman standing there at a hand-mill singing to it amazingly beautifully as she was grinding. The king dismounted from his horse and went inside to the woman and lay with her. And as he rode away, then [326] Farmer Símun realised what the king had been up to there. But she was called Þóra and she was Farmer Símun's servant woman. Afterwards Símun had her taken care of. And later on this woman gave birth to a child, and this boy was named Hákon and was said to be King Sigurðr's son. Hákon was brought up there with Símun Þorbergsson and his wife Gunnhildr. Also brought up there were her and Símun's sons Ǫnundr and Andreas, and they were very fond of Hákon, so that nothing could part them but death.

CHAPTER NINETEEN

King Eysteinn Haraldsson was located east in Vík close to the border. He had a dispute with landowners, Renir and Hísingsbúar. They assembled troops

---

[408] *arnar hungrs eyðandi*: 'destroyer of the eagle's hunger', warrior.

[409] *vágfylvingi*: 'dark thing of the wave', ship. This interpretation was suggested by E. A. Kock (*NN* §348A), although the form *fylvingr*, which he derives from the adjective *fǫlr*, is not otherwise attested.

[410] *vígskarð*: 'war-cut', a slit through which weapons could be fired (known as an arrow-loop).

against him, and he fought a battle with them and was victorious. The place
where they fought is called Leikberg. He also set fire to very many places
in Hísing. After that the landowners submitted and paid great fines, and the
king took hostages from them. So says Einarr Skúlason:

219. The generous, bold king—   *Runhenda* 2
    so things for them went wrong—   *Mork* II 216
    the Víkverjar pays   *Skald* II 552
    for arbitrary ways.
    Most were afraid
    before terms were made,
    and hostages takes
    he who harsh payment makes.

220. The sovereign fought   *Runhenda* 3
    the stout cohort—   *Mork* II 217
    to his men praise is clear—   *Skald* II 553
    Leikberg near.
[327]   Renir fled a lot
    and rendered what—
    riches men paid—
    the ruler bade.

CHAPTER TWENTY

A little later King Eysteinn set out on a journey abroad west across the sea
and sailed to Katanes. He got intelligence about Jarl Haraldr Maddaðarson
in Þórsá. He attacked him with three small warships and came upon them
unawares, though the jarl had a thirty-benched ship with eighty men
aboard. Yet as they were unprepared for it, King Eysteinn and his men now
immediately managed to board the ship and captured the jarl and took him
with them onto one of their ships. He ransomed himself with three marks of
gold, and they parted without more ado. So says Einarr Skúlason:

221. Eighty men were aiding   *Eysteinsdrápa* 1
    the offspring of Maddaðr;   *Mork* 217
    the wound-fiord gull's feeder[411]   *Skald* II 559
    forwards[412] himself, mighty.

---

[411] *sára sogns mǫgrennir*: 'feeder of the gull (raven) of the fiord (blood) of wounds',
warrior, King Eysteinn.
[412] *fremsk*: the reading of *Morkinskinna* and some manuscripts of *Heimskringla*.
Other manuscripts have *fekksk* 'was captured', in which case the 'warrior' kenning
would refer instead to Haraldr Maddaðarson, and he would be the subject of the clause.

The tide-horse's tirer[413]
took that jarl with three vessels.
The bold baiter of the corpse-skua[414]
bowed his head[415] to the fine ruler.

[328] King Eysteinn sailed on from there southwards along the eastern coast of Scotland and made for the market town in Scotland that is called Apardjón, and there killed many people and plundered the place. So says Einarr Skúlason:

222.	The troop, I've heard tell,	*Runhenda* 5
	of Apardjón fell.	*Mork* 218
	Smashed was war-ice;[416]	*Skald* II 554
	the prince spoiled peace.	

He fought a second battle south by Hjartapollr with a mounted troop and forced them to flee. They cleared some ships there. So says Einarr:

223.	The king's sword did pierce.	*Runhenda* 6
	Blood fell on spears.	*Mork* 218
	The troop kept together loyally	*Skáldsk* 104 (ll. 1–2)
	by Hjartapollr.	*Skald* II 555
	Hot sword-hilt-Rhine[417] —	
	the wolf got more wine[418] —	
	Huginn[419] cheered;	
	English ships were cleared.	

Then he sailed southwards again to England and there fought a third battle by Hvítabýr and was victorious and burned the town. So says Einarr:

224.	The prince increased war,	*Runhenda* 7
	swords chanted[420] there,	*Mork* II 219
[329]	war-clouds[421] were hewn,	*Skáldsk* 104 (ll. 3–4)
	by Hvítabýr town.	*Skald* II 555
	Strongly played on each house—	
	people endured woes,	
	the wolf's tooth grew red—	
	the Garmr of fir-wood.[422]	

---

[413] *drasils hranna þreytir*: 'tirer of the horse of waves (ship)', seafarer.

[414] *hræskúfs nistir*: 'feeder of the carrion-skua (raven)', warrior.

[415] literally 'gave his head', i.e. surrendered.

[416] *folksvell*: 'battle-ice', weapons.

[417] *valbasta Rín*: 'the Rhine (water) of (the metal cladding of) the sword-hilt', blood.

[418] *vitnis vín*: 'wolf's wine', blood.

[419] *Huginn*: the name of a raven.   [420] i.e. clashed.

[421] *hildar ský*: 'cloud of battle', shield.

[422] *fyriskógar Garmr*: 'the Garmr (hound; damager, enemy) of fir forest', fire.

After that he made raids in many places across England. Stefnir was now king in England. Next King Eysteinn fought a battle by Skarpasker with some mounted troops. So says Einarr:

225. The able king—
    rain drove of bow-string[423]—
    by Skǫrpusker killed
    the troop shield-skilled.

                    Runhenda 8
                    Mork II 220
                    Skald II 556

Next he fought in Pílavík and was victorious. So says Einarr:

226. In Pilavík the lord
    reddened the sword.
    Tore the wolf's band
    Partar corpses grand.
    He made, the king—
    sword on brow did sing—
    all Langatún
    west of sea burn.

                    Runhenda 9
                    Mork II 220
                    Skald II 557

There they burned Langatún, a large village, and people say that this town hardly recovered afterwards. After this [330] King Eysteinn travelled away from England and in the autumn back to Norway, and people gave very varying reports of this expedition.

CHAPTER TWENTY-ONE

There was satisfactory peace in Norway in the early days of Haraldr's sons, and there was fairly reasonable concord between them as long as their original advisers lived, indeed Ingi and Sigurðr were more or less children. At that time they both had a single following, while Eysteinn had one of his own. He was a full-grown man in age. But when Ingi and Sigurðr's guardians were dead, Sáða-Gyrðr Bárðarson, Ámundi Gyrðarson, Þjóstólfr Álason, Óttarr birtingr, Qgmundr sviptir and Erlingr skakki's brother Qgmundr dengir (Hammerer)—Erlingr was taken little notice of while Qgmundr was alive—after that Ingi and Sigurðr split their following, and then Gregorius, son of Dagr Eilífsson and Skopti Qgmundarson's daughter Ragnhildr, ruled as a support to King Ingi. Gregorius had great wealth and was himself a most outstanding person. He came to be in charge of the government of the country alongside King Ingi, and the king allowed him to take what he wished of his own possessions. King Sigurðr became a very overbearing person and unruly in every way as soon as he was grown up, and so was Eysteinn too, and this was even more true in the case of Eysteinn, indeed

---

[423] *strengjar regn*: 'rain of the bow-string', arrows.

he was the most greedy for wealth and most avaricious of them all. King Sigurðr grew into a big and strong man, a valiant man in looks, with brown hair and ugly mouth, but all right in his other features. He was of all men the most well-spoken and readiest of speech. Einarr Skúlason mentions this:

[331] 227.   The speech-craft of Sigurðr   *Sigurðardrápa* II 1
              excels, he who reddens   *Skald* II 550
              with gore sharp[424] fires of gash-floods.[425]
              God himself has given the king success.
              It is, if the Raumar's ruler[426]
              orates, angry-worded, as if—
              the glad-spoken king displays splendour—
              silent are other people.[427]

CHAPTER TWENTY-TWO

King Eysteinn was a swarthy man and dark in colouring, of quite tall average build, a sensible and intelligent person, but what was most detrimental to his authority was that he was avaricious and greedy for wealth. He married Níkolás mási's (Seagull's) daughter Ragna. King Ingi was the most handsome of men in his features. He had yellow hair, and it was rather thin and very curly. He had not grown very tall, and he could scarcely walk on his own, one leg was so withered, and his shoulders and chest were deformed. He was cheerful of speech and pleasant with his friends, generous with wealth, mostly letting leading men make decisions about the government with him, popular with ordinary people, and all of this very much attracted power and followers to him.

King Haraldr gilli's daughter was called Brígiða. She was first of all married to King Ingi Hallsteinsson [332] of the Svíar, and later to Jarl Karl Sónason and then to King Magnús of the Svíar. He and King Ingi Haraldsson were sons of the same mother. Last of all she was married to Jarl Birgir brosa (Smile). They had four sons, one Jarl Philippus, second Jarl Knútr, third Fólki, fourth Magnús. Their daughters were Ingigerðr, who was married to King Sørkvir—their son was King Jón—second Kristín, third Margrét. Haraldr gilli's second daughter was called Maria. She was married to Hallkell húkr's (Bowed's) son Símun skálpr (Sheath). Their son was called Níkolás. Haraldr gilli's third daughter was called Margrét. She was married to Símun's brother Jón Hallkelsson.

Now many things happened with these brothers that led to differences between them, but yet I shall only mention what seems to me to have had the most significant consequences.

---

[424] *snarpa* emended from *snarpra* (all manuscripts).

[425] *sárflóðs eldr*: 'fire of wound-flood (blood)', sword.

[426] *Rauma ræsir*: 'ruler of the Raumar', king of Norway.

[427] i.e. it seems that other people's words are worth nothing.

CHAPTER TWENTY-THREE

Cardinal Níkolás from the City of Rome came to Norway in the time of the sons of Haraldr, and the Pope had sent him to Norway. Now the cardinal was angry with Sigurðr and Eysteinn, and they had to make atonement with him, but he was very well pleased with Ingi and called him his son. So when they were all at peace with him, he granted them that he would consecrate Jón Birgisson as archbishop in Þrándheimr and gave him the vestment that is called pallium and declared this, that the archbishop's see was to be in Niðaróss at Christchurch, where King Óláfr the Saint rests, though previously there had only been suffragan bishops in Norway. The cardinal brought it about that no one should bear weapons [333] in marketplaces with impunity excpt the twelve men that were the king's bodyguard. He in many ways improved people's practices in Norway while he was there in the country. No foreigner has visited Norway that everyone thought as highly of or that had as much authority over the common people as he. He returned south afterwards with great gifts of friendship and declared he would always be the greatest friend of Norwegians. And when he got south to the City of Rome, then the previous pope died suddenly, and all the people of the City of Rome wanted to take Níkolás as Pope. So he was consecrated Pope with the name of Adrianus. Those people that visited the City of Rome in his time say that he never had such urgent business with other people that he did not always speak with Norwegians first when they wanted an audience with him. He was not Pope for long, and he is said to be a saint.

[334] CHAPTER TWENTY-FOUR

In the time of the sons of Haraldr gilli an event took place in which a man that is named Halldórr came across some Vinðr, and they captured him and caused him injuries, cutting his throat and pulling out his tongue from there and cutting it off at the roots of his tongue. Afterwards he made his way to the blessed King Óláfr, meditated devoutly on this holy person and weeping bitterly, begged King Óláfr to grant him speech and health. Next he received his speech and grace from that good king and immediately became his servant all the days of his life and turned into a glorious and faithful person. This miracle took place a fortnight before the later St Óláfr's day,[428] on the day that Cardinal Níkolás reached land.

---

[428] *Óláfsmessa in síðari*: the anniversary of his translation, 3rd August. Earlier versions of *Óláfs saga helga* say a fortnight before the earlier feast, which was 29th July.

CHAPTER TWENTY-FIVE

There were two brothers in Upplǫnd, men of high lineage and well off, Einarr and Andreas, sons of Guthormr grábarðr (Greybearded), maternal uncles of King Sigurðr Haraldsson. They had their ancestral property there and all their possessions. They had a sister quite handsome to look at, but yet not too prudent about what wicked people say, as later became apparent. She was very friendly with an English priest that was called Ríkarðr, who was living there with her brothers, and she did him many favours and frequently great benefits out of kindness. This led to no better result than that there got about and flew around monstrous words about this woman. After this had become common talk, then everyone believed this was the priest's fault, as also her brothers did, as soon as they became aware of this, then they declared him the most likely one to be reponsible before the public[429] in the [335] great friendship that existed between them. This turned out to be the greatest misfortune for them [the couple] afterwards, as was not unexpected, since they [the brothers] remained silent about their concealed plot and let no sign of it be apparent in them. So one day they called the priest to them—he was expecting nothing from them but just something good—, enticed him away with them saying that they had to go to another district to see to something there that they needed done, and told him to go with them; taking with them a member of their household who was in the plot with them. They went by ship along the lake that is called Rǫnd, and on along the shore of the lake and landed on a promontory that is called Skiptisandr. There they went ashore and played for a little while. Then they went to a certain secret place, then told their workman to strike him a blow with the back of an axe. He struck the priest so that he lay in a daze. But when he came to himself, he said:

'Why must you play so roughly with me?'

They replied: 'Even if no one tells you, yet you shall now discover what you have done.'

After that they put forward their charges against him. He denied them and spoke, bidding God and the blessed King Óláfr judge between them. After that they broke his leg in two. Then they dragged him between them to the forest and bound his hands behind his back. After that they passed cords round his head and a plank beneath his shoulders and head and put in a stick and twisted the cord.[430] Then Einarr took a peg and put it in the priest's eye, and his servant stood above and struck it with the axe and forced out the eye so that it immediately flew down onto his moustache. So then he put the peg in the other eye and said to his servant:

---

[429] *fyrir alþýðu í þeiri miklu blíðu* is most likely a corruption of *fyrir þýðu þá mikla ok blíðu* 'because of the great and kindly friendship'. Cf. *Legendary Saga* 216.

[430] So as to tighten it.

'Strike somewhat more gently.'

He did so. Then the peg shot off his eyeball and tore away his eyelid. After that Einarr took hold of the eyelid in his hand and stretched it up and saw that the eyeball was still there. Then he put the peg out on his cheek and the servant struck it then, and the eyeball sprang down onto the cheekbone [336] where it was most prominent. After that they opened his mouth and took hold of his tongue and pulled it out and cut it off, and after that freed his hands and head. As soon as he came to himself it occurred to him to place his eyeballs up against his eyebrows in their places and he held them there with both hands as well as he could. So then they carried him to the ship and went to the farm that is known as at Sæheimruð and landed there. They sent a man to the farm to say that a priest was lying there by a ship on the shore. While the man that had been sent was gone up there, then they asked if the priest was able to speak, but he fluttered his tongue and wanted to try to speak with it. Then Einarr spoke to his brother:

'If he recovers and the stump of his tongue grows, then it occurs to me that he may speak.'

After that they pinched the stump of his tongue with tongs and pulled at it and twice cut pieces off it, and a third time from in the roots of his tongue and left him lying there half dead. The housewife there on the farm was poor, and yet she went immediately and her daughter with her and they carried him back to the house in their shawls. After that they fetched a priest, and when he got there, then he bound up all his wounds and they tried to relieve him as much as they could. He lay there, the wounded priest, in a sad state, hoping constantly for God's grace and never doubting it, praying to God in his mind and with sorrowful heart without speaking, all the more trusting the more he was distressed, and meditated in his mind on the gracious king, Óláfr the Saint, God's darling, having previously heard much said about his glorious works and trusting in him all the more zealously with his whole heart for every help in his need. So as he lay there maimed and devoid of any strength, then he wept bitterly and sighed, begging with sorrowful breast the saint, King Óláfr, to succour him. So then after midnight [337] the wounded priest fell asleep. Then he dreamt he saw a noble-looking man come to him and speak with him:

'Badly have you now been treated, Ríkarðr my friend. I can see that now your strength is not great.'

He dreamt he agreed on this. Then this person spoke to him:

'You are in need of grace.'

The priest says: 'I would need the grace of almighty God and of the blessed King Óláfr.'

He says: 'And you shall have it.'

Next he took hold of the stump of his tongue and pulled it so hard that it was painful for the priest. Next he rubbed over his eyes with his hand, and over his leg, also over his other limbs that were painful. Then the priest asked who it was there. He looked at him and said:

'It is Óláfr here from the north in Þrándheimr.'

And after that he disappeared, but the priest awoke completely cured, and immediately began to speak.

'Blessed am I,' he said, 'thanks to God and the blessed King Óláfr. He has cured me.'

And miserably as he had previously been treated, so he received swift remedy for all his misfortune, and it felt to him as if he had neither been wounded nor distressed, his tongue whole, both his eyes come in their correct positions, the fractures in his bones grown together and all his other wounds healed and free from pain, back in the best of health. And it was now as a sign that his eyes had been put out that there grew a white scar on each of his eyelids in order that the glory of this noble king might be seen in this man that had been in such a miserable state.

CHAPTER TWENTY-SIX

Eysteinn and Sigurðr had been in dispute because King Sigurðr had killed a follower of King Eysteinn's, Haraldr inn víkverski (the Man from Vík), who had premises in Bjǫrgyn, and another, the priest Jón son of Táparðr (Tabard), Bjarni Sigurðarson.[431] [338] Because of this they arranged a peace meeting between them for in the winter in Upplǫnd. The two of them sat in discussion for a long time, and the outcome of their talk was that they would meet in Bjǫrgyn, all the brothers, the following summer. It was also part of their statement that they wanted King Ingi to have two or three estates and enough other wealth for him to keep thirty men with him, saying they felt he did not have the health to be king. Ingi and Gregorius heard this news and went to Bjǫrgyn and gathered a very large troop. Sigurðr arrived a little later, and he had considerably fewer troops. Ingi and Sigurðr had now been kings over Norway for nineteen winters. Eysteinn was longer coming from the Vík in the east than they coming from the north. Then King Ingi had a trumpet blown for an assembly in Hólmr, and Sigurðr and Ingi with their men and a large number of people turned up there. Gregorius had two longships and a good ninety men for whom he provided all their food and drink. He maintained his following better than other landed men, for he never drank in taverns without all his following drinking with him. He wore a gilt helmet to the assembly, and all his following were helmeted. King Ingi stood up and told people about what he had heard, how his brothers wanted

---

[431] i.e. Táparðr was the nickname of Jón's father Bjarni Sigurðarson.

to deal with him, and asked for support, and the common people applauded what he said loudly and said they would stand by him.

CHAPTER TWENTY-SEVEN

Then King Sigurðr stood up and speaks, saying it was untrue what King Ingi had accused them of, declared Gregorius had made it up, and said it should not be long before such a meeting between them should take place, if he had his way, at which he would cast down that gilt helmet there, and ended his speech by saying that they would not both be walking about for long. Gregorius answers, saying he thought that he [King Sigurðr] had little need to be eager for that, and [339] declaring he was ready for it. A few days later one of Gregorius's menservants was killed out in the street, and the killer was one of King Sigurðr's menservants. Then Gregorius wanted to attack King Sigurðr and his men, but Ingi dissuaded him, as did many other people. But as King Ingi's mother Ingiríðr was returning from evensong, then she came across where Sigurðr skrúðhyrna (Decorated Axe-Head) had been killed. He was one of King Ingi's followers and was an old man and had been in the service of many kings. And he had been killed by King Sigurðr's men Hallvarðr Gunnarsson and Eysteinn trafali's (Hindrance's) son Sigurðr, and people blamed their action on King Sigurðr. So she went straight to King Ingi and told him, said he would always be an insignificant king if he was unwilling to do anything even when his followers were slaughtered one after another just like pigs. The king got angry at her criticism, and as they were arguing together, Gregorius came walking in, helmeted and mailcoated, telling the king not to be angry, saying she was quite right.

'But I have come here to support you if you want to make an attack on King Sigurðr, and there are more than a hundred men out here in the courtyard, my followers, helmeted and mailcoated, and we shall attack them from there where it seems hardest to others to do so.'

But most people were against it and declared that Sigurðr would be willing to atone for his unlucky deed. So when Gregorius saw that it would be decided against, he spoke to King Ingi:

'They are plucking your men off, killing my manservant a little while ago, and now your follower, and they will be wanting to hunt down me or some other landed man that they think will be the greatest loss to you, since they can see that you are doing nothing about it, and will deprive you of the kingdom after your friends have been killed. Now whichever way your other landed men want to go, I am not willing to wait to be slaughtered like an ox, and Sigurðr and I shall [340] conclude our business tonight in whatever way may turn out to be possible. But it is both that you are in a bad way on account of your poor health, and moreover I think you have little desire to keep your friends. But I am now quite ready to go from here to face Sigurðr, for my standard is here outside.'

King Ingi stood up and called for his clothes, told everyone to get ready who wanted to stand by him, saying it would do no good to hold him back, declaring he had given way a long time, affirming now they must fight it out to the finish.

CHAPTER TWENTY-EIGHT

King Sigurðr was drinking on Sigríðr sæta's (Grass Widow's) premises and was getting ready and thought that nothing would come of the attack. After that they approached the premises, King Ingi down from the smiths' shops, the king's brother-in-law Árni from out at Sandbrú, Áslákr Erlendsson from his premises, and Gregorius from the street, and it was considered to be hardest from there. Sigurðr and his men shot a great deal from upstairs windows and broke up ovens and threw the stones at them. Gregorius and his men broke down the gate of the enclosure, and it was there in the gateway that Laxa-Páll's son Einarr fell of King Sigurðr's troop, and Hallvarðr Gunnarsson. He was shot in through the upstairs room and no one grieved for him. They knocked down the buildings and Sigurðr's troops left his side to receive quarter. Then Sigurðr went to an upper room and tried to ask for a hearing, but he had a gilt shield and people recognised him and would not listen to him. People shot at him, so that it was like looking at a snowstorm, and he could not stay there. So when the troops had left his side and people were knocking down the buildings very rapidly, [341] then he went out and his follower Þórðr húsfreyja (Housewife) with him, a man from Vík, and they wanted to go up to where King Ingi was to be found, and Sigurðr called to his brother Ingi, that he should give him quarter, but they were both cut down. Þórðr húsfreyja fell with great glory. Many men fell there, though I name but few, of Sigurðr's troops and also of Ingi's troops, and four men of Gregorius's troops, and also those that were with neither, and they were hit by missiles down on the jetties or out on the ships. They fought a fortnight before the feast of John the Baptist,[432] and that was a Friday.

King Sigurðr was buried at the old Christchurch out at Hólmr. King Ingi gave Gregorius the ship that had been King Sigurðr's. And two or three nights later King Eysteinn arrived from the east with thirty ships and brought his nephew Hákon along with him and did not go to Bjǫrgyn but stayed in Flóruvágar, and people passed between them and tried to reconcile them. But Gregorius wanted them to sail out against them, saying there would not be a better opportunity in the future, declaring that he would be the leader in this.

---

[432] The feast for the birthday of St John the Baptist (Jónsmessa baptista) is 24th June.

'But you, king, are not to go. There is now no lack of troops for it.'

But many were against it, and so nothing came of the expedition. King Eysteinn travelled east to the Vík, but King Ingi north to Þrándheimr and they were now nominally reconciled, but did not meet in person.

CHAPTER TWENTY-NINE

Gregorius Dagsson travelled east a short time after King Eysteinn and stayed up in Hǫfund on Bratsberg at his residence. King Eysteinn stayed in Oslo and had his ships dragged more than two sea-miles over the ice, because there was a lot of ice lying over the Vík. He went up to Hǫfund and was going to capture Gregorius, but he found out about it and went away up into Þelamǫrk with ninety men and on north there across [342] the mountains and came down in Harðangr and went after that into Eðni to Stuðla. Erlingr skakki had a residence there, but he was gone north to Bjǫrgyn, though his wife Kristín, King Sigurðr's daughter, was at home and offered Gregorius whatever he wanted from there. Gregorius was warmly welcomed there. He took a longship from there that was Erlingr's, and everything that he needed. Gregorius thanked her heartily and said she had become a magnificent person, as one might have expected. After that they travelled to Bjǫrgyn and found Erlingr, and he thought she had acted well.

CHAPTER THIRTY

After that Gregorius Dagsson travelled north to Kaupangr and arrived there before Yule. King Ingi was delighted to see him and bade him have everything he wanted of his possessions. King Eysteinn burned Gregorius's farm and slaughtered his stock. And the boat sheds that the elder King Eysteinn had had built north in Kaupangr, which were the most splendid constructions, were then burnt during the winter and some fine ships with them that were King Ingi's, and this act was very ill thought of, and the idea was attributed to King Eysteinn and King Sigurðr's foster-brother Philippus Gyrðarson. The following summer King Ingi travelled from the north and acquired a very large following, and King Eysteinn from the east, and he too gathered troops to himself. They met in Seleyjar to the north of Líðandisnes, and King Ingi had the larger force. They were on the point of fighting. They were reconciled, and the terms of their agreement were that Eysteinn was to pledge himself to pay forty-five marks of gold. King Ingi was to have thirty marks as compensation for Eysteinn having instigated the burning of the ships and also of the boat sheds, and then Philippus was to be outlawed and also all those that had been [343] at the burning when the ships were burnt. The men were also to be outlawed who were guilty of wounding King

Sigurðr, for King Eysteinn accused King Ingi of protecting those men. And Gregorius was to have fifteen marks in compensation for King Eysteinn having burned him out of house and home. King Eysteinn was displeased and felt it had been a forced settlement. King Ingi travelled east into Vík from the meeting, and Eysteinn north into Þrándheimr. After that King Ingi stayed in the Vík, and King Eysteinn in the north, and they did not meet. And the only contacts they had were not such as to be conducive to peace, and also each had friends of the other killed and nothing came of the compensation payments on Eysteinn's part. And each blamed the other for what had been agreed not being fulfilled. King Ingi and Gregorius's party attracted many troops from King Eysteinn's side, Bárðr standali (Strutter) Brynjólfsson and Hallkell húkr's son Símun skálpr and many other landed men, Halldórr Brynjólfsson and Jón Hallkelsson.

CHAPTER THIRTY-ONE

When two winters had passed after the fall of King Sigurðr, the kings gathered armies together, Ingi from the east of the country, and he got eighty ships, and King Eysteinn from the north and he got forty-five ships. Now he had the great dragon ship that King Eysteinn Magnússon had had built, and they had very fine troops and large numbers of them. King Ingi lay with his ships south off Mostr, and King Eysteinn a little further north in Grœningasund. Eysteinn sent Áslákr ungi (the Young) Jónsson and Árni sturla Sæbjarnarson south to Ingi. They had a single ship. So when Ingi's men recognised them, they attacked them and killed many men of theirs, capturing their ship and everything that was on it, and all their goods. But Áslákr and [344] Árni and some men with them got ashore and went to see King Eysteinn and told him how King Ingi had received them. King Eysteinn now called a meeting of his men and tells people what hostile acts Ingi and his men were willing to commit and asked his supporters to stand by him.

'And we have such a large and good force that I am by no means going to flee away if you are willing to stand by me.'

But there was no applause for what he said. Hallkell húkr was there, but both his sons, Símun and Jón, were with Ingi. Hallkell replied, so that many heard:

'Let your chests of gold stand by you now and defend your land!'

CHAPTER THIRTY-TWO

During the following night they rowed away in secret on many ships, some to join King Ingi, some to Bjǫrgyn, some into the fiords. So in the morning when it was light, then the king had only ten ships remaining. So he left the great dragon ship behind there as it was heavy to row, and other ships and largely knocked the dragon ship to pieces, and also they cut open their beer barrels and destroyed everything they could not take with them. King Eysteinn went aboard Jón mǫrnefr's (Suet Nose's) son Eindriði's ship, and they travelled north and in to Sogn and from there overland east to Vík. King Ingi took the ships and travelled east to the Vík along the coast. But now on the eastern side of Fold, Eysteinn was there and he had nearly twelve hundred men. Then they saw king Ingi's naval force and felt they did not have the troops to face him and ran off into the forest. Then they fled all in different directions, so that the king was just with one other man. King Ingi and his men got to know of Eysteinn's movements, and also that he had few men with him. They went to [345] search for him. Símun skálpr came across him as he was coming out towards them from a clump of bushes. Símun greeted him:

'Hail, lord,' he says.

The king says: 'I am not sure whether you don't think you are my lord now,' he says.

'That's as may be,' says Símun.

The king asked him to get him away, saying that would be fitting for him.

'Because for a long time things have been well between us, though now it is different.'

Símun said that now nothing could come of anything of that kind. The king asked that he might hear Mass first, and this was done. Then he lay face down and stretched out his arms to both sides of him and asked that he be struck in the cross between his shoulders, saying that then it should be put to the test whether he could endure being cut by weapons or not, as Ingi's comrades had claimed. Símun spoke with the man that was to execute him, telling him to act now, saying that the king had been crouching there over the heather far too long. He was then dispatched and was thought to have reacted manfully. His body was conveyed to Fors, and south of the church beneath the slope his body was placed for the vigil.

King Eysteinn was buried at Fors church, and his tomb is in the centre of the floor of the church and there is a fringed covering spread over it, and people say that he is a saint. Where he was executed and his blood fell onto the ground a spring came up, and another there beneath the slope where his body had been placed for the vigil. From the water of each of these many men claim to have received cures. It is said by the Víkverjar that many miracles have been performed at King Eysteinn's tomb, until his enemies poured broth made of the flesh of a dog over the tomb.

It was Símun skálpr that was most criticised for this deed, and this was how the common people reacted to it. But some say that when King Eysteinn was captured, Símun sent someone to see King Ingi, and the king said [346]

Eysteinn was not to come before his sight. That is what King Sverrir has had written. But this is what Einarr Skúlason says about it:

228.　Late will be saved Símun　　　　*Eysteinsdrápa* 2
　　　skalpr by such actions,　　　　　*Fsk* 341
　　　who, most evil, oft committed　　*Skald* II 560
　　　murders, and betrayed his ruler.

[347] **Hákonar saga herðibreiðs**

CHAPTER ONE

King Sigurðr's son Hákon was accepted as leader of the troop that had previously followed King Eysteinn, and the men of this troop gave him the title of king. He was now ten winters old. There were with him there now Hávarðr hǫlðr (Freeholder) of Reyrr's son Sigurðr and Hákon's foster-brothers, Símun's sons Andreas and Ǫnundr, and many other leading men and friends of King Eysteinn and King Sigurðr. They first went up into Gautland. King Ingi took possession of all that they owned in Norway, and made them outlaws. King Ingi travelled to the north of the Vík and stayed there, though sometimes in the north of the country. Gregorius was facing the danger in Konungahella and defended the land from there.

CHAPTER TWO

The next summer Hákon and his party came down from Gautland and went to Konungahella taking a very large and fine troop. Gregorius was there in the town and called a large assembly with landowners and townspeople and requested troops. He felt the people were not very responsive and said he placed little trust in them. He went away with two ships and in to the Vík and was very gloomy. He was planning to go to see King Ingi. [348] He had heard that King Ingi was travelling with a great army from the north around the Vík. But when Gregorius had got a short way north, then he met King Ingi's foster-brothers Símun skálpr and Halldórr Brynjólfsson and Gyrðr Ámundason. Gregorius was very pleased to see them. So he turned back and all of them together and had eleven ships. But when they rowed up to Konungahella, then Hákon and his party were holding a meeting outside the town and saw them coming. Then said Sigurðr of Reyrr:

'Now Gregorius is doomed, coming into our hands with a small force.'

Gregorius came to land opposite the town and was going to wait for King Ingi, for he was expected, but he did not arrive. King Hákon got ready in the town and made Þorljótr skaufuskalli (Cleft-Cheek Baldy) leader in the force that was in the merchant ships that were floating in front of the town. He was a pirate and a freebooter. But Hákon and Sigurðr and the whole army were in the town and drew up their forces on the jetties. Everyone there had become subject to Hákon.

CHAPTER THREE

Gregorius and his party rowed up along the river and let the ships be carried down by the current against Þorljótr's party. They shot at each other for a while, until Þorljótr leapt overboard and his fellows. Some were killed, but some reached land. Then Gregorius and his party rowed to the jetties, and Gregorius immediately had gangways shoved up under Hákon's men's feet. Then the man that was carrying his standard fell when he was about to go up. Then Gregorius called on Auðunn Hallsson's son Hallr to pick up the standard. He did so and after that carried the standard up onto the jetties, and Gregorius went straight after him and shoved his shield forward above his head. But as soon as Gregorius got onto [349] the jetties and Hákon's men recognised him, then they drew back and immediately there was space made on both sides. So when more of his troops came up from the ships, then Gregorius and his men pushed forward, and Hákon's men first drew back and next they were running up into the town, and Gregorius and his men chased them and twice drove them up out of the town and killed many of them. There never was a more glorious attack than this, according to what people say, that Gregorius made, because Hákon had more than forty hundred men, and Gregorius not fully four hundred. Then Gregorius spoke to Hallr Auðunarson after the battle:

'Many people seem to me less fierce in attacking than you Icelanders, for you are less accustomed to it than we Norwegians, but none seem to me to be bolder in fighting than you.'

Then Ingi arrived a little later and had many men killed that had accepted Hákon, though some he made pay fines, and he burnt some people's dwellings, and some he drove out of the country and treated harshly in many ways. In the winter Hákon travelled overland north into Þrándheimr and arrived before Easter, and the Þrœndir took him as king there to rule over what he inherited from his father, a third part of Norway to be shared with King Ingi. Ingi stayed in the Vík, and Gregorius, and Gregorius wanted to travel north against them, but many were against it, and nothing came of this that winter.

CHAPTER FOUR

Hákon travelled from the north in the spring taking nearly thirty ships. The Víkverjar had left Hákon's force with eight ships and gone ahead, raiding in both Mœrrs. No one remembers raids having been made before between the market towns. Hallkell húkr's son Jón assembled a troop of landowners and went against them and captured Kolbeinn óði (the Furious) and killed every mother's son on his ship. After that he searched for the rest and found them with seven [350] ships, and they fought, but his father Hallkell did not go to meet him, as they had arranged. There fell many good landowners there, and he was wounded himself. Hákon travelled south to Bjǫrgyn with his troops, and when they got to Stjórnvelta they learnt that King Ingi had arrived in

Bjǫrgyn from the east a few nights before, and Gregorius, and then they dared not sail that way. They sailed south past Bjǫrgyn by the outer route[433] and then came across comrades of King Ingi's on three ships that had happened to arrive from the east later. On them were King Ingi's foster-brother Gyrðr Ámundason—he was married to Gregorius's sister Gyríðr—and secondly Gyrðr lǫgmaðr (Lawman) Gunnhildarson, thirdly Hávarðr klíningr (Buttered Cake). So Hákon had Gyrðr Ámundason killed and secondly Hávarðr klíningr, but took Lawman Gyrðr with him and travelled east into the Vík.

CHAPTER FIVE

So when King Ingi learnt of this, then he travelled east after them. They met east on the Elfr. King Ingi sailed up into the river along the more northerly branch and sent out for intelligence for himself concerning Hákon and his men. But King Ingi came to land out by Hísing and waited there for the intelligence. And when his intelligence men got back, then they went to the king and said that they had seen Hákon's force and all their arrangements, saying that they were lying up by the stakes[434] and had tied the stems of their smaller ships together up between the stakes.

'They have two merchant ships that trade with the Baltic and have positioned them outermost of their ships.'

There were fortified crows' nests on the merchant ships, which they also had forward at the stems of both. So [351] when the king learnt this, what preparations they had made, then he had a trumpet blown for a meeting of his whole force. So when the assembly had been summoned and was in session, then the king seeks advice from his troops and addresses Gregorius Dagsson and his brother-in-law Erlingr skakki and other landed men and ships' masters and tells them of all Hákon's men's preparations. Gregorius was the first to reply and made known what he wanted, saying this:

'Encounters between us and Hákon have taken place a few times, and they have generally had more troops and yet had the worst of it in our dealings. But now we have many more troops, and it will now seem likely to those people who have recently lost good kinsmen of theirs at their hands that now vengeance may well take place, for they have this summer for some time up to now escaped from us. We have often said this, that if they wait for us, as it is said that they are doing now, it may be that we should risk a fight with them. Now there is this to say about my disposition, that I want to engage in battle with them, if this is not contrary to the king's wishes,

---

[433] Outside the islands, rather than the usual route between the islands and the mainland, so as to be less visible from the coast.

[434] Poles driven into the river by the banks to moor ships to. Cf. note 383 above.

for I think that, as has happened before, they will again be forced to yield if we attack vigorously. I will launch my attack from where it seems to others most difficult.'

There was great applause for Gregorius's speech, and everyone said they were ready to engage in battle with Hákon and his troops. Then all the ships were rowed up along the river until each side could see the other. Then King Ingi and his troops turned out of the current of the river behind the island. The king then had a talk with all the ships' captains and told them to prepare to attack and then called on Erlingr skakki, saying, as was true, that there was no person in that troop more sensible, nor one more expert in battle, though there were some that were even more impetuous. The king then again turned to speak to other landed men, addressing some by name, and ended his speech by saying that he was urging everyone to make their attack when they saw that it would be useful, and afterwards all to be united in one effort.

[352] CHAPTER SIX

Erlingr skakki replied to the king's speech:

'It is my duty, king, not to be silent in response to your speech. And if you want to know what my strategy will be, then I shall let you hear what it is. This plan that is now being adopted is quite contrary to my inclination, for I consider it to be an impossibility to fight with them in these circumstances, even though we have many troops and fine ones. If we are to make an attack on them and row at them against this current, where there are three men on one side of a rowing bench, then one must row and another must hold a shield over that one. What is there then but a third of our troops available to fight? It seems to me that they will be coming into battle quite unable to fight that are at the oars turning their backs towards their enemies. Give me some time to make plans, and I promise you in return that I shall work out a strategy for this before three days are passed, so that we may more easily sail to battle with them.'

And it was very clear from what Erlingr said that he was against attacking them, but nevertheless many others urged it, saying that Hákon and his men would leap up ashore again like before.

'And then we shall get none of them,' they say, 'and they now have few forces, and we have their fate entirely in our hands.'

Gregorius made little comment about it and spoke slightingly of it as if the main reason for Erlingr being so against the attack was that he wanted to put aside the plan that Gregorius proposed, rather than that he was able to understand everything better than anyone else.

CHAPTER SEVEN

King Ingi then spoke to Erlingr:

'Brother-in-law,' he says, 'we shall now carry out your advice as to how to manage the attack, but since the advisers are more keen for this, we shall now make our attack on them today.'

Then [353] spoke Erlingr: 'All the smaller ships and light vessels shall row out round the island and up the more easterly branch and so downstream against them and try whether they can loose them from the stakes, and then we shall row the large ships against them up from below, and I am not sure until we have put it to the test whether they will attack the better than I in that they are in a greater fury.'

This plan appealed to everyone. A sort of headland jutted out between them and Hákon, and neither ships could be seen from the others. So when the fleet of light ships rowed down along the river, then Hákon's party saw it, but before that they had been holding a discussion and making their plans. Some supposed that King Ingi and his troops would attack, but many thought that they probably did not dare to, since the attack seemed to be much delayed, and they had great confidence in their preparations and troops. In their party there were many important men. Sigurðr of Reyrr was there, and the two sons of Símun. Níkolás Skjaldvararson was also there, and Jón mǫrnefr's son Eindriði, who was now the best known and most popular man in Þrændalǫg. Many other landed men and troop-leaders were there. Now when they saw that Ingi's men were rowing many ships down along the river, then Hákon and his men thought that Ingi and his troops were trying to flee, and they cut the cables from their ships, grabbed at their oars and rowed after them and were going to chase them. The ships drifted quickly with the current, and when they were brought down along the river past the headland that before was between them, then they saw that Ingi's main fleet was lying out by the island Hísing. Ingi's comrades then saw where Hákon's ships were moving, and assumed that they would be attacking. Then there was a great turmoil and clashing of weapons and shouting of encouragement and they raised up war-cries, and Hákon and his troops turned their ship towards the north of the country, and there is there a sort of sheltering bay, and they got out of the current. They got themselves ready there, took cables from their sterns up ashore and turned their prows outwards and tied all their ships together, let the two Baltic merchant ships lie out at the ends of the line of other ships, the one above them, and the other below them, and tied them to the longships. And [354] in the middle of the fleet lay the king's ship, and next to it Sigurðr's ship, and on the other side of the king's ships lay Níkolás, and next to him

Eindriði Jónsson. All the smaller ships lay further out from them. They had loaded nearly all their ships up with stones and weapons.

CHAPTER EIGHT

Sigurðr of Reyrr made a speech and spoke as follows:

'It is now likely that what we have long been promised will come about, that a battle between us and Ingi will take place. We have also now for a long time been expecting this, and many of our comrades have boasted proudly that they would not flee or flinch in the face of King Ingi or Gregorius, and it is good now to call to mind what they have said. Yet we can with less confidence speak about how we have in the past suffered something of a toothache in our dealings, and it is true, as everyone has heard, that we have very often been given a rough ride by them. But none the less it is necessary for us to behave in as manly a way as possible and to stand as firmly as we can, for that is the only way out for us so that we may be victorious. And though we have somewhat fewer forces, yet fate can decide which side shall come out on top. This is our best hope in our situation, that God knows that we have the better case. Ingi has already cut down his two brothers, and no one is blind to what compensation is intended for King Hákon for the death of his father. It is to be cut down like his other kinsmen, and this will become apparent today. From the beginning Hákon has asked for no more of Norway than the third of it that his father had had, and this was refused him. But by my reckoning Hákon has a better claim to inherit from his uncle Eysteinn than Ingi or Símun skálpr or the other men that deprived Eysteinn of life. To many a one that [355] is concerned for the salvation of his soul and that has such great crimes on their consciences as Ingi it would seem that he would not dare before God to give himself the title of king, and I am surprised that God permits him such impudence, and it must be God's will that we overthrow him. Let us fight boldly, for God will give us victory. But if we fall, then God will reward us for it with manifold joys if he grants evil men the power to overcome us. Let men behave with moderation and not be afraid if battle takes place. Let each look after himself and his comrades, and God after all of us.'

Sigurðr's speech was applauded warmly, and everyone made sincere promises to respond to it properly. King Hákon went aboard one of the Baltic merchant ships, and a shield wall was formed round him, but his standard was on the longship that he had previously been on.

CHAPTER NINE

Now this is to be said about Ingi's men, that when they saw that Hákon's men were getting ready for battle—now there was only the river between them—then they sent out a swift boat after their troops that had rowed away to tell them to turn back, while the king and the rest of the troops waited for them and lined up their forces for an attack. Then the leaders made speeches and told the troops their plans, this first, which ships were to lie closest. Gregorius spoke:

'We have a large and fine force. This is now my advice, that you, king, be not in the attack, because everything is taken care of if you are, and one cannot tell where a bad marksman's arrow may end up. Their dispositions are such that from the fortified crows' nests on the merchant ships stones and missiles will be thrown. This is a little less dangerous for those that are far off. They have no more troops than are within the capacity of us landed men to fight a battle with. I shall sail my ship at that one [356] of their ships that is largest. I still expect that fighting them will be a brief test for us. Thus it has generally been in our encounters up to now, even when the odds have been the reverse of what they are now.'

It appealed to everyone when Gregorius said that the king himself should not be in the battle. Then Erlingr skakki spoke:

'I shall support this advice that you, king, should not go into the battle. It looks to me from their dispositions that we shall need to take great care if we are not to receive many casualties from them. It seems to me best only to have unwounded men to bandage up. In the planning that we were doing earlier today, then many people spoke against what I advised, claiming that I did not want to fight. But it seems to us that the situation has changed much for the better now that they are away from the stakes. And now the point has been reached where I shall not oppose engaging in battle, for I can see what everyone is aware of, how very necessary it is to drive off this band of villains that has roamed all over the country robbing and plundering, so that afterwards people may inhabit the land in peace serving one king that is as good and just as King Ingi is and yet has for long suffered hardship and trouble from the overbearing and injustice of his kinsmen and has borne the brunt of it on behalf of the whole population and exposed himself to manifold dangers to bring peace to the land.'

Erlingr spoke much and eloquently, and so did still other leaders, and they all ended on the same note, that everyone urged the attack. They waited until all their force had assembled. King Ingi now had Bœkisúðin, and submitted to his friends' entreaty that he should not go into battle, and he lay behind by the island.

CHAPTER TEN

So when the troops were ready, then they rowed hard forward to make their attack and both sides raised their war cries. Ingi's men did not tie their ships together and did not row linked together, for they were rowing [357] across all the currents and the large ships were forced sideways a great deal. Erlingr skakki attacked King Hákon's ship and thrust his prow in between it and Sigurðr's ship. Then the battle began. But Gregorius's ship drifted sideways up onto the shallows and listed heavily, and to begin with they could not join in the attack. So when Hákon's men saw that, then they sailed towards it and attacked them, and Gregorius's ship lay open before them. Then Hákon magi's son Ívarr sailed up to it and the raised decks ran into each other. Ívarr hooked a grappling iron round Gregorius where he was thinnest and hauled him towards himself, and Gregorius was forced out to the ship's side and the grappling iron up along the side and it came close to hooking him overboard. Gregorius was not much wounded, for he had a coat of plate-mail. Ívarr shouted to him and said he had thick boards round him. Gregorius spoke, saying he had so arranged it that it should be what was necessary and no more. Then it came very close to Gregorius and his men having to go overboard until Áslákr ungi got an anchor onto their ship and pulled them off the shallows. Then Gregorius attacked Ívarr's ship and they then fought together for a long while. Gregorius's ship was bigger and had more men on it. The troops on Ívarr's ship fell in large numbers, but some leapt overboard. Ívarr was badly wounded so that he was unable to fight, but when the ship had been cleared, then Gregorius had him conveyed ashore and got him away, and they were friends after that.

CHAPTER ELEVEN

So when King Ingi and his comrades saw that Gregorius was on the shallows then the king shouted to the troops that they were to row over to him. He said:

'This is the worst kind of tactics for us to lie behind here when our friends have gone into battle. We have the ship that is the biggest and best manned in the whole fleet. Now I see that Gregorius is in need of support, [358] the person that I owe most to, so let us join in battle as hard as we can. It is also most proper that I should be in the battle, since I want to win the victory, if it is going to be won. But even if I knew in advance that our men would not be victorious, yet it would be our only course to be where our other men are, because I cannot do anything if I lose the men who are my shield and are the most valiant and have long been in charge of me and my kingdom.'

Then he told them to set up the standards, and this was done, and they rowed across the river. The battle was now at its fiercest and the king found no space to attack, the ships were crowded so tightly together. So they sailed beneath the Baltic merchant ships.[435] Then halberds and pointed staves

[435] Probably ought to be 'one of the Baltic merchant ships', cf. the other manuscripts, some of which have the singular.

were used on them from above and such a load of stones that they could not withstand them, and they found they could not stay there. So when the men in the troop realised that the king was come, then they made room for him, and then he attacked Eindriði Jónsson's ship. Now Hákon's men left the small ships and went up onto the merchant ships, but some of them went ashore. Erlingr skakki and his men had a hard fight. He was in the position forward of the raised deck. He shouted to his forecastle men telling them to board the king's ship. They replied that that was not possible and there were iron spikes on the rails in front of them. Erlingr went forward to the stem and stayed there a short while before they forced their way up aboard the king's ship and cleared that ship. Then the whole force began to flee. After this many of the troops leapt into the sea and many fell, but a whole multitude reached land, as Einarr Skúlason says:

229. From the bloody sea-steed's[436] *Elfarvísur* 1
       stem to the depths fell many.   *Skald* II 566
       The ogress' Glaumr[437] fed amply.
       On the stream carrion drifted.
[359] The surge of wounds,[438] scalding, *Skáldsk* 87
       stained the Elfr, poison-cold;
       wolf-ale[439] flowed with the water,
       warm, into Kǫrmt's necklace.[440]

230. In the swift stream floated,   *Elfarvísur* 2
       deserted, many vessels,   *Skald* II 567
       prows bloody—the troop bent
       the bow—red darts flew at wet helmets,
       until the lords' following
       fled ashore from—Hǫkon's—
       deer of the deep[441]—company
       dwindled in the shield's clamour.[442]

Einarr composed a *flokkr* about Gregorius Dagsson that is called *Elfarvísur*.

King Ingi gave quarter to Níkolás Skjaldvararson when his ship had been cleared, and he then went over to King Ingi and stayed with him afterwards as long as he lived. Eindriði Jónsson leapt onto King Ingi's ship when his

---

[436] *marblakkr*: 'sea's horse', ship.
[437] *gýgjar Glaumr*: 'Glaumr (horse) of the giantess', wolf.
[438] *unda gjalfr*: 'surge of wounds', blood.
[439] *vitnis ǫlðr*: 'wolf's ale', blood.
[440] *Karmtar men*: 'the necklace of Kǫrmt (an island)', the sea.
[441] *grœðis dýr*: 'animals of the ocean', ships.
[442] *rítar rymr*: 'roar of the shield', battle.

own ship was cleared, and asked for quarter for himself. The king wanted to give him quarter, but Hávarðr klíningr's son leapt up and struck him his death blow and this deed was much criticised, but [360] he said that Eindriði had been behind the killing of his father Hávarðr. Eindriði was much lamented, and yet most of all in Þrœndalǫg. There many of Hákon's troops had fallen, though no further leaders. Few fell of Ingi's troops, though many were wounded. Hákon fled up inland while Ingi travelled north into the Vík with his troops. He stayed in the Vík during the winter, and Gregorius. And when they got to Bjǫrgyn from the battle, King Ingi's men, Bergljótr and his brother, sons of Ívarr of Elda, they then killed Níkolás skegg (Beard), who had been a steward, and afterwards went back north to Þrándheimr. King Hákon came north before Yule, but Sigurðr was sometimes at home up in Reyrr. Gregorius had received quarter for him from Ingi, so that he might keep all his possessions, for Gregorius and Sigurðr were close relatives. King Hákon was in Kaupangr over Yule, and his men had a fight one evening over Yule in the royal hall early in the Yule season and seven men were killed and many were wounded. And afterwards on the eighth day of Yule, then these comrades of Hákon travelled in to Elda, Óttarr birtingr's son Álfr hroði and nearly eighty men, and they arrived in the early part of the night when the others were drunk, and they set fire to the hall, while the others went out and defended themselves. And Ívarr's son Bergljótr and his brother Ǫgmundr fell there, and very many men. There had been nearly thirty men inside there. In the winter north in Kaupangr King Hákon's foster-brother Andreas Símunarson died, and he was lamented most of all. Erlingr skakki and those of Ingi's men that were in Bjǫrgyn went on as though they were going to go north during that same winter and capture Hákon, but nothing came of it. Gregorius sent this message from the east in Konungahella that if he was staying as close as Erlingr and his men, he would not stay put in Bjǫrgyn, if Hákon was having King Ingi's friends in Þrándheimr and their mates killed.

[361] CHAPTER TWELVE

King Ingi and Gregorius travelled from the east to Bjǫrgyn in the spring. So as soon as Hákon learnt this, and Sigurðr and his men, that Ingi had left the Vík, then they travelled eastwards overland into the Vík. And when King Ingi and his men got to Bjǫrgyn, then a quarrel arose between Halldórr Brynjólfsson and Bjǫrn Níkolásson. And Bjǫrn's manservant had asked his opposite number why he was so pale when they met down on the jetties, and he said he had been being bled.

'I would not want to look as pale as chaff like you are with bloodletting.'

'And I guess,' said the other, 'that you would have borne it worse and less manfully.'

And the start of it was no more than that. Then one word led to another until they quarrelled and next they were fighting. So Halldórr Brynjólfsson was told that his manservant had been wounded on the jetties. Now Halldórr was drinking nearby on his premises. Then he went down there, though already Bjǫrn's menservants had got there, and Halldórr thought they had parted on unequal terms, and they drove Bjǫrn's menservants off and knocked them about. Then Bjǫrn bukkr was told that the Víkverjar were beating his menservants down at the jetties. Then Bjǫrn and his men took their weapons and went down and were going to avenge their men. Then there were serious woundings. Now Gregorius was told that his brother-in-law Halldórr needed support and his menservants were being slaughtered out on the street. Then Gregorius and his men leapt into their mailcoats and went down. Now Erlingr skakki heard that his nephew Bjǫrn was fighting with Halldórr and Gregorius in on the jetties and that he needed support.[443] So he went over there and had a very large number of men and told people to give him support, saying that it would be shameful

'If one man from the Vík is going to trample over us here in our native place, and that will be [362] remembered against us for evermore.'

Fourteen men fell there, and nine were killed immediately, though five died later from their wounds, and many were wounded. Then word reached King Ingi that they were fighting in there on the jetties, Gregorius and Erlingr, and he went up and tried to part them and could do nothing about it, for both sides were in such a fury. Then Gregorius shouted to King Ingi telling him to go away, saying he would not be able to do anything about it as things were, and saying that it would be the greatest disaster if anything happened to him,

'For one cannot tell who it would be that would hold himself back from any calamity if he felt it was within his power.'

So the king went away. And when the worst of the fighting was over, then Gregorius and his men went up to Níkoláskirkja and Erlingr and his men after them, and they shouted at each other. After that King Ingi came a second time and made peace between them, and both sides were now in favour of him alone arbitrating between them. Then they learnt that Hákon was in the Vík, and King Ingi and Gregorius travelled east and had a very large number of ships. So when they got to the east, then Hákon and his men fled and there was no battle. Then King Ingi travelled in to Oslo, but Gregorius stayed in Konungahella.

CHAPTER THIRTEEN

Gregorius heard of the whereabouts of Hákon and his men a little later, in a place called Saurbýir. It is up by the forests. He went there and arrived at

[443] Bjǫrn's mother was Ása daughter of Kyrpinga-Ormr.

night, thinking that Hákon and Sigurðr must be in the larger farmstead, and
set the buildings there on fire. Hákon and his men were in the smaller [363]
farmhouse. They made their way to where they saw the fire, wanting to help
the others. Áli óskeyndr's (Unshielded's) son Munán, brother of Hákon's
father King Sigurðr fell there. Gregorius and his men killed him when he
tried to help those that were being burned in the building. They went out,
and a large number of men was killed there. Ásbjǫrn jalda (Mare) got away
from the farm—he was a very great robber— and had been badly wounded.
But a farmer met him and Ásbjǫrn asked the farmer to let him escape, saying
he would give him payment for it. The farmer said he would do what he was
keener for, saying he had often gone in fear of him, and struck him his death
blow. Hákon and Sigurðr got away, but a large number of their troops was
killed. Afterwards Gregorius travelled east to Konungahella. A little later
Hákon and Sigurðr went to Halldórr Brynjólfsson's estate in Vettaland and set
fire to the buildings and burnt them. Halldórr went out and was immediately
killed and his menservants with him. There were killed nearly twenty men
in all. His wife Sigríðr, Gregorius's sister, her they let go away to the wood
in just her nightshirt. There they captured Gregorius's nephew Ámundi, son
of Gyrðr Ámundason and Gyríðr Dagsdóttir, and took him with them. He
was five winters old at the time.

CHAPTER FOURTEEN

Gregorius heard about these events, and he was greatly affected by them. He
made detailed enquiries about where they were. Gregorius left Konungahella
towards the end of the Yule season with a large troop, and they came to Fors
on the thirteenth day of Yule and stayed there for the night and held mattins
there on the last day of Yule,[444] and the Gospel was read to him afterwards. This
was a Saturday. And when Gregorius and his men saw Hákon's party, then it
seemed to them that [364] Hákon's men's troop was much smaller than their
troop. There was a river between them when they met. It is called Befja. The
ice on the river was unsafe, because there was a current running under the ice
round the edges. Hákon's party had knocked holes in the ice on the river and
shovelled debris over them so that they could not be seen. When Gregorius
got to the river, he spoke, saying the ice looked unsafe to him, telling them it
was advisable to go to the crossings that were a little higher up the river. The
troop of farmers spoke, saying that they could not understand what reason he
had for not daring to attack them over the ice, when they had no more troops
facing them than were there, declared the ice perfectly sound, saying that it
seemed to have been passed over by people. Gregorius replied, saying that it
had seldom been necessary to taunt him for lack of courage very much, and

[444] January 6th. Cf. note 380 above.

that it would not be so now, told them to back him up well and not to stay standing on the land if he went onto the ice, and said their advice should be adopted to walk onto unsafe ice though he declared himself to be unwilling.

'But I refuse to put up with your taunts,' he says, and ordered his standard to be carried forward. He then went out onto the ice. But as soon as the troop of farmers realised that the ice was unsafe, then their troop turned back. Gregorius sank into the ice, though not deeply. He told his men to go carefully, but no more followed him than nearly twenty men, and all the rest of his men turned back. Someone from Hákon's party shot an arrow at him and hit him in the throat. Gregorius fell there and twenty men with him, and this is now the end of his life. And it was universally said that he has been the greatest leader out of the landed men in Norway that those that were alive at the time could remember, and has been the most well-disposed to us Icelanders since the elder King Eysteinn died. Gregorius's body was conveyed up to Hǫfund and buried on Gimsey at a nunnery that is there. At that time Gregorius's sister Baugeið was abbess there.

[365] CHAPTER FIFTEEN

Two royal stewards travelled in to Oslo to tell the news to King Ingi. And when they got there, then they called the king to speak with them. He asked what news they had to tell.

'The fall of Gregorius Dagsson,' they said.

'How have things turned out so badly?' said the king.

They told him. The king replied:

'Then they had their way who understood the least.'

It is said that he took this so badly that he wept like a child. But when he got over this, he spoke as follows:

'I wanted to go to see Gregorius as soon as I heard about the killing of Halldórr, for I felt sure that Gregorius would not hang about for long before deciding to avenge him. But those people behaved as if nothing was as important as that Yule drinking feast and it could not be interrupted. For I am certain, that if I had been there, either more circumspection would have been employed or else Gregorius and I would have shared the same night's lodging.[445] So has passed away there the man that has been best to me and has done most to keep the land in my hands. But I had thought until now that our deaths would not have been far apart. Now I shall make it my first priority to go to battle with Hákon and his men and there will be one of two outcomes, I shall either be killed or else overcome Hákon and his men. For such a man as Gregorius was will not be too much avenged even if they all die to pay for his death.'

[445] i.e. would have died together.

Someone replies, saying he would not have to search far for them, declared they were about to come there to meet with him. King Sigurðr's daughter, King Ingi's cousin Kristín was there in Oslo. The king heard that she was intending to leave the town, and sent word to her asking why she wanted to leave the town. So she said she thought it was dangerous and not a place for women to be in. The king asked her not to go away.

'If it turns out that we are victorious, as I [366] intend, then you will be well looked after here, but if it turns out that I fall, then my friends will get no chance to see to my corpse, and yet you will be able to request permission to see to the corpse. Thus you will best be able to repay me for having treated you kindly.'

CHAPTER SIXTEEN

On the evening of Blasius's Day[446] intelligence reached King Ingi that Hákon was now expected to arrive in the town. Then King Ingi had his troops called up from the town by a trumpet, and nearly forty hundred men were now called out. The king had his battle line made a long one and no more than five men deep. Then people told the king that he was not to be in the battle, saying that there was much at stake in him.

'And let your brother Ormr be the leader of the troops.'

The king says: 'I think that if Gregorius were alive and were here now, and I were fallen and had to be avenged, that he would not lie in hiding, but would be in battle himself. And though I am in a worse state because of my poor health than he was, yet I shall not be less determined in his case, and there is no chance of my not being in the battle.'

People say that Gunnhildr, who had been married to Hákon's foster-brother Símun, had someone sit outside [at night to cast a spell] to bring victory to Hákon, but it was revealed that they should fight Ingi by night, and never by day, and it said that then it would work. And the woman who it is said sat outside is named as Þórdís skeggja (Bearded Woman), but I do not know the truth of it. Símun skálpr, he had gone into the town and lain down to sleep and had woken up at the war cry. And towards the end of the night intelligence came to King Ingi. He was told that Hákon and his men were now coming in over the ice, for the ice was lying all the way from the town out to Hǫfuðey.

[367] CHAPTER SEVENTEEN

King Ingi then went out onto the ice with his army and set up his battle line in front of the town. Símun skálpr was in the wing that reached out

---

[446] St Blaise's day (Blasius' Day) (in the west) is 3rd February.

towards Þrælaborg, but in the wing that went in, in front of Nunnusetr, was Óláfr klíningr's (Buttered Cake's) son Guðrøðr Suðreyjakonungr and Jón son of Sveinn son of Bergþórr bukkr (Buck). So when Hákon and his men got to where King Ingi's battle line was, then both sides shouted a war cry. Guðrøðr and Jón made signs to Hákon's force and let them know where they were to be found. After that Hákon's men turned to where they were and Guðrøðr and his men immediately fled, and that must have been nearly fifteen hundred men. But Jón and a large troop with him ran over to Hákon's troop and fought alongside them. King Ingi was told of this. He replies thus:

'There has been a wide difference between my friends. Gregorius would never have behaved thus as long as he lived.'

Then people spoke, begging the king that a horse might be shoved under him and that he should ride out of the battle and up into Raumaríki.

'There you will get plenty of help straight away today.'

'I have no heart for that,' says the king. 'I have often heard you say this, and it seems true to me, that little came of my brother King Eysteinn after he took to flight, and he was very well endowed in every way that beseems a king. Now I can see what poor prospects I shall have with my poor health if [368] I take up the course that was so great a disaster for him, considering how greatly our activity and health and all our endurance differ. I was then in my second winter when I was taken as king in Norway, and now I am at least twenty-five. I feel that I have had more difficulties and troubles during my kingship than pleasure and comfort. I have had many battles, sometimes with larger forces, sometimes with fewer. That has been my greatest good fortune that I have never had to flee. Let God decide about my life, how long it is to be, but never shall I take to flight.'

CHAPTER EIGHTEEN

So when Jón and his comrades had severed King Ingi's battle line, then many of those that had been nearest there also fled, and then the battle line broke up and fell into disorder, but Hákon's party then pressed forward hard. Day was also about to break. Then an attack was made on Ingi's standard. In that storm King Ingi fell, but his brother Ormr then carried on the battle. Many of the host then fled up into the town. Ormr went twice into the town after the king had fallen, and urged on the troops, and each time he went out onto the ice and carried on the battle. Then Hákon and his men attacked the wing of the formation that Símun skálpr was in charge of, and in that onslaught the king's kinsman-in-law[447] Guðbrandr Skafhǫggsson fell from

---

[447] Guðbrandr's wife was a cousin of Ingi's.

Ingi's troop, and Símun skálpr and Hallvarðr hikri (Dawdler) went at each other and fought each other with their companies and drove each other out in front of Prælaborg. In this onset they both fell, Símun and Hallvarðr. The king's brother Ormr achieved very great renown and yet fled in the end. Earlier in the winter Ormr had engaged himself to Níkolás masi's daughter Ragna, who had been married to King Eysteinn Haraldsson, and [369] was now to have gone to his wedding the next Sunday. Blasius's Day was on a Friday. Ormr fled to Svíþjóð to his brother Magnús, who was now king there, while their brother Rǫgnvaldr was jarl there. They were sons of Ingiríðr and Heinrekr halti (the Lame). He was King Sveinn Sveinsson of the Danes' son. The king's daughter Kristín saw to King Ingi's corpse, and he was laid in the stone wall in Hallvarðskirkja on the outer side of the choir on the southern side. He had now been king for twenty-five years. In this battle many men fell from both sides and yet many more from Ingi's troops. Árni Fríreksson fell from Hákon's troops. But Hákon's men took possession of the wedding banquet and a very great deal of other booty.

CHAPTER NINETEEN

King Hákon then subjected the whole land to himself and appointed his own men to all the stewardships and likewise the market towns. King Hákon and his men held their meetings in Hallvarðskirkja when they were deciding national policies. The king's daughter Kristín gave money to the priest that was in charge of the keys of the church to hide one of her men in the church so as to be able to hear what Hákon and his men were talking about. And when she found out what they were planning, she sent word to her husband Erlingr skakki in Bjǫrgyn saying that he was never to trust them.

CHAPTER TWENTY

The event took place in the battle at Stiklarstaðir, as was written above, in which King Óláfr threw away from himself his sword Hneitir when he had been wounded.[448] Now some man or other, Swedish by descent, had broken his sword, and he picked up the sword Hneitir and fought with it. Now this man got away out of [370] the battle and went with other men that were fleeing. He turned up in Svíþjóð and went back to where he lived. He kept this sword all his life, and afterwards his son, and one after another of their kinsmen, and it was always a condition of owning the sword that each owner told the next the sword's name and also where it had come from. Now it was much later, in the days of Emperor Kirjalax of Mikligarðr, that there were there in Garðr large companies of Væringjar. Then it came about one

448 See Vol. II 385, ch. 228.

summer when the emperor was on some military expedition and they were
lying in their camp, that the Væringjar were keeping watch and were staying
awake to guard the king, lying out on the level ground round the outside of
the camp. They divided the night into watches among themselves, and those
that had just been on the watch then lay down and slept. They were all fully
armed. It was their custom when they lay down to sleep for each one to have
his helmet on his head and his shield on top of him, and his sword under his
head, and he was to lay his right hand on the handle. A certain one of their
comrades to whose lot had fallen the watch in the last part of the night, now
awoke at dawn. Then his sword was gone. And when he searched for it, then
he saw the sword lying on the ground a long way off from him. He stood
up and picked up the sword. He thought his comrades who had been on the
watch must have done it for a joke, taking his sword from him by a trick. They
denied this as far as they were concerned. Similar things happened for three
nights. Then he was quite amazed himself and so also were the others who
saw this or heard about it, and men enquired of him what this could mean.
Then he said that this sword was called Hneitir and the blessed Óláfr had
owned it and carried it himself in the battle at Stiklarstaðir. He recounts what
had happened to the sword after that. Afterwards King Kirjalax was told. So
he had the man who was wearing this sword called to him, gave him gold,
three times the value of the sword. And the king had the sword taken into
Óláfskirkja which is maintained by the Væringjar. It stayed there afterwards
above the altar. [371] Eindriði ungi was in Mikligarðr at the time when these
events took place. He told this story in Norway, as Einarr Skúlason bears
witness in the *drápa* that he composed about the blessed King Óláfr, and in
it there is a passage that tells of this happening.

CHAPTER TWENTY-ONE

The event took place in Grikland when Kirjalax was king there, that the
king went on a military expedition to Blǫkumannaland. And when he got
to Pézínavellir, then there came against him there a heathen king with an
invincible army. They had brought there a mounted troop and very large
waggons with battlements up on them. And when they prepared their night
quarters, then they arranged their waggons side by side round the outside of
their camp, and around them they dug a great ditch. All this then became a
stronghold as big as if it were a castle. The heathen king was blind.

Now when the king of the Greeks arrived, then the heathens drew up their
battle line on the level ground in front of their waggon-castle. Then the
Greeks drew up their battle line facing it, and both sides rode and fought. It
then went badly and unfortunately. The Greeks now fled and had suffered a

large loss of men, and the heathens gained the victory. Then the king drew up a battle line of Frakkar and Flemings, and after that they rode forward against the heathens and fought with them and it went the same as with the previous ones, that many were killed and all that escaped fled. Then the king of the Greeks got very angry with his soldiers, but they replied to him telling him now to get in the Væringjar, his wine bags. The king replies, saying that he will not waste his treasures by taking a small number of men, though they were valiant, against such a large army. Then Þórir helsingr (man from Helsingjaland), who was then the leader of the Væringjar, replied to what the king had said:

'Though we were faced by raging fire, yet I and my troops would [372] leap straight in if I knew that the result would be that you, king, would have peace thereafter.'

So the king replied: 'Make a vow to your king, the blessed Óláfr, for help and victory for yourselves.'

The Væringjar had four hundred and fifty men. They made their vow by joining hands and vowed to raise a church in Mikligarðr at their own expense and with the support of good men and to have this church dedicated to the honour and glory of the blessed King Óláfr. After that the Væringjar ran forward onto the battlefield, and when the heathens saw this, then they told their king that another detachment of the King of the Greeks' army was now coming.

'And this one,' they said, 'is but a handful of men.'

Then the king replies: 'Who is that noble-looking man that is riding there on the white horse at the head of their troops?'

'We do not see such a man,' they say.

The odds there were no less than sixty heathens against one Christian, but nevertheless the Væringjar advanced into battle very boldly. And as soon as they engaged, then fear came over the troop of heathens and terror so that they immediately began to flee, and the Væringjar chased them and soon killed a huge number of them. And when the Greeks and Frakkar saw this, they that had previously fled before the heathens, they now joined in and pursued the rout with them. The Væringjar were now come up into the waggon-castle.There a very great number of casualties took place. And after the heathens had fled, then the heathen king was captured and the Væringjar took him with them. Then the Christians captured the heathens' camp and the waggon-castle.

[373] Magnúss saga Erlingssonar

CHAPTER ONE

After Erlingr became aware of what the plans of Hákon and his men were, then he sent messages to all the leaders that he knew had been trusty friends of King Ingi, and also to the king's personal following and the men in his service that had got away, and Gregorius's men, and arranged to meet them. And when they met and had their discussion, then it was immediately decided that they should keep their company together, and they confirmed this arrangement between them. After that they discussed whom they should take as their king. Now Erlingr skakki spoke, enquiring whether it was the opinion of leaders or other landed men that King Haraldr gilli's daughter's son, Símun skálpr's son, should be taken as king, and that Jón Hallkelsson should take on the leadership of their company. Jón declined. Then it was enquired of King Magnús berfœttr's sister's son Níkolás Skjaldvararson whether he was willing to become leader of their company. He replied in this way, that it was his advice that they should take one as king that was descended from a kingly line, but take one as leader of the company that was likely to turn out to be intelligent, saying he would find it easier to get followers. It was enquired of the king's brother-in-law Árni whether he was willing to have some one of his sons, the brothers of King Ingi, taken as king. His reply was that Kristín's son, King Sigurðr's daughter's son, had the best descent entitling him to the kingdom in Norway.

'There is for him,' he says, 'the man to govern with him [374] that is duty bound to be in charge of him and the kingdom in his father Erlingr, an intelligent man, determined and well tried in battles and a good ruler. He will not lack success in this enterprise if good luck is on his side.'

Many seconded this suggestion readily. Erlingr replies:

'From what I have heard, most of those that have been enquired of for this business are rather reluctant to take on this responsibility. Now it seems to me to lie in the balance, if we carry out this proposal, which is more likely, that the honour goes to the person that is put at the head of this company, or that it should turn out the contrary, which has now previously befallen very many of those that have taken up such a dangerous course, that as a result they have lost all their possessions and their lives as well. But if this business is concluded successfully, then it may be that there will be some that would have liked to have taken up this opportunity. The person that takes on this responsibility will need to set up strong safeguards against his then suffering opposition or hostility from those that are now taking part in these negotiations.'

Everyone agreed to set up this alliance in all good faith. Erlingr spoke:

'It can be said as far as I am concerned that it seems to me almost the same as my death to serve Hákon, and though this seems to me the most dangerous course, yet I am willing to risk letting you arrange things, and I will take on the leadership of the company if that is what you all consent to and want, and if you are all willing to confirm this by oaths.'

Everyone agreed to this, and it was decided at this meeting that they should take Magnús Erlingsson as king. After that they held an assembly in the town, and at this assembly Magnús was taken as king over the whole country. He was now five winters old. After that everyone that was present and had been in the service of King Ingi paid allegiance to him, and each of them kept the same titles as he had previously had with King Ingi.

[375] CHAPTER TWO

Erlingr skakki set out on his journey and committed himself to some ships, taking with him King Magnús and all the landed men that were there. In company there with him were the king's brother-in-law Árni and King Ingi's mother Ingiríðr and her two sons and Sigurðr storkr's son Jón kútiza (Udder) and Erlingr's personal following and also those that had been followers of Gregorius, and they had in all ten ships. They travelled south to Denmark to see King Valdamarr and King Ingi's brother Búriz Heinreksson. King Valdamarr was King Magnús's blood relative. They were sisters, the daughters of King Haraldr of Garðar in the east—he was Valdamarr Jarizleifsson's son[449]—King Valdamarr's mother Ingilborg and King Magnús's mother Kristín's mother Málmfríðr. King Valdamarr welcomed them and he and Erlingr spent a long time on meetings and planning, and the outcome of their talk was that King Valdamarr was to provide King Magnús with all the support from his kingdom that he needed in order to gain possession of Norway and thereafter keep it, while Valdamarr was to have the rule in Norway that his previous relatives Haraldr Gormsson and Sveinn tjúgusjegg had had, the whole of the Vík as far north as Rýgjarbit. This plan was confirmed by oaths and special agreements. After that Erlingr set out from Denmark and sailed out from Vendilskagi.

[376] CHAPTER THREE

In the spring immediately after Easter King Hákon went north to Þrándheimr. He now had all the ships that King Ingi had possessed. Hákon held an assembly in the town in Kaupangr and at it he was taken as king over the whole country. Then he gave Sigurðr of Reyrr a jarldom, and there he was accepted as jarl.

---

[449] Valdamarr was actually son of Járizleifr's son Vissivaldr.

After that Hákon and he travelled back south and all the way east to Vík. The king went to Túnsberg, but sent Jarl Sigurðr east to Konungahella to defend the land with part of their force, in case Erlingr should come from the south. Erlingr and his company got to Agðir and immediately made north for Bjǫrgyn. There they killed King Hákon's steward Árni Brígiðarskalli (Brígið's Old Man) and went back east from there to meet with King Hákon. Now Jarl Sigurðr had not become aware of Erlingr's journey from the south, and he was still now east by the Elfr, while King Hákon was in Túnsberg. Erlingr sailed to near Hrossanes and lay there for a few nights. King Hákon got ready in the town. Erlingr sailed to the town. They captured a trading ship and loaded it with wood and straw and set it on fire, and the wind got up towards the town and drove the trading ship up to the town. He had two cables put aboard the trading ship and two small ships tied to it, had these row along behind as the trading ship was blown ahead. And when the fire was very nearly got into the town, then they held the cables that were on the trading ship so that the town could not catch fire. Smoke blew so thickly into the town that they could not be seen from the jetties where the king's battle line was standing. After that Erlingr sailed all his force in behind where the wind was blowing the fire and shot up at them. So when the townspeople saw that the fire was getting close to their houses, and many were getting wounded from the missiles, then they made up [377] their minds and sent the priest Hróaldr langtala (Long Speech) out to see Erlingr to receive quarter for themselves and the town from Erlingr, and they broke up the king's battle line when Hróaldr told them that the quarter had been accepted. So when the troop of townspeople was gone away, then the troops on the jetties became thinned out. Then some urged Hákon's men that they should fight back, but Ǫnundr Símunarson, who now had the greatest say over the troop said this:

'I am not going to fight for Jarl Sigurðr's realm when he is nowhere near.'

After that Ǫnundr fled, and then the whole troop with the king, and they went up inland and a very large number of men of Hákon's troops fell there. Then this was composed:

231. Ǫnundr would not enter   *Skald* II 840
       into battle, he declared,
       until from the south Jarl Sigurðr
       sailed bringing the housecarls.
       Up the street Magnús's soldiers,
       splendid, are rushing,
       but the hawks[450] of Hǫkon
       hurried away quickly.

[450] brave fellows (ironical).

Þorbjǫrn Skakkaskáld says this:

232. It turned out in broad Túnsberg—   *Erlingsdrápa* 2
teeth of Gríðr's steed[451] you are not   *Skald* II 634
[378]   reluctant to redden—lord of men,
I learned, for you smoothly.
Townspeople took fright at
the torrent of bright spear-points.
Trees of weapon-tumult[452] felt
terror of fire and bent elm-bow.

King Hákon travelled by the inland route north into Þrándheimr. And when Jarl Sigurðr learnt of this, then he travelled with all the ships he could get hold of by the coastal route north to meet with King Hákon.

CHAPTER FOUR

Erlingr skakki captured all the ships in Túnsberg that King Hákon possessed. Along with them he got Bœkisúðin, which had been King Ingi's. Erlingr went after that and subjected the whole of the Vík to Magnús, and also on northwards wherever he went, and stayed the winter in Bjǫrgyn. Then Erlingr had King Hákon's landed man Ingibjǫrn sipill (Slurp) killed north in Firðir. King Hákon stayed in Þrándheimr during the winter, but the following spring he called out a levy and got ready to travel south to meet with Erlingr. There with him then were Jarl Sigurðr, Jón Sveinsson, Eindriði ungi and Ǫnundr Símunarson, Philippus Pétrsson, Philippus Gyrðarson, Rǫgnvaldr kunta (Cunt), Sigurðr kápa (Hooded Cloak), Sigurðr hjúpa (Overcoat), Frírekr kœna (Boat), Áskell at Forland, Gunnarr gjaldkeri's (Steward's) son Þorbjǫrn, Strað-Bjarni (Fuck-).

[379] CHAPTER FIVE

Erlingr stayed in Bjǫrgyn and had a large force and came to the decision to impose an embargo on all trading ships that were intending to travel north to Kaupangr, since he thought that intelligence would reach Hákon too soon if the ships were to sail from one to the other, though he gave as his reason that the Bjǫrgynjarmenn were more deserving of having the goods that were on the ships even though they were being purchased at a lower price from the crews of the trading ships than they thought suitable, rather than that they should be transported 'into the hands of our enemies and foes for their support'. So the number of ships gathered at the town increased, for many

---

[451] *Gríðar fákr*: 'steed of Gríðr (a giantess)', wolf.
[452] *malma dynviðir*: 'trees (men) of the din of weapons (battle)', warriors.

arrived each day, and none left. Then Erlingr had the lightest of his ships drawn up ashore, and allowed the rumour to get about that he was going to stay there and give a welcome to the support coming from his friends and relations. And one day Erlingr had a trumpet blown for a meeting of the skippers and then gave permission for all the skippers of trading ships to depart for wherever they wanted to go. So when men had got leave from Erlingr skakki, those that were in charge of trading ships and had previously been lying fully prepared to travel with their wares, some with their purchases and some that had other business, there being then too weather that was very favourable for sailing north along the coast, and before mid-afternoon of that day had come, all those that were ready had sailed. Then whoever had the fastest ship pushed ahead most energetically. They all raced each other. So when this fleet got north to Mœrr there was then there facing them King Hákon's force, and he himself was there assembling and preparing his troops and he was summoning to him landed men and the men of his levy, not having had for a long time before this learnt any news from Bjǫrgyn, but now they got the same news from all the ships that were travelling from the south that Erlingr skakki had beached his ships in Bjǫrgyn and that they would have to seek him there, and they said that [380] he had a large force. From there Hákon sailed to Véey and sent out Jarl Sigurðr and Ǫnundr Símunarson in to Raumsdalr to get him forces and ships, and he sent out men into both Mœrrs.

But when King Hákon had stayed a few nights in the market town, then he sailed away and a bit further south, thinking that then their journey would be sooner started and forces would sooner reach him. Erlingr skakki had given permission for the trading ships to sail out of Bjǫrgyn on Sunday, and on Tuesday when mattins was over the king's trumpet was blown and the men of the levy and the people of the town were summoned to him to launch the ships that had previously been beached. Erlingr held an assembly with his own troops and the men of the levy, saying what his plan was now, naming men to captain ships, having who were enrolled onto the king's ship read out. This assembly ended with Erlingr telling everyone to get ready in his place, wherever they had been assigned, and saying that anyone that was then waiting behind in the town when he sailed Bœkisúðin away should lose life or limbs. The king's brother-in-law Ormr sailed his ship away straight away in the evening, and most ships had already been afloat.

CHAPTER SIX

On Wednesday, before the Masses were sung in the town, Erlingr had sailed all his forces away out of the town. They had twenty-one ships. There was now a fresh wind from the south along the coast. Erlingr had

his son King Magnús with him. There were many landed men there and
they had a very fine troop. While Erlingr was sailing north past Firðir he
sent a light ship aside from their route in to Jón Hallkelsson's dwelling
and had Níkolás, son of Símun skálpr and son of Haraldr gilli's daughter
Maria captured, and they brought him with them out to the troop. He went
on the king's ship. Straight away in the last part of the night on Friday they
sailed [381] to Steinavágr. King Hákon was then lying in the harbour that
is called . . .,[453] and had fourteen ships. He himself and his men were up
on the island playing a game, and his landed men were sitting on a kind of
mound. They saw that some boat or other was rowing to the island from
the south. There were two men on it, and they were leaning back down to
the keel and pulling forward on the oars with no little vigour, and when
they got to land, they did not tie up the boat but both ran. So the ruling men
saw this and discussed among themselves that these men must have some
tidings to tell. They stood up and went towards them. And as soon as they
met, Ǫnundr Símunarson asked:

'Are you able to tell anything of Erlingr skakki, as you are going in such
a rush?'

The one that was first able to get out a word because of his exhaustion
replied:

'Erlingr is sailing at you here with twenty ships or thereabouts and many
of them pretty large, and you will soon see their sails now.'

Then said Eindriði ungi: '"Too close to my nose," said the old man, he
had been shot in the eye.'[454]

Then they went hastily to where the game was being played, and next a
trumpet sounded, and a war summons called all the troops to the ships in as
much haste as possible, and this was at the time of day when the cooking
was nearly done. All the people made for the ships. Each man leapt out onto
the ship that was closest to him there, and the ships were unequally manned.
They take to the oars, some are raising the masts and they turn the ships
to the north and make for Véey, since they were expecting a great deal of
support for themselves there from the townspeople.

CHAPTER SEVEN

The next thing was that they see the sails of Erlingr and his troops, and each
side sees the others. Eindriði ungi had the ship that was called Draglaun,
a large longship built like a transport vessel,[455] and it had now got short of
crew, as those that had [382] previously been on it had leapt onto other ships.

[453] All manuscripts have a gap here.

[454] Presumably a proverbial expression to mean that danger was close.

[455] *langskipsbúza*, cf. note 194 above.

This was the slowest of Hákon's ships. So when Eindriði got opposite the island of Sekkr, then Bœkisúðin came after them, which was skippered by Erlingr skakki, and these two ships got fastened together. But Hákon was now nearly come in to Véey when they heard the sound of trumpets, since the ships that were closest had turned back, wanting to help Eindriði, and now both sides engaged in battle as far they could. Many of the sails went down across the ships, but none of them were tied together and they came side by side. This battle did not go on long before the organisation broke down on King Hákon's ship. Some fell, some leapt overboard. Hákon threw a grey hooded cloak over himself and leapt onto another ship. And when he had been on it a short time then he realised that he had come where he was surrounded by enemies, and when he thought about it, then he could see none of his own men nor of his own ships very close. Then he went onto Bœkisúðin and forward into the company of forecastlemen and asked for quarter, and the forecastlemen received him and gave him quarter. But in this onslaught there had been a large number of casualties, and yet more of them among Hákon's men. There had now fallen on Bœkisúðin Símun skálpr's son Níkolás, and his killing was attributed to Erlingr's men themselves. After this there was a lull in the fighting and the ships on the two sides were disentangled. Now Erlingr was told that King Hákon was there on the ship and his forecastlemen had taken charge of him and had promised to defend him. Erlingr sent someone forward on the ship and bade him tell the forecastlemen that they were to guard Hákon so that he did not go away, and said that he was not against the king getting quarter if this was what the ruling men decided and if peace terms were negotiated based on that. The forecastlemen all spoke, blessing him for saying that. Then Erlingr had the trumpet sounded vigorously and gave men orders that they were to attack the ships that had not been cleared, saying that they would never have a better opportunity to avenge King Ingi. Then they all shouted a [383] war cry and each urged on the next and went to the attack. In this tumult King Hákon was mortally wounded. And after his fall and when his men became aware of it, then they rowed hard forwards and threw down their shields and hewed with both hands, caring nothing for their lives. This rashness soon caused them great harm, for Erlingr's men could see unprotected parts of their bodies to strike at. A large part of Hákon's force fell. This was for the most part because the difference in numbers was great and Hákon's men protected themselves so little, and there was no point in any of Hákon's men speaking of quarter except just those that men of the ruling class took into their power and pledged ransom for. These men fell of Hákon's troop, Sigurðr kápa, Sigurðr hjúpa, Rǫgnvaldr kunta. But some ships got away and rowed in into the fiords and so saved their lives. King Hákon's body was conveyed in into Raumsdalr and was buried there. His brother King Sverrir had King Hákon's body conveyed north to Kaupangr and laid in the stone wall in Christchurch in the choir on the south side.

CHAPTER EIGHT

Sigurðr and Eindriði ungi, Ǫnundr Símunarson, Frírekr kœna and yet more leaders kept the troop together, abandoned the ships in Raumsdalr and after that travelled to Upplǫnd. Erlingr skakki and King Magnús went with their troop north to Kaupangr and subjected the whole land to themselves wherever they went. After that Erlingr had Eyraþing summoned. There Magnús was taken as king over the whole country. Erlingr stayed there a short time, since he thought the Þrœndir [384] were not faithful to him and his son. Magnús was now said to be king over the whole country.

King Hákon was a quite handsome person in looks, well shaped, tall and thin. He was very broad-shouldered. Therefore his followers called him Hákon herðibreiðr (Broad-Shouldered). But because he was young of age, other leaders took part in policy-making with him. He was cheerful and unassuming in speech, playful and had the nature of a youthful person. He was popular with the common people.

CHAPTER NINE

There was a man of Upplǫnd called Markús in Skógr, a kinsman of Jarl Sigurðr. Markús fostered a son of King Sigurðr. He was called Sigurðr. Afterwards the Upplendingar took Sigurðr as king with the consent of Jarl Sigurðr and other leaders that had followed King Hákon, and they had now still the support of a large troop. The band was often divided ino two groups. The king and Markús were less in exposed positions, while Jarl Sigurðr and other leaders with their troops were more exposed to dangers. They travelled with this band mostly round Upplǫnd, and sometimes down into the Vík.

Erlingr skakki always kept his son Magnús with him. He had the whole fleet and the defence of the country in his charge. He stayed in Bjǫrgyn for some time in the autumn and travelled from there east into the Vík and established himself in Túnsberg, making arrangements for winter quarters there and gathering to himself the taxes and dues that belonged to the king round the Vík. He also had a fine and large troop of men. But because Jarl Sigurðr had a small part of the country and his following was large, there was soon a shortage of money, and where there were no leaders near, then money was demanded very unlawfully, some by harsh accusations of wrongdoing, and some straightforwardly by plundering.

[385] CHAPTER TEN

At this time the realm of Norway was in a properous condition. The farming community was wealthy and powerful and unused to lack of freedom and the hostility of the bands of men. There soon got to be many reports and detailed accounts when plundering took place. The Víkverjar were staunch friends of King Magnús and Erlingr. This was chiefly on account of the popularity of King Ingi Haraldsson, for the Víkverjar had often served under that standard with their support. Erlingr had guards kept on watch in the towns, and twelve men were on the watch every night. Erlingr was always holding an assembly with the farmers and at them the unruliness of Sigurðr's men was often discussed and with the encouragement of Erlingr and other members of the troop there came to be great support among the farmers for the idea that it would be a very fortunate act for people to ensure that that band never prospered. The king's brother-in-law Árni spoke at length on this matter and fiercely towards the end. He asked everyone that was at the assembly, both men from the troop and farmers and townsfolk that people should pass a resolution to condemn according to the law Jarl Sigurðr and all their band to the Devil, both during their lives and after their deaths. And with the vehemence and rage of the crowd everyone now assented to this. This unprecedented act was carried out and confirmed in the way that the law provided for judgments to be passed at assemblies. The priest Hróaldr langtala spoke about this business. He was an eloquent man, and this speech came to very much the same conclusion as had previously been expressed. Erlingr gave a banquet in Túnsberg at Yule and he distributed pay there at Candlemas.[456]

CHAPTER ELEVEN

Jarl Sigurðr travelled round the Vík with his finest body of men, and many men submitted to him as a result of bullying, and many paid money. In this way he travelled widely up inland and [386] turned up in various places. There were many in the band that secretly sought quarter from Erlingr, and this answer came in reply that everyone that asked for it should have mercy on his life but only those would be allowed to remain in the country that had not committed serious offences against him. So when the men in the band learned that people were not to be allowed to remain in the country, then this held the band together to a large extent, for there were many that knew they could be so truly charged that Erlingr would think them very guilty. Philippus Gyrðarson reached an agreement with Erlingr and got back his property and returned to his estates. A little later Sigurðr's men came there and killed him. Each side struck many blows on the other in persecutions

---

[456] See note 289 above.

or in killing of people and that is not recorded in writing when leading men were not involved.

CHAPTER TWELVE

It was in the first part of Lent that intelligence came to Erlingr that Jarl Sigurðr must be coming to fight him, and he was heard of here and there, sometimes nearby, and sometimes further off. Erlingr sent out scouts so that he should know about it wherever they might turn up. He also had his whole troop called out every evening from the town by trumpet, and they lay assembled during the nights with the troop all set out in battle array. Then intelligence reached Erlingr that Jarl Sigurðr and his men were a short way off up in Ré. Erlingr then set out from the town taking with him all the townspeople that were capable of fighting and had arms, and also the merchants, except for twelve men that were left behind to guard the town. He left the town on Tuesday in the second week of Lent[457] after mid-afternoon, and every man had with him two days' provisions. Then they travelled during the night and they took a long time to get their troops out of the town. [387] There were two men to each horse and each shield. When the troop was counted then there were nearly thirteen hundred men.

Now when intelligence came to meet them, they were told that Jarl Sigurðr was in Ré at the farm that is called Hrafnsnes with five hundred men. Then Erlingr had his troops called together and told them the news that he had heard, and everyone urged that they should hurry and capture them in the building or fight straight away during the night. Erlingr made a speech and spoke as follows:

'It would seem likely that our meeting with Jarl Sigurðr will come about soon. In their band there are many other men too whose handiwork may stick in our memory when they cut down King Ingi and also many others of our friends whom it would take long to number. They carried out these deeds with the help of fiends and witchcraft and villainy, for it stands here in our statutes and laws of the land that no one is so degenerate that he not call it an act of villainy or murderous crime if people are killed by night. This band have sought to find their salvation, on the instruction of those skilled in the black arts, in fighting by night and not under the sun. They have also by such methods achieved the victory of overcoming such a ruler as they have laid low. Now we have often maintained and demonstrated how hateful their way of going on seems to us when they have engaged in battle by night. We shall therefore rather follow the example of those other leaders, that are better known to us and better models to imitate, by fighting in the light of day and in a properly organised way, and not stealing upon sleeping men by night. We have a good force against them,

---

[457] i.e. 19th February 1163.

no larger an army than they have. We shall wait for daytime and the dawn and
keep together in our formation in case they decide to make some attack on us.'

After this the whole troop sat down. Some spread out some haystacks
[388] and made themselves beds, some sat on their shields and thus waited
for dawn. The weather was cool and and there was sleet falling.

CHAPTER THIRTEEN

Jarl Sigurðr had so far received the intelligence that the force was come close
to them. His men got up and armed themselves, not knowing precisely how
large a force Erlingr and his men had. Some wanted to flee, though most
wanted to wait. Jarl Sigurðr was a sensible person and a good speaker, but
was not said to be a man of great daring. He also was now more keen to
flee, and because of this came in for a great deal of criticism from his troops.
But when it began to get light, both sides began to draw up their troops.
Jarl Sigurðr drew up his on a kind of slope above the bridge between it and
the town. A small river was flowing there. And Erlingr and his men drew
up theirs on the other side of the river. Behind their formation were men on
horseback, well armed. They had the king with them. The jarl's men saw
now that the difference in numbers was going to be great, and reckoned it
was advisable to make for the forest. The jarl replies:

'You say that I have no courage in me, but now it will be put to the test,
so now each one must take care that he does not flee or flinch before I do.
We have a good vantage position, we shall let them go over the bridge, and
when their standard gets over the bridge, then we shall throw ourselves on
them in front of the slope, and let no one flee from anyone else.'

Jarl Sigurðr had a dark-coloured tunic and a red cloak with the skirts
tucked up, skin boots on his feet. He had a shield and a sword that was called
Bastard. The jarl spoke:

'God knows with me, that rather than get a lot of gold I would like to
manage to get one blow on Erlingr skakki with Bastard.'

[389] CHAPTER FOURTEEN

Erlingr skakki's troop wanted to advance to the bridge. He spoke, telling
them to turn up along the river.

'This river is small and not difficult to cross, for it is level ground up to it.'

This was done. The jarl's battle-line went up along the slope keeping opposite
to them. And when the slope came to an end and it was level and straightforward
across the river, then Erlingr said that his men should sing the Paternoster
and pray that the side should be victorious that was most proper. Then they
(Sigurðr's men) all sang the Kyrie in a loud voice and all beat their weapons

on their shields. And at that noise three hundred men of Erlingr's troop shot off and fled. Erlingr and his troop went across the river, and the jarl's men shouted a war cry, but their rush forward broke off at the bottom of the slope at Erlingr's battle line. The battle began at the beginning of the slope. First there were spear thrusts and soon it was already a hand-to-hand fight. The jarl's standard turned tail, so that Erlingr and his men got up onto the slope. There was then a short battle before the jarl's force fled into the forest that was behind them before. Now Jarl Sigurðr was told, and men told him to flee. He replied:

'Forward with us now, while we still can!'

Then they went forward very valiantly and hewed to both sides. In this onset Jarl Sigurðr and Jón Sveinsson and nearly sixty men fell. Erlingr and his troop lost few men and pursued the rout up to the forest. Then Erlingr reviewed his troops and turned back. He came to where the king's slaves were trying to drag the clothes off Jarl Sigurðr and he was not entirely dead though he was unconscious. He had put his sword in its sheath, and it was lying next to him. Erlingr picked it up and hit the slaves with it, telling them to creep off. [390] After that Erlingr turned back with his force and established himself in Túnsberg. Seven nights after the jarl fell some of Erlingr's men caught Eindriði ungi, and he was killed.

CHAPTER FIFTEEN

Markús of Skógr and his foster-son Sigurðr decided to go down into the Vík when spring came, and there got themselves a ship. So when Erlingr learnt that, then he went east after them and they met in Konungahella. Markús and his companion fled out onto the island of Hísing. The people of the country, the Hísingsbúar, rushed down there and joined the battle array with Markús's men. Erlingr and his men rowed to land, and Markús's men shot at them. Then Erlingr spoke with his men:

'Let us take their ships and not go ashore to fight with the country's army. The Hísingsbúar are bad to visit, rough people and stupid. They will not keep this band with them for long, for Hísing is a small country.'

This was done, they took the ships and conveyed them over to Konungahella. Markús and his troop went up into Markir and planned to launch attacks from there. They each had watch kept on the other. Erlingr had a large number of men, calling out troops to join them from the surrounding areas. Now neither side made attacks on the other.

CHAPTER SIXTEEN

Erlendr hímaldi's son Eysteinn was chosen as archbishop after the death of Archbishop Jón. Eysteinn was consecrated in the same year as King Ingi fell. And when Archbishop Eysteinn came to his see, he was well liked [391] by all the people of the land. He was a very outstanding person, a man of noble family. The Þrœndir welcomed him, for most of the men of rank in Þrœndalǫg were related to or had some link with the archbishop, and all were firm friends of his. The archbishop then started negotiations with the landowners, speaking first of the foundation's need of money, and also of what great development the foundation needed to have if it was now to be as much more decently maintained than before as it was more dignified than before now that an archbishop's see was established there. He asked the landowners that they should grant him the equivalent of an ounce of pure silver as his share of fines. Now previously he had had an ounce in ordinary currency, which was legal tender for the king's share of fines, but there is a fifty per cent difference in the value of this ounce by which the one he wanted to have, the ounce of pure silver, is greater.[458] So with the support of kinsmen of the archbishop and his friends, and his own management ability, this change was brought about, and it was made law over the whole of Þrœndalǫg, and it was brought about too throughout the area that came under his authority as archbishop.

CHAPTER SEVENTEEN

Sigurðr and Markús, after they had lost their ships on the Elfr, realised that they would not be able to get hold of Erlingr. So they turned up towards Upplǫnd and thus travelled overland north to Þrándheimr. They were welcomed there. Sigurðr was taken as king there at Eyraþing. Many good men's sons joined the band there. They took to ships there and made quick preparations, travelling, when summer came, south to Mœrr and received all the royal dues wherever they went. There were these landed men in Bjǫrgyn to defend the land, Níkolás Sigurðarson, Nǫkkvi Pálsson and yet more [392] leaders of troops, Þórólfr dryllr (Stocky), Þorbjǫrn gjaldkeri and many others. Markús and his party sailed from the north and learnt that Erlingr's men were with large numbers in Bjǫrgyn. They sailed past there to the south by the outer route [outside the islands]. People commented on the fact that that summer Markús's men had a favourable wind wherever they wanted to go.

CHAPTER EIGHTEEN

Erlingr skakki, as soon as he learnt that Markús's party had turned to the north, then he sailed north into the Vík and gathered troops to himself, and soon had a large following and had large and numerous ships. But when he

---

[458] 'Silver' coins were always mixed with copper. Pure silver had double the value of silver coins, weight for weight.

tried to sail out into the Vík, he got a contrary wind and lay here and there in harbours all that summer. So when Markús and his band came east to Listi, then they learnt that Erlingr had an invincible army in the Vík, and turned back north. And when they got to Hǫrðaland, then they planned to go to Bjǫrgyn, and when they got in front of the town, then Níkolás and his men were rowing out towards them and had a much larger force and larger ships. Markús and his party then saw they had no other choice but to row away south. Some make out to sea, some south into the sounds, some in into the fiords, but Markús and some men with him leapt ashore up onto the island that is called Skarpa. Níkolás and his men took their ships, gave Jón Hallkelsson and some other men quarter, but killed most of those they caught. A few days later Eindriði heiðafylja (Heath Mare) found Sigurðr and Markús. They were conveyed to Bjǫrgyn. Sigurðr was beheaded out from Grafdalr, and Markús hanged with another man on Hvarfsnes, and that was at Michaelmas.[459] The band that had followed them then dispersed.

[393] CHAPTER NINETEEN

Frírekr kœna and Bjarni inn illi (the Evil), Ǫnundr Símunarson, Ǫrnólfr skorpa (Crust), they had rowed out to sea with some ships and sailed the outer route along the ocean past the coast, and wherever they came to land they plundered and killed Erlingr's friends. But when Erlingr learnt of the killing of Markús and his men, then he gave the landed men and the men of the levy leave to return home, and he himself then sailed with his troops east across Foldin, for he had heard of some of Markús's men being there. Erlingr sailed to Konungahella and stayed there during the autumn. In the first week of winter Erlingr went out to the island of Hísing with a large troop and requested an assembly there. The Hísingsbúar came down and opened an assembly. Erlingr brought charges against them for having rushed to join Markús's men and for drawing up their forces against him. Ǫzurr was the man that was the most powerful of the farmers that spoke on their behalf. The assembly lasted a long time, but in the end the farmers entrusted the judgment to Erlingr, and he gave them an appointment for a meeting for a week later and appointed fifteen men of the farmers to come to it. And when they came, Erlingr sentenced them to pay three hundred cattle. The farmers went back home dissatisfied with their lot. A little later the river froze over and Erlingr's ship was stuck in the ice. Now the farmers withheld the payment and lay assembled for a while. Erlingr prepared his Yule banquet there, and the Hísingsbúar held a joint feast and had a party together over Yule. In the night after the fifth day of Yule,[460] Erlingr went

---

[459] *Mikjálsmessa*, 29th September.
[460] 29th December.

out onto the island and captured Ǫzurr's house [394] and burnt him inside, and in all he slew a hundred men and burnt three farms, after that travelling back to Konungahella. Afterwards the farmers came to him and paid the fine.

CHAPTER TWENTY

In the spring Erlingr skakki got ready as soon as he could get his ships afloat because of the ice and left Konungahella. He learnt that those that had previously been Markús's men were making raids north in the Vík. Erlingr had watch kept on their movements and went to look for them and found them while they were lying in a certain harbour. Ǫnundr Símunarson and Ǫrnólfr skorpa got away, but Frírekr kœna and Bjarni inn illi were captured and many of their troops killed. Erlingr had Frírekr tied to an anchor and thrown overboard. For this deed Erlingr was very greatly disliked in Þrœndalǫg, for Frírekr had very noble relatives there. Erlingr had Bjarni hanged, and then, before he was hanged, he uttered the most horrible words, as he usually did. So says Þorbjǫrn Skakkaskáld:

233.	East of the fiord Erlingr	*Erlingsdrápa* 3
	issued death to the vikings—	*Skald* II 635
	many men got from Kœna	
	misery—when he went there.	
	A fluke was fastened between	
	Frírekr's shoulders; ill-eager,	
[395]	hung on a tree somewhat higher,	
	harmful to people, Bjarni.	

Ǫnundr and Ǫrnólfr and the groups that had got away fled to Denmark, but were sometimes to be found in Gautland or in the Vík.

CHAPTER TWENTY-ONE

Erlingr skakki sailed after that to Túnsberg and stayed there a long time during the spring. But when summer came he sailed north to Bjǫrgyn. There was at the time a very large number of people there. The legate Stephanus was there from the city of Rome and archbishop Eysteinn and other native bishops. There also was bishop Brandr, who had now been consecrated bishop for Iceland. There also was King Magnús berfœttr's grandson Jón Loptsson. King Magnús and other kinsmen of Jón's had now acknowledged his kinship to them. Archbishop Eysteinn and Erlingr skakki were often in conversation and in private talks. And on one occasion it came up in their discussion that Erlingr asked:

'Is that accurate, lord, what people say, that you have increased the standard of money for your share of fines among farmers in the north of the country?'

The archbishop replies: 'It is indeed true that farmers have granted me an increase in the standard of money for my share of fines. They have done this voluntarily, and under no compulsion, thus increasing God's glory and the wealth of our foundation.'

Erlingr says: 'Is this the law, lord, of the blessed King Óláfr, or have [396] you interpreted this provision rather more rigorously than the way it is written in the lawbook?'

The archbishop says: 'The blessed King Óláfr will have set up the laws in accordance with what was accepted and agreed to by the people, but one cannot find in his laws that it is forbidden to increase God's due.'

Erlingr replies: 'If you are going to increase your dues, then you will want to support us in increasing the king's dues by the same amount.'

The archbishop says: 'You have already now increased sufficiently the name and power of your son. And if I have now taken an unlawful standard of money from the Þrœndir, then I maintain that it amounts to a greater breach of the law that he is king over the land that is not the son of a king. There are neither laws nor precedents in this country to justify this.'

Erlingr says: 'When Magnús was taken as king over the realm of Norway, it was done with your knowledge and consent and also with that of other bishops in this country.'

The archbishop says: 'You promised, Erlingr, that if we agreed with you that Magnús should be taken as king, you would support God's rights in all respects with all your power.'

'I acknowledge this,' says Erlingr, 'that I have promised to uphold God's law and the laws of the land with all my strength and that of the king. Now I can see a better way forward than for each of us to accuse the other of breaking his promises. Let us rather keep all our personal promises. You support King Magnús in his power, as you have promised, and I shall support your power in all profitable matters.'

The whole discussion now proceeded smoothly between them. Now Erlingr spoke:

'If Magnús has not been taken as king in accordance with what has been the ancient custom in this country, then you can use your power to give him a crown, in accordance with what God's laws are for annointing a king to power. And though I am not a king nor descended from a kingly line, yet have most kings in our memory now been such as have not been as well acquainted with the statutes and laws of the land as I. For King Magnús's mother is a legitimate daughter of a king and queen. Magnús is also [397] son of a queen and son of a lawfully wedded wife. So if you are willing to grant him consecration as king, then no one will afterwards be able to deprive him of the kingdom lawfully. Viljálmr Bastard was not a king's son, and he was consecrated and crowned king over England, and since then the kingdom has remained in his family in England and all of them have been crowned. Sveinn Úlfsson in Denmark was not a king's son, and yet he was crowned king there and afterwards his sons and one after another of that family has been crowned king.[461] There is now an archbishop's see here in this country. That is a great glory and honour for our country. Let us enhance it further with good things, let us have a crowned king no less than English people or Danes.'

After this the archbishop and Erlingr frequently discussed this business, and everything proceeded in a peaceable way. Afterwards the archbishop put this to the legate and easily brought the legate into agreement with himself. The archbishop then had a meeting with his suffragan bishops and other clerics and put this matter to them, and all replied in the same way, saying they consented to whatever the archbishop wished to have done, and all were eager for the consecration to go ahead as soon as they found that that was what the archbishop wished to have done. That was the decision of them all.

CHAPTER TWENTY-TWO

Erlingr skakki had preparations made in the royal palace for a great banquet, and the great hall was hung with precious cloths and tapestries and adorned in the most expensive way. Then the court and all the people in the king's service were given entertainment. There was a huge number of guests and many leaders there. Magnús then received consecration as king from Archbishop Eysteinn, and there were present at [398] the consecration five other bishops and the legate and a huge number of clerics. Erlingr skakki and twelve landed men with him swore legally binding oaths together with the king. And on the day that the consecration took place, the king and Erlingr had as their guests the archbishop and the legate and all the bishops, and this banquet was the most glorious. Father and son gave out there many great gifts. King Magnús was now eight winters old. He had now been king for three winters.

[399] CHAPTER TWENTY-THREE

King Valdamarr of the Danes had now heard the news from Norway that Magnús was now sole king there. Now all other groups in that country had been got rid of. Then the king sent men of his with letters to King Magnús and Erlingr, reminding them of the personal agreement that Erlingr had entered into with King Valdamarr, as was written here above, that King

---

[461] This is incorrect. Knútr Valdimarsson was in 1170 the first king of Denmark to be crowned.

Valdamarr was to gain possession of the Vík from the east to Rýgjarbit if
Magnús became sole king in Norway. So when the messengers came forward
and showed Erlingr the letters from the king of the Danes, and he realises
the claim that the king of the Danes has in Norway, then Erlingr put this
before other people that he went to for advice, and they all said the same
thing, that never should the Danes be given a share of Norway, for people
said that the time that had been worst in the country was when Danes had
power over Norway. The messengers of the king of the Danes discussed
their request with Erlingr and asked him for a decision. Erlingr told them to
go with him east into Vík in the autumn, saying that he would then give his
decision when he had seen the men in the Vík that were most knowlegeable.

[400] CHAPTER TWENTY-FOUR

In the autumn Erlingr skakki travelled east into Vík and stayed in Túnsberg,
sending men over to Borg and having a four-district assembly called there
in the Borg. After that Erlingr went there with his troops. And when the
assembly was in session, then Erlingr spoke and told about what plans had
been agreed between him and the king of the Danes when Erlingr and his
party had set up their band for the first time.

'I am moreover willing,' he says, 'to keep to all the personal agreements
that we entered into then, if it is what you farmers wish and consent to, to
serve the king of the Danes rather than this king that is here consecrated and
crowned king over the country.'

The farmers answered Erlingr and said as follows:

'By no means are we willing to become subjects of the king of the Danes
as long as one of us Víkverjar is alive.'

Then the whole crowd rushed up with shouts and cries bidding Erlingr
keep his oaths that he had sworn to all the people of the land to defend 'your
son's land, and we shall all follow you.'

Thus this assembly was broken up. After this the messengers of the king
of the Danes went back south to Denmark and told the result of their errand
such as it was. The Danes subjected Erlingr and all the Norwegians to much
criticism, saying that one never got anything from them but what was bad.
The word got around that the next spring the king of the Danes would take
out an army and make raids in Norway. In the autumn Erlingr went north to
Bjǫrgyn and stayed there during the winter and distributed wages there.

CHAPTER TWENTY-FIVE

That winter some Danish men travelled round the country overland saying
what is very common, that they were on their way to the blessed King Óláfr

for the vigil.[462] But when they got to Þrándheimr, then they went to see many men of rank, saying [401] now that their business was that the king of the Danes had sent them to seek their friendship towards him, and their welcome if he came to the country, and he was promising to give them both power and wealth. This message was accompanied by a letter and seal of the king of the Danes, and the instruction that the Þrœndir[463] were to send in reply their letters and seals. They did so and most responded positively to the message of the king of the Danes. The messengers went back east towards the end of Lent. Erlingr was staying in Bjǫrgyn. And when spring came, Erlingr's friends told him the rumour they had heard from men on trading ships that were come from Þrándheimr in the north that the Þrœndir had come out in open hostility to him and they had announced at their assemblies that if Erlingr came to Þrándheimr he should never get out past Agðanes with his life. Erlingr said that this was a false rumour and nonsense.

Erlingr announced that he was going to go south to Unarheimr for the Rogation Days assembly, and had a warship prepared, a twenty-benched one, and a lighter ship, a fifteen-benched one, and also a ship to carry stores. So when the ships were ready, then there arose a fresh southerly wind. On the Tuesday in Rogation Days Erlingr had his troops summoned to the ships by trumpet, but men were reluctant to leave the town and thought it unpleasant to have to row against the wind. Erlingr sailed north into Byskupshǫfn. Then said Erlingr:

'You are grumbling a lot about rowing against the wind, get out now and raise the masts, after that hoist the sails, and let us sail the ships north.'

They did so, sailed north during the day and during the night. Wednesday in the evening they sailed in past Agðanes. Then they found before them a great collection of ships, cargo ships and rowing boats and light ocean-going vessels—these were for people attending the festival[464]—going in to the town, some ahead of them, some behind. The townspeople therefore took no notice of longships sailing past.

[402] CHAPTER TWENTY-SIX

Erlingr skakki arrived in the town at the time that mattins was being sung up at Christchurch. Erlingr and his men ran into the town, and they were told that Óttarr birtingr's son Álfr hroði, a landed man, was still sitting and drinking with his men. Erlingr made an attack on them. Álfr was killed and nearly all his men. Few other men fell, for most had gone to church. This

---

[462] This would have been in Þrándheimr on the eve of 29th July or 3rd August.

[463] *Kringla* had *bœndrnir*, other manuscripts *Þrœndir* or *Þrœndirnir*.

[464] Ascension Day (Thursday in Rogation week), the 40th day after Easter. Cf. note 396 above.

was the night before Ascension Day. Straightway in the morning Erlingr had all his troops called out onto Eyrar by trumpet for an assembly, and at the assembly Erlingr brought charges against the Þrœndir, accusing them of treason against the king and himself, and naming as responsible Bárðr standali and Páll Andreasson and Raza-Bárðr (Arse-) — he at that time was town steward — and very many others as well. They replied, denying the charges. Then Erlingr's chaplain stood up holding up many letters and seals and asked if they recognised their seals there that they had sent in the spring to the king of the Danes. Then the letters were then also read aloud. Also present there with Erlingr were the Danish men that had brought letters during the winter. Erlingr had got hold of them for this purpose. Then they repeated before all the people the words that each of them had spoken:

'Thus you spoke, Raza-Bárðr, and you smote your chest: "From this breast came all these plans originally".'

Bárðr replied: 'I was mad then, my lord, when I said that.'

There was no other choice then but to hand over the judgment of the whole affair to Erlingr. He then took on the spot an immense amount of money from many people, and pronounced all those that had been killed to have forfeited compensation. Afterwards he went back south to Bjǫrgyn.

[403] CHAPTER TWENTY-SEVEN

That spring King Valdamarr had a great army out in Denmark and sailed his troops north into the Vík. As soon as he got into the realm of the king of Norway, then the farmers brought out against him a host and a crowd of men. The king travelled peaceably and sensibly, but wherever they travelled by the mainland, then men shot at them even if they were one or two, and it seemed to the Danes like the absolute hostility of the people of the country. So when they got to Túnsberg, then King Valdamarr called an assembly there on Haugar, but no one attended from the surrounding districts. Then King Valdamarr made a speech, saying this:

'It is obvious as regards the people of this land, that all are opposed to us. We now have two options open to us. The one is to lay waste this land and spare nothing, neither cattle nor men. The other option is to go back south without more ado. But it is more to my mind to go rather to the eastern Baltic to heathen countries of which there are plenty available, and not to kill Christian folk here even though they deserve it well enough.'

But all the others were eager to make raids, and yet the king prevailed, so that they went back south, and yet there was plundering very widely round the outlying islands and everywhere when the king was not nearby. They travelled south to Denmark.

[404] CHAPTER TWENTY-EIGHT

Erlingr skakki heard that an army of Danes was come into the Vík. Then he called out a levy over the whole country of troops and ships, and this turned out to be a huge rush to arms and he took this army east along the coast. But when he got to Líðandisnes, he learnt that the army of Danes was gone back south to Denmark and they had plundered widely in the Vík. Then Erlingr gave leave to all the levy troops to return home, but he himself and some landed men sailed with a very large number of ships south after the Danes to Jótland. And when they got to the place called Dýrsá, then they found before them Danes returned from an expedition, and they had many ships. Erlingr attacked them and fought with them. The Danes soon fled and lost many men, but Erlingr and his men plundered the ships and also the market town and got a very large amount of wealth there and afterwards went back to Norway. Then there was for a time warfare between Norway and Denmark.

[405] CHAPTER TWENTY-NINE

The king's daughter Kristín travelled in the autumn south to Denmark. She went to see her kinsman King Valdamarr. They were the children of sisters. The king welcomed her extremely warmly and presented her with banquets with him there, so that she could maintain her following there well. She was often in conversation with the king, and he was very friendly with her. So the following spring Kristín sent men to Erlingr and bade him go to see the king of the Danes and be reconciled with him. The next summer Erlingr was in the Vík. He prepared a single longship and manned it with his finest troops. After that he sailed over to Jótland. He learnt that King Valdamarr was in Randaróss. Erlingr sailed there and arrived in the town at the time when most people were sitting over their food. So when they had put up their awnings and made fast their ship, Erlingr went ashore in a party of twelve and all mailcoated, having hoods over their helmets and swords under their cloaks. They went to the king's quarters. Just then dishes were being carried in, and the doors were open. Erlingr and his men went straight in before the high seat. Erlingr spoke:

'We wish to have a truce, king, both here and for our journey back.'

The king looked at him and said:

'Is it you there, Erlingr?'

He replied: 'It is Erlingr here, so tell us quickly whether we shall have a truce.'

There were inside there eighty of the king's men and all of them unarmed. The king said:

'You shall have a truce, Erlingr, as you ask. I do not act the villain to any man if he comes to see me.'

Erlingr kissed the king's hand and after that went out and to his ship. He stayed there for a while with the king. They spoke about making peace between themselves and their countries, and it was agreed that Erlingr should stay there as hostage with [406] the king of the Danes, while Archbishop Absalon's brother Ásbjǫrn snara (Snare) travelled to Norway as hostage in return.

CHAPTER THIRTY

It happened on one occasion that King Valdamarr and Erlingr were in conversation. Erlingr spoke:

'Lord, it seems to me that the best way to reach a settlement is for you to have all of that part of Norway that you were promised in our personal agreement. So if that were the case, what leader would you put in charge there? Would it be some Danish one? No,' he says, 'no leaders of the Danes would be willing to go to Norway and have to deal with a tough and disobedient people, when he has previously been well enough off here with you. It was for this reason that I came here, that I wish under no circumstances to lose your friendship. In the past men have travelled here to Denmark from Norway, Hákon Ívarsson and Finnr Árnason, and your kinsman King Sveinn made both of them his jarls. I am not now a person of less power in Norway than they were then, and the king gave them the administration of Halland, a realm that he had held previously. Now it seems to me, lord, that you might well grant me this land[465] if I pledge my fealty to you so that I shall be holding this realm from you. Moreover my son King Magnús cannot refuse me this, so I shall be subject and bound to you for every service that belongs to this title.'

Erlingr said this and other similar things, and it came about in the end that Erlingr became subject to King Valdamarr, and the king led Erlingr to his seat and gave him a jarldom and the Vík as his fief and to administer. Then Erlingr went back to Norway and afterwards was jarl as long as he lived, and remained at peace with the king of the Danes for ever after.

Erlingr had four sons by concubines. One was called Hreiðarr, [407] the second Ǫgmundr; they had their own separate mothers. The third was Finnr, the fourth Sigurðr; their mother was Ása in ljósa (the Bright). They were younger. The king's daughter Kristín and Erlingr had a daughter that was called Ragnhildr. She was married to Jón Þorbergsson of Randaberg. Kristín left the country with a man that was called Grímr rusli (Useless). They went out to Mikligarðr and stayed there a while, and they had some children.

---

[465] i.e. the part of Norway claimed by Valdamarr.

CHAPTER THIRTY-ONE

Óláfr, son of Guðbrandr Skafhǫggsson and son of King Eysteinn Magnússon's daughter Maria, was being fostered with Sigurðr agnhǫttr (Bait-Hood) in Upplǫnd. Now while Erlingr was in Denmark, then the foster-father and -son, Óláfr and Sigurðr, started a band of men and many Upplendingar joined it. Óláfr was taken as king of it. They travelled round Upplǫnd with this band, and sometimes into the Vík, sometimes east to Markir. They were not aboard ships. So when Jarl Erlingr heard about this band, then he took his troops into the Vík and was on board ships during the summer and in the autumn in Oslo and gave banquets there over Yule. He had watch kept up inland on the band and went himself up inland to look for them, and with [408] him the king's brother Ormr. And when they got to the lake that is called . . .[466] then they captured all the ships that were by the lake.

CHAPTER THIRTY-TWO

The priest that officiated at Ryðjǫkull—this is by the lake—invited the jarl and his men to a banquet and to come there at Candlemas.[467] The jarl promised to go, he felt it would be a good thing to go to the services there. They rowed there across the lake during the evening before the feast day. But this priest had a different plan in hand. He sent men to bring intelligence to Óláfr and his men about Erlingr's movements. He gave Erlingr and his party strong drink in the evening and made them drink a great deal. And when the jarl went to sleep, then there were beds for them made in the banqueting hall. Now when they had slept a little while, the jarl awoke and asked if it was now time for mattins. The priest said that little of the night had passed, bade them sleep in peace. The jarl replied:

'I am having a lot of dreams tonight, and I am sleeping badly.'

After that he fell asleep. He awoke a second time and told the priest to stand up and sing the service. The priest told the jarl to sleep, saying it was now midnight. The jarl lay down and slept a short time and leapt up and told his men to get dressed. They did so and took their weapons, went to church and laid their weapons outside while the priest sang mattins.

CHAPTER THIRTY-THREE

Intelligence reached Óláfr during the evening, and they walked during the night along six leagues of pathways, and people thought this was a great deal of travelling. They arrived in Ryðjǫkull during mattins. It was absolutely pitch-dark. Óláfr and his men went to the banqueting hall and shouted a

---

[466] This must have been part of the Raumelfr (Glomma).

[467] Cf. note 289 above.

war cry, killing a few men inside there that had not gone to mattins. But when Erlingr and his men heard the [409] shout they ran to their weapons and after that made off down for the ships. Óláfr and his men met them by a sort of enclosure. There was a battle there. Erlingr and his men retreated down by the side of the enclosure, and the enclosure protected them. They had a much smaller troop. Many of them fell, and many were wounded. What helped them most was that Óláfr and his men could not distinguish them, it was so dark. So Erlingr's men made straight for the ships. Bishop Guðmundr's father Ari Þorgeirsson fell there and many others of Erlingr's followers. Erlingr was wounded in his left side, and some people say that he scraped the sword against himself when he was drawing it. Ormr was also badly wounded. With difficulty they got aboard their ships and immediately drew away from the shore.

It was said that Óláfr and his men had had very bad luck in the encounter, considering how Erlingr and his men had been delivered up to them if Óláfr had proceeded more sensibly. Afterwards people called him Óláfr ógæfa (Bad Luck), but some called them Hettusveinar (Hood Boys).[468] They went up round the countryside with this band again as before, but Jarl Erlingr went out into the Vík to his ships and stayed behind in the Vík during the summer, while Óláfr and his men were in Upplǫnd and sometimes east in Markir. They had the band like that a second winter.

CHAPTER THIRTY-FOUR

The next spring Óláfr and his band went out into the Vík and took all the royal dues there, staying there a long time during the summer. Jarl Erlingr heard about this and took his troops east to find them, and their meeting was on the eastern side of the fiord in a place that is called at Stangir.[469] A great battle took place there and [410] Erlingr was victorious. Sigurðr agnhǫttr fell there and many of Óláfr's men, but Óláfr got away by flight. He travelled after that south to Denmark and stayed in Jótland at Álaborg the next winter after that. And the following spring Óláfr caught an illness that led to his death, and he is buried there at Máríukirkja, and the Danes call him a saint.

CHAPTER THIRTY-FIVE

Páll Skoptason's son Níkolás kúfungr (Snail) was one of King Magnús's landed men. He captured Haraldr, who was said to have been son of King Sigurðr Haraldsson and the king's daughter Kristín and half-brother of King Magnús. Níkolás conveyed Haraldr to Bjǫrgyn and handed him over to Jarl

---

[468] Perhaps alluding to Óláfr's foster-father's nickname agnhǫttr (Bait-Hood).

[469] Stangir, modern Stange, is on the eastern side of Lake Mjǫrs (Mjøsa) so *austan fjarðar* must mean east of Mjǫrs, rather than east of the Vík. Cf. Fritzner s.v. fjǫrðr.

Erlingr. It was Erlingr's custom, if enemies of his came before him, that he spoke nothing or very little to them, and calmly what he did say, if he was resolved to kill them, while those that he wanted to have life he verbally abused most bitterly. Erlingr said little to Haraldr, and people were suspicious about what he was intending. Then people bade King Magnús to intercede for Haraldr with the jarl. The king did so. The jarl replied:

'That is what your friends advise. But you will not long rule the country in peace if you are always going to act with goodwill towards everyone.'

Afterwards Erlingr had Haraldr conveyed across to Norðnes and he was beheaded there.

CHAPTER THIRTY-SIX

There is a man called Eysteinn that claimed to be King Eysteinn Haraldsson's son. He was then a young man, not completely full-grown, when it is told that [411] he turned up one summer east in Svíaveldi and went to see Birgir brosa. He was now married to Haraldr gilli's daughter Brígiða, Eysteinn's aunt. Eysteinn put before them his purpose and asked for their help for himself. The jarl and his wife too welcomed what he said and promised him their support. He stayed there a while. Jarl Birgir gave Eysteinn some troops and a good sum of money for his immediate needs and sent him on his way generously. They both assured him of their friendship. Eysteinn then went north in Norway and came down in the Vík. Now troops immediately rushed to him, and this band expanded. They took Eysteinn as king, and they stayed with this band in the Vík during the winter. But because they were short of money, then they plundered widely, and the landed men and farmers brought a troop against them. So when they were overpowered, then they fled away into the forests and lay for long periods in deserted places. Then their clothing wore out, so they fastened birch bark round their legs. The farmers then called them Birkibeinar (Birch-Legs). They often rushed into settlements and turned up here and there and launched an attack if they were not faced by large numbers. They fought some battles with farmers, and now one side, now the other was victorious. The Birkibeinar had three pitched battles and were victorious in all of them. At Krókaskógr they narrowly escaped disaster. A gathering of farmers came against them, a huge number of troops. The Birkibeinar felled heaps of trees in front of them and afterwards ran into the forest. The Birkibeinar were two winters in the Vík without going to the north of the country.

CHAPTER THIRTY-SEVEN

King Magnús had then been king for thirteen winters when the Birkibeinar started up. The third summer they took to ships, then went out along the coast,

getting themselves wealth and troops. They were at first in the Vík, but towards
the end of summer [412] they made for the north of the country, travelling so
fast that no intelligence preceded them before they reached Þrándheimr. The
Birkibeinar's band consisted mainly of men from Markir and Elfargrímar,
and they had a large number from Þelamǫrk, and they were now well armed.
Their king, Eysteinn, was handsome and fair of feature, small of face, not a big
person. By many people he was known as Eysteinn meyla (Maidenly). King
Magnús and Jarl Erlingr were staying in Bjǫrgyn when the Birkibeinar sailed
past to the north, and they were not aware of them. Erlingr was a powerful
man, intelligent in mind, a very great warrior when there was war, a good
ruler of the land and authoritarian, said to be rather severe and harsh. But the
real thing was that he gave only a few of his enemies permission to stay in the
country, even when they begged for quarter, and for this reason many ended
up running off to join the bands when these rose against him. Erlingr was a tall
man and tough in build, rather high-shouldered, long-faced, sharp-featured,
light-coloured and growing very grey-haired, carried his head rather on one
side, pleasant in manner and dignified, wore old-fashioned clothing, tunics
and shirts long in the body and sleeves, French cloaks, boots high in the leg.
He made the king wear similar clothing while he was young, but when he
could decide for himself he dressed in great finery. King Magnús was high-
spirited and playful, a very sociable person and a great man for the ladies.

CHAPTER THIRTY-EIGHT

Sigurðr Hranason's son Níkolás, he was son of Brynjólfr úlfaldi's (Camel's)
daughter Skjaldvǫr, sister of Halldórr Brynjólfsson and half-sister of King
Magnús [413] berfœttr. Níkolás was a very great leader. He had an estate
in Hálogaland on Ǫngull at a place called at Steig. Níkolás had a dwelling
in Niðaróss down from Jóanskirkja where the chaplain Þorgeirr had lived.
Níkolás was frequently in Kaupangr, and he had complete authority over
the people of the town. Níkolás's daughter Skjaldvǫr was married to Eiríkr
Árnason. He was a landed man too.

CHAPTER THIRTY-NINE

It was on the later Máríumass,[470] when people were returning from mattins
in the town, that Eiríkr went to Níkolás and spoke:
  'Father-in-law, some fishermen that have come in are saying that longships
were sailing in along the fiord, and people suppose that it must be Birkibeinar,
and the thing to do, father-in-law, is to have the whole town militia with
arms summoned by trumpet call out onto Eyrar.'

---

[470] The feast of the Nativity of the Blessed Virgin Mary, 8th September.

Níkolás replied: 'I do not, son-in-law, go by rumours of fishermen. I shall set a watch out in the fiord, and we shall hold an assembly today.'

Eiríkr went home, and when the bell was rung for High Mass, Níkolás went to church. Now Eiríkr came to him and spoke:

'I think, father-in-law, that the information is true. There are now men here that say they have seen the sails. It seems to me advisable for us to ride out of the town and muster troops for ourselves.'

Níkolás replied: 'You are chattering on again, son-in-law. Let us first hear Mass, then decide what to do afterwards.'

Níkolás went to church. And when Mass had been sung, Eiríkr went to Níkolás and spoke:

'Father-in-law, now my horses are ready. I am going to ride out.'

Níkolás replied: 'Farewell then! We shall hold an assembly on Eyrar and find out what troops are in the town.'

Then Eiríkr rode away, but Níkolás went to his premises and afterwards to eat.

[414] CHAPTER FORTY

Now just when food was being served, a man came in and told Níkolás that now Birkibeinar were rowing into the river. Then Níkolás called out that his men were to arm themselves, and when they were armed, Níkolás told them to go inside into the upper part of the building, and this was the most unwise thing to do, for if they had guarded the courtyard, then the townspeople would have come up to help them, for the Birkibeinar went and filled the whole courtyard and then went to the upper storeys all round. They shouted to each other. The Birkibeinar offered Níkolás quarter, but he refused. After that they fought. Níkolás and his men defended themselves with bowshots and handshots and oven stones, but the Birkibeinar knocked down the buildings and shot as often as they could. Níkolás had a red shield with gilt studs in it and stars on it, a Viljálmr's make. The Birkibeinar shot so that the arrows stuck in as far as the binding of the heads. Níkolás spoke:

'The shield is now proving false to me.'

There Níkolás fell and a large part of his company and he was very greatly mourned. The Birkibeinar gave quarter to all the people of the town.

CHAPTER FORTY-ONE

Afterwards Eysteinn was taken as king there, and all the people submitted to him. He stayed for a while in the town, after that travelled in into Þrándheimr. Many troops joined him there. Þorfinnr svarti (the Black) of Snǫs joined him there, and he had a troop of men. At the beginning of winter they travelled out to the town. Then Guðrún of Saltnes's sons, Jón kettlingr (Kitten), Sigurðr and Viljálmr, joined them. They travelled up out of Niðaróss to Orkadalr—then there were calculated to be nearly twenty hundred men there—travelling on to Upplǫnd and then out across Þótn and Haðaland, then to Hringaríki.

[415] CHAPTER FORTY-TWO

In the autumn King Magnús travelled east into Vík with some of the troops, and the king's brother Ormr as well. Jarl Erlingr stayed behind in Bjǫrgyn and kept a large force there and was to go against the Birkibeinar if they travelled down the coastal route. King Magnús established himself in Túnsberg, he and Ormr as well. The king gave a banquet there over Yule. King Magnús heard about the Birkibeinar up in Ré. After that the king left the town with his troop and Ormr as well and they reached Ré. There was a lot of snow and the weather was amazingly cold. So when they got to this farm, then they went out of the enclosure onto the road, and on the outside of the fence they lined up and trod the snow down hard for themselves. They had just less than fifteen hundred men. The Birkibeinar were at another farm but some of their troops were in buildings here and there. But when they became aware of King Magnús's army, they gathered together and set up a battle line. And when they saw King Magnús's troops, then they thought, as was true, that their force was greater. They immediately went into battle. But when they advanced along the road, then few at a time were able to move forward, and those that jumped out off the road found the snow so deep that they could hardly get forward, and now their line broke up, while those that went forward along the road first fell. Then their standard was cut down, and those that were next in line retreated, while some took to flight. King Magnús's men pursued them and killed them one after the other when they caught them. Then the Birkibeinar could not get their battle line formed and were exposed to weapons, and now many fell and many fled. It was then as can often happen, that though men are brave and bold in battle, if they suffer heavy blows and start to flee, most find it difficult to turn around again. Then the main force of Birkibeinar began to flee, and a multitude fell, for King Magnús's men killed all they could, and none [416] of those they caught were granted quarter, and the rout scattered widely.

King Eysteinn took to flight. He ran into a certain building and begged for quarter for himself and also that the farmer would hide him. But the farmer killed him, afterwards going to see King Magnús and finding him at Hrafnsnes. The king was inside in a room and was warming himself by the fire, and there were many people there. Afterwards men went and conveyed the body there, carrying it into the room. Then the king told men to go and identify the body. There was a man sitting on the corner bench, and it was a Birkibeinn, and no one had taken any notice of him. But when he saw the corpse of his leader and recognised it, then he stood up quickly and sharply. He had an axe in his hand, he ran quickly further in across the floor and struck at King Magnús, hitting him on the neck by the shoulders. Some man or other saw the axe swing down and shoved him away. That caused the axe to turn down onto the shoulders, and it was a great wound. Then he swung the axe up a second time and struck at the king's brother Ormr. He was lying on the bench. The blow was aimed at both his legs. So when Ormr saw that the man was trying to kill him, he moved quickly, throwing his feet forwards over his head, and the blow fell on the edge of the bench frame. The axe stuck fast. But weapons were sticking so thickly on the Birkibeinn that he was hardly able to fall. Then they saw that he had dragged his intestines across the floor after him, and this man's valour is very highly praised.

King Magnús's men pursued the rout for a long time and they killed all they could. Þorfinnr at Snǫs fell there, and many other Þrœndir fell there too.

CHAPTER FORTY-THREE

This band, that were called Birkibeinar, had gathered together with a great multitude. These people were tough and the most valiant fighters and were a rather unruly crew, going about quite furiously and madly, once they felt they had [417] a great force. They had in their band few men that were good planners or were accustomed to the administration of land or laws or managing an army, and although some knew better, yet the majority[471] all wanted to do what each himself thought fit. They felt themselves secure with the numbers in their band and their valour. But of the troops that got away, many were wounded and had lost their weapons and clothing, and all were without money. Some made their way east to Markir and many to Þelamǫrk, mostly those that had relatives there. Some went all the way east to Svíaveldi. They all ran away because they had little hope of quarter from King Magnús or Jarl Erlingr.

CHAPTER FORTY-FOUR

After this King Magnús travelled back out to Túnsberg, and he came to be very celebrated for this victory, for everyone said that Jarl Erlingr was the shield and organiser of the pair, but after King Magnús had gained victory over such a powerful and numerous band when he had a smaller force, then it seemed to everyone as if he was going to overcome all, and he would then be as much greater a warrior than the jarl as he was a younger one.

---

[471] *Kringla* had *flokkrinn*, but other manuscripts *fjǫldinn*.

Index of Names

Page references are to the page numbers of the *Íslenzk fornrit* edition, which are noted in square brackets within the text of the translation.

Dýrsá (Djurså, river on the eastern side of Jutland) 404.

Dœlir (people of Dalar, Guðbrandsdalar (valleys in Upplǫnd)) 251 (verse).

Eaðvarðr (Eat-, Ját-) (Eadward the Confessor) inn góði (the Good) son of Aðalráðr, king of the English (died 1066) 32, 65, 66, 168, 170, 171, 174, 193.

East-Vinðr (Austr-Vinðr, eastern Wends) 70 (verse).

Eatmundr son of Aðalráðr (Edmund Ironside, King Edmund II of the English, died 1016) 66.

Eðni (Etne, Hǫrðaland) 342.

Egðir (people of Agðir) 84, 87, 90, 223 (verses).

Egg (Egge, Sogn) 24, 25.

Egill son of Áslákr of Forland 214, 216–17.

Eilífr, Danish jarl 254.

Eilífr son of Jarl Rǫgnvaldr Úlfsson 70.

Einarr Andreasmágr (Andreas Brúnsson's son-in-law) 289, 290.

Einarr son of Ari of Reykjahólar 311, 316.

Einarr þambarskelfir or -skelmir (Bowstring-shaker) Eindriðason 24, 37, 107, 122–26.

Einarr son of Guthormr grábarðr (Greybeard) 334–36.

Einarr Pálsson, Laxa-Pálsson (Salmon-) 313, 340.

Einarr Skúlason, Icelandic poet and priest, twelfth century 239, 240, 249, 251, 271, 286, 296, 321, 326–30, 346, 358, 359, 371.

Einarr son of Ǫgmundr of Sandr 311.

Eindriði in Gautdalr 311.

Eindriði heiðafylja (Heath Mare) 392.

Eindriði ungi (the Young) 324, 370–71, 378, 38–383, 390.

Eindriði son of Einarr þambarskelfir 122, 125, 126, 128, 129.

Eindriði son of Jón mǫrnefr 344, 353–54, 358–60.

Eiríkr brother of Benedikt 304.

Eiríkr inn ársæli (of the Prosperous Seasons), king of the Svíar (died 1088) 263.

Eiríkr Árnason, landed man 413.

Eiríkr inn sigursæli (the Victorious) Bjarnarson, king of the Swedes (died c. 995) 36.

Eiríkr hæll (Peg) son of Eindriði in Gautdalr 311.

Eiríkr eimuni (Ever Remembered) Eiríksson, king of the Danes (1134–37) 276, 282, 289–90, 307–08.

Eiríkr Ívarsson, archbishop in Niðaróss (1189–1205) 316.

Eiríkr Oddsson, author of *Hryggjarstykki* (fl. mid-twelfth century) 313, 317–320.

Eiríkr góði (the Good) Sveinsson, king of the Danes (1095–1103) 207–08, 228–29, 258, 262.

Elbr 141, see Elfr.

Elda (in northern Þrándheimr) 360.

Elfargrímar (dwellers on the banks of the Elfr) 285, 412.

Elfarvísur, a poem by Einarr Skúlason 359.

Elfr(in) 12, 36, 38 (verse), 112, 113, 115, 144, 159, 162, 227, 228, 309, 350, 359 (verse), 376, 391; see Elbr and Gautelfr.

Elisabeth daughter of King Jarizleifr 90, see Ellisif.

Ellipaltar (perhaps a compound derived from Greek ἕλη and Latin *paludes*, which both mean 'fen'; the word seems to be used of the mouth of the Dnieper) 89.

Rýgjarbit (boundary between Agðir and the Vík, near the place now known as Gjernestangen) 375, 399.

Rǫgnir, a name for Óðinn, in kenning for warrior 115 (verse).

Rǫgnvaldr kunta (Cunt) 378, 383.

Rǫgnvaldr son of Jarl Brúsi, jarl in Orkney (c.1037–c. 1045) 68, 69.

Rǫgnvaldr, jarl, son of Heinrekr halti 369.

Rǫgnvaldr son of Ingi Steinkellsson 279.

Rǫgnvaldr Kali Kolsson, jarl in Orkney (1136–58) 324–25.

Rǫgnvaldr Úlfsson, jarl 70.

Rǫnd (Randsfjord), lake in Haðaland 335.

Sáða-Gyrðr (Seed-) Bárðarson, Gyrðr 292, 303, 313, 314, 317, 330, 342, 378, 386.

Saltíri (Kintyre in western Scotland) 219, 220, 224; see also Sanntíri; Saltíriseið (the isthmus of Kintyre, at Tarbert) 224.

Saltnes (Saltnes, Østfold, Norway) 414.

Sandbrú, in Bjǫrgvin 340.

Sandey (Sanda), island in the Hebrides 221 (verse).

Sandr (Sand, east of Tjaldasund, on Tjaldey?) 311.

Sanntíri = Saltíri 221 (verse).

Sarpr (Sarp, Sarpsfossen, waterfall north of the Vík) 283.

Sarpsborg (in Vingulmǫrk, eastern side of the Vík) 257, 283. Cf. Borg.

Sauða-Úlfr (Sheep-) 120, 303, 313, 315.

Saurbýir (now Sörbygden), in Ranriki 362.

Saxons (Saxar) 37.

Saxi in Vik 229, 297.

Saxland (north Germany) 32, 41.

Scotland (Skotland) 25, 179, 220, 224, 233, 298, 321, 328; the fiords of Scotland (Skotlandsfirðir) 219, 224.

Scots (Skotar) 220 (verse); king of the Scots (Skotakonungr) 224, 298; the court of the king of the Scots (hirð Skotakonungs) 233.

Sekkr (or Sekk; now Sekken), island in Romsdalsfjord, Norway 382.

Selárdalr, near Arnarfjǫrðr, Western Fiords, Iceland 45.

Seleyjar (Seløyar, north of Líðandisnes) 342.

Seljuhverfi (now Jøssund district in Sør-Trøndelag, Norway) 215.

Selund (Sjáland) 53, 93 (verses); Selund-dwellers (Selundbyggvar, inhabitants of Selund) 198 (verse).

Serkir (Saracens) 75, 245 (verses).

Serkland (Saracen-land, north Africa) 74, 75, 81, 244, 261.

Serkr Brynjólfsson from Sogn 233.

Sigarðr, landed man 292.

Sigríðr sæta (Grass Widow) 340.

Sigríðr daughter of Bárðr and sister of King Ingi 297.

Sigríðr daughter of Dagr Eilífsson 363.

Sigríðr daughter of Finnr Árnason 128, 306.

Sigríðr daughter of Ketill kálfr 122.

Sigríðr daughter of Saxi in Vík 229, 297.

Sigríðr daughter of Jarl Sveinn Hákonarson 122.

Steigar-Þórir Þórðarson 99, 101, 201, 210–11, 213–16, 217 (verse), 256. see Þórir of Steig.

Steinavágr (Steinvåg), on the island of Heissa, Sunnmœrr 381.

Steinbjǫrg (Steinberget), just outside Niðaróss 212.

Steinkell [son of Rǫgnvaldr Úlfsson], king of the Svíar (1060–66) 158, 163, 164 (verse), 225, 258, 279.

Steinn Herdísarson, Icelandic poet, eleventh century 120, 145, 147–49, 180–81, 202–03.

Stephanus, legate from Rome (sent by Pope Alexander III, arrived from England 1163) 395, 397, 398.

Stígr hvítaleðr (White Leather) 258.

Stikla(r)staðir (Stiklestad, in the northern part of Þrándheimr) 14, 23–25, 68, 200, 369–70.

Stimr (Stemmet), mountain near the sea on the boundary of Norð-Mœrr and Raumsdalr 262.

Stjórnvelta (unidentified) 350.

Stoðreimr (Ståreim, Nordfjord, in Firðir) 323.

Strað-Bjarni (Fuck-) 378.

Stuðla (Stole, Sunn-Hǫrðaland) 323, 342.

Stúfr [blindi] Þórðarson, Icelandic poet, eleventh century 83, 84, 90, 112, 114, 206.

Styrjaldar-Magnús (Warfare-), i.e. Magnús berfœttr 230.

Styrkárr, Haraldr Sigurðarson's marshal 192–93.

Styrkárr glæsirófa (Splendid Tail) 312.

Súðaþorp (Suderup), in Jótland 105.

Suðreyjar (Hebrides) 25, 219, 221, 224, 233, 265, 324; king of the Suðreyjar, Suðreyjakonungr (king in the Hebrides) 221, 367. Cf. verse 179, line 8.

Súl [or Súla] (Sulstua), highest farm in Veradalr 23.

Sunndalr (Sundal, west of Lake Vænir) 225.

Sunn-Hǫrðaland (south Hordaland, south-west Norway) 10, 324.

Sunn-Mœrr (Sunnmøre, western Norway) 214, 225.

Sváfa (Swabia) 254.

Svartahaf (the Black Sea) 88.

Sveinki Steinarsson 323.

Sveinn, priest 312.

Sveinn 263, see Blót-Sveinn.

Sveinn Álfífuson, see Sveinn son of Knútr inn ríki.

Sveinn son of Bergþórr bukkr 367, 378, 389.

Sveinn Eiríksson, king of the Danes (1146–57) 258.

Sveinn son of Erlendr from Gerði 323.

Sveinn Guðinason, jarl (?Swegen Godwineson, died 1052) 168, 194.

Sveinn Hákonarson, jarl (died 1016) 122.

Sveinn tjúguskegg (Forkbeard) Haraldsson, king of the Danes (986–1014) 36, 375.

Sveinn son of Haraldr flettir 213, 214, 216, 218.

Sveinn Hrímhildarson 270–71.

Sveinn son of Knútr inn ríki and Álfífa, king of the Danes (1030–35) 8, 10, 11, 12 (verse), 16, 256.

Sveinn son of Sveinn Erlendsson 323.

Viljálmr Bastard (bastarðr) (Róðbjartsson, William the Conqueror, died 1087) 168–70, 193–97, 239, 397.

Viljálmr son of Roðgeirr, king of Sicily (William I the Bad, son of Roger II) (1154–66) 248.

Viljálmr's make (Viljálmsgørð), a type of shield, perhaps named after its maker or inventer 414.

Vimur a mythical river (*Skáldsk* 25), in a kenning for ship 240 (in verse).

Vinðland (Wendland, on the southern shore of the Baltic) 38–40, 272, 296.

Vinðr (Wends, people of Wendland) 37–39, 41–45, 63 (verse), 130, 289–93, 309, 334; Vinðr country (Vinða grund, verse) 39; king of the Vinðr (Vinðakonungr) 290; army of Vinðr (herr Vinða, Vinðaherr) 41, 43; Wendish warships,warships of Vinðr (Vinðasnekkjur) 290, 309; see East-Vinðr.

Viskardalr, in Halland 212.

Vist (Viste), in Jaðarr (?) 311.

Visundr (Bison), a ship 33 (verse), 34.

Vænir, Væni (Lake Vänern in Sweden) 162, 225, 226.

Væringjar (Varangians, Scandinavian warriors in the service of the Greek emperors) 71–74, 78–82, 85, 86, 88, 90, 370–72; army of the Væringjar (Væringjaherr) 81.

Vǫllr (probably Völlur in Rangárvallasýsla in southern Iceland) 91.

Vǫrsar, people of Vǫrs (Voss, area in Hǫrðafylki, western Norway, i.e. Norwegians) 213 (verse).

White-Chist (Hvíta-Kristr, Jesus Christ) 17 (verse). See Christ.

Winchester (Vincestr), in England 11, 31.

Yggr, a name of Óðinn, in a kenning for warrior 195 (verse).

Yrjar (Ørland, in Austrátt) 126.

Zoë in ríka (the Great), Porphyrogenita, joint ruler in Constantinople (1028–50, queen of Michael Catalactus and later of Konstantinus Monomakus) 71, 85, 88.

Þelamǫrk (Telemark, southern Norway) 341, 412, 417.

Þexdalr (Teksdal), in Norð-Mœrr 215.

Þjóð (Thy), in Jótland 114, 115.

Þjóðólfr Arnórsson, Icelandic poet, eleventh century 7, 11, 33, 38, 44, 48–52, 54–55, 57–61, 64, 68, 70, 75, 82, 86, 91, 95, 97, 109, 123, 141–44, 146, 149, 151, 164, 166–67, 188, 190, 198–99.

Þjóstólfr Álason, 280, 303, 305–08, 318, 320, 330.

Þjótta (Tjøtta), island off Hálogaland 22.

Þóra mother of Sigurðr Jórsalafari son of Magnús berfœttr 229, 271.

Þóra mother of Hákon herðibreiðr son of Sigurðr munnr 325–26.

Þóra daughter of Guthormr grábarði, Haraldr gilli's concubine, mother of Sigurðr munnr 279, 300, 301.

Þóra daughter of Jóan (in *Morkinskinna* and *Fagrskinna* daughter of Árni lági), mother of Magnús berfœttr 208.

Þóra daughter of Saxi in Vík, mother of Sigurðr slembidjákn 297.

Þóra daughter of Skopti Ǫgmundarson, wife of Ásólfr Skúlason 198, 225.

Þótn (Toten, an area of Haðaland near Lake Mjǫrs) 414.

Þrándheimr, district of northern Norway, modern Trøndelag (cf. Þrœndalǫg) 8–9, 15, 22, 31, 102, 120, 122–23, 126, 128–29, 140, 158, 178, 210–11, 214–15, 218, 229, 272, 285, 303–04, 316, 321–22, 332, 337, 341, 343, 349, 360, 376, 378, 391, 400–01, 412, 414.

Þrándheimsmynni (the entrance to Trondheimsfjord) 312, 314.

Þrándr gjaldkeri (Steward) 317–18.

Þróttr, a name of Óðinn, in kenning for warrior 246 (in verse).

Þrælaborg, south of Oslo 367, 368.

Þrœndalǫg (Trondelag; = Þrándheimr) 137, 353, 360, 391, 394.

Þrœndir, Þrœndr (people of Þrándheimr) 49 (verse), 54 (verse), 65 (verse), 107, 117 (verse), 126–27, 147, 203 (verse), 210, 213 (verse), 222 (verse), 303, 321, 349, 383, 391, 396, 401–02, 416; host of Þrœndir (Þrœndaherr, þrœnzk drótt) 107, 218 (verse).

Þumli, in Hísing, perhaps the place now called Tumlehed 145 (verse).

Ægisfjǫrðr (Øksfjord), in the very north of Norway 311.

Ǫgmundr of Sandr 311.

Ǫgmundr sviptir (Loss) 314, 330.

Ǫgmundr son of Erlingr skakki 407.

Ǫgmundr Ívarsson of Elda 360.

Ǫgmundr dengir (Hammerer) son of Kyrpinga-Ormr 330.

Ǫgmundr son of Jarl Ormr Eilífsson 306.

Ǫgmundr son of Skopti Ǫgmundarson 225, 227–28, 231–32.

Ǫgmundr son of Þorbergr Árnason 198, 214, 225, 230–31, 238, 330.

Ólafar, the Óláfrs, i.e. Óláfr Tryggvason and Óláfr helgi 27 (verse).

Ǫleifr, i.e. Ólafr Eiríksson 5 (verse).

Ǫleifr, i.e. Ólafr Haraldsson 6, 16, 17, 21, 25, 38, 51, 59, 64, 68, 98 (verses).

Ǫleifr, i.e. Ólafr kyrri 202, 211 (verses).

Ǫlvir miklimunnr (Big-Mouth), farmer 291–92.

Ǫngull (Engeløy), island in Vestfjorden, Hálogaland 413.

Ǫngulsey (Anglesey, north Wales) 223.

Ǫngulseyjarsund (Menai Strait, between Anglesey and the mainland) 135, 222.

Ǫngulssund 222 (verse) = Ǫngulseyjarsund.

Ǫnundr (Jákob) Ólafsson, king of the Svíar (1022–c. 1050) 18.

Ǫnundr Símunarson, foster-brother of Hákon herðibreiðr 326, 347, 353, 377–78, 380–81, 383, 393–95.

Ǫrnólfr skorpa (Crust) 393–95.

Ǫzurr (Asser/Ascer Þorkelsson), archbishop in Lund (1104–37) 289.

Ǫzurr, farmer on Hísing 393–94.